Jones' Instrument Technology Volume 1

Mechanical Measurements

Contents of other volumes

Fourth Edition

Jones' Instrument Technology Volume 1

Mechanical Measurements

Edited by **B E Noltingk**

Butterworths
London · Boston · Durban · Singapore
Sydney · Toronto · Wellington

First published 1985

Reprinted 1987

British Library Cataloguing in Publication Data

Instrument technology.—4th ed.
Vol. 1: Mechanical instruments
1. Measuring instruments
I. Noltingk, B. E. II. Jones, E. B.
Instrument technology
620′.0044 QC100.5

ISBN 0-408-01231-5

Library of Congress Cataloging in Publication Data
Main entry under title:

Instrument technology.

Fourth ed. of: Instrument technology/E. B. Jones.
3rd ed. London: Newnes-Butterworths, 1974.
Includes index.
Contents: v. 1. Mechanical measurements.
1. Engineering instruments. I. Noltingk, B. E.
II. Jones, E. B. (Ernest Beachcroft). Instrument technology.
TA165.I59674 1984 620′.0028 84-4273
ISBN 0-408-01231-5 (v. 1)

Filmset by Mid-County Press, London SW15
Printed by The Thetford Press Ltd, Thetford, Norfolk

Contents

Contributors

C S Bahra, BSc, MSc, CEng, MIMechE, is Development Manager at Transducer Systems Ltd

G Fowles, is now a Senior Development Engineer with the Severn-Trent Water Authority after some time as a Section Leader in the Instrumentation Group of the Water Research Centre

E H Higham, MA, CEng, FIEE, MIMechE, MIERE, MInstMc, is with Foxboro Great Britain Ltd

W M Jones, BSc, DPhil, FInstP, is a Reader in the Physics Department at the University College of Wales Aberystwith

B E Noltingk, BSc, PhD, CEng, FIEE, FInstP, is now a Consultant after some time as Head of the Instrumentation Section at Central Electricity Research Laboratories

D J Pacey, BSc, FInstP, was, until recently, a Senior Lecturer in the Physics Department at Brunel University

W L Snowsill, BSc, is a Research Officer in the Control and Instrumentation Branch of the Central Electricity Research Laboratories

P H Sydenham, ME, PhD, FInstMC, FIIC, AMIEAust, is Head of and Professor at the School of Electronic Engineering, the South Australia Institute of Technology

K Walters, MSc, PhD, is a Professor in the Department of Applied Mathematics at the University College of Wales Aberystwith

Preface

E. B. Jones was a remarkable man. His career had included teaching and practising and he brought together the wisdom acquired in both these activities. The result was a book—or set of three books if you distinguish the volumes—for which instrument men have had cause to be grateful over a number of years. In a quickly changing technology, it was a long-lasting book as he undertook successive revisions.

E. B. Jones was an irreplaceable man. No one could have quite the experience and knowledge to cover his ground, describing instrument technology for students as we approach the end of the century. Perhaps he is smiling in heaven to realize that it has taken a couple of dozen contributors to step into his shoes.

Anyone concerned with authorship must remain true to himself. So it is inevitable that a change of writer brings some shift of emphasis. However, in our updated *Instrument Technology*, the shift is only small; it is a tribute to the original that an appreciable part of earlier editions has still been suitable for reproduction this time. More of the changes simply mirror a technology that is never stationary. A great deal of instrumentation is concerned with process control; that might have justified the use of those words in the titles of the old volumes. Since they are not in the titles, I have felt there should be some widening of scope and chapters have been added to cover the measurement of length, strain, vibrations, force, vacuum, particle size, electrical and optical quantities and noise.

On the other hand, the subject of control has been omitted. It is now very much a topic in its own right—it would perhaps like to be thought of as the parent, rather than the child, of instrumentation. Control could not be dealt with adquately while sufficient space was still left for the many facets of instrumentation itself. Because this is a book for the general practitioner, we have also deliberately left out fields of application where a considerable body of specialist knowledge has been built up, notably instrumentation for meteorological, military, medical and other biological purposes. In process control, instrumentation and control form a trio with the actuators that regulate the process; we have also omitted detailed reference to them.

This updated *Instrument Technology* is aimed at a technician readership, as were earlier editions. Inasmuch as the poor modern technician is expected to have a greater depth of knowledge, that corresponds to a move up-market. The specialist instrument designer will of course read whole books on the subject matter of one of our chapters but we hope he will still find here a sound foundation on which he can build. The would-be graduate engineer who does not specialize in instrumentation (and, alas, all too few of them do) will find here the broad coverage he needs. A continuing hope is that *Instrument Technology* will be found on the shelves and in the libraries of designers and factories for the enlightenment of people who want a general appreciation of the situation before they call in the experts who will have to work out the details.

Readers will find differences between chapters in their style of treatment. This is partly because different subjects call for different approaches and partly, of course, because individual writers show their individuality. I hope that, as an editor guiding contributors, I have steered a middle course between—to mix the metaphors—a Procrustean bed and a rope long enough to hang on. A problematic choice is always that of the right balance between talking abstract fundamentals and providing a mere manual for instrument hardware. Earlier editions of *Instrument Technology* made a feature of outlining the science fringing on particular fields of instrumentation; we have retained some of this but not over-emphasized it.

A Preface is the place for thank-yous. Many people have contributed to the book. Of course I should thank my contributors for painstaking work. Some of them should be thanked for their patience, after punctual completion of their own tasks, at delays while the whole work was assembled; and perhaps with some contributors I could hint at my own impatience for their contribution to those delays! Many writers thank their (respective) wives for their tolerance. My gratitude to mine is, at least partly, that she, at least sometimes, got on with her own good works, leaving me to my labours without the niggling sense of guilt that I was neglecting her.

B.E.N.

Introduction

1 Techniques and applications

In instrumentation research, there is a divide that does not arise so acutely in research on other technologies. This is that the research can be either techniques oriented or applications oriented. In the first case, some new scientific principle is considered and then as many ways as possible in which it can be used for measurement are worked out. In the second case, we start with a need: something is to be measured, perhaps something quite new or perhaps the requirement is for it to be done under difficult conditions or with unprecedented accuracy. Applications-oriented research then considers any and every way in which the measurement needed might be made.

A similar problem arises when thinking how to group the material in a book on instrumentation. For the most part, we have chosen to categorize by application, but we have supplemented this by one or two 'techniques' chapters. An appreciation of nuclear techniques needs to be based on some understanding of radiation, so it is natural for their applications to be combined in a single chapter.

A few decades ago, pneumatic devices formed a large part of the instrumentation installed on plant; earlier editions of *Instrument Technology* described equally what was based on pneumatics and on electronics. In recent years, the electronic side has grown disproportionately and authors writing today tend to emphasize that category. But pneumatics is still widely used and to redress the balance we have included a 'techniques-oriented' chapter devoted to it.

2 Further reading

Instrument Technology is primarily a 'stand alone' description of current practice. For the greatest part its readers will learn most from it simply by reading what it says itself. It is certainly not an academic treatise that needs to justify much of what it says by quoting previous writers.

Because this book does not go into the greatest detail we have, in most chapters, listed more specialized books where particular subjects are dealt with more fully. The extensiveness of the lists varies with the availability of appropriate books and with the inclination of the contributor.

The reader may sometimes want to do yet more reading: instrumentation tends to be a difficult subject in which to trace references to earlier work. This is partly because the alternative approaches—techniques and applications—that we have mentioned complicate the issue. It is partly because much useful information is to be found in manufacturers' publications rather than conventional scientific journals. Perhaps most of all it is because some instrument technology will be described in papers that have the use made of that technology as their main topic and consequently as the subject under which they are indexed. Sydenham has discussed the overall problem and also edited a classified compilation listing many papers on 'measurement science and technology in the physical sciences'.

3 Accuracy

A supremely important question in all matters of instrumentation is the accuracy with which a measurement is made. An attitude of robust scepticism is healthy in an instrument engineer: he should tend to distrust what he is told about equipment and he should equally hesitate to accept his own reasoning about systems he has assembled. He should demand evidence and preferably proof. Accuracy is important but complex.

A first analysis distinguishes 'systematic' and 'random' errors in an instrument. The concept is based on the idea of making a series of measurements of the same quantity under the same conditions. There will generally be differences in the results, but even their average may differ from the 'true value'—an abstract concept but often replaceable by the 'conventional true value' that has been measured by an instrument or technique known to have a very high accuracy. The difference can be equated roughly with systematic error and can be eliminated by calibration, a subject we return to in several chapters of *Instrument*

Technology. Calibration is concerned with the chain linking a local measurement to fundamental standards and with the 'traceability' of this chain.

The phrase *random errors* gives a hint that probability comes into the assessment of the results of measurement, but in a deterministic world where does the randomness come from? Some variations in readings, though clearly observed, are difficult to explain and most random errors can be treated statistically without knowing their cause. In most cases it is assumed that the probability of error is such that errors in individual measurements have a normal distribution about the mean (which is zero if there is no systematic error). This implies that errors should be quoted, not as indicating that it is impossible that a true value lies outside a certain range, but that a certain probability can be attached to its whereabouts, the probability growing steadily larger as the range where it might be grows wider.

When we consider a measurement chain with several links, the two approaches give increasingly different figures. For if we think of possibilities/impossibilities then we must allow that the errors in each link can be extreme and in the same direction, calling for a simple addition when calculating the possible total error. On the other hand, this is *improbable* so the 'chain error' that corresponds to a given probability, e_c, is appreciably smaller. In fact, statistically,

$$e_c = \sqrt{e_1^2 + e_2^2 + \cdots}$$

where e_1, e_2, etc. are the errors in the different links each corresponding to the same probability as e_c.

The causes of random errors can often be appreciated by thinking of 'influence quantities'. Most devices intended to measure some physical quantity make some response to other quantities: they come under their *influence*. Even in the simple case of a tape measure being used to measure an unknown length, the tape will itself expand with temperature, so giving a false reading unless the influence is allowed for. It is desirable for any instrument to be insensitive to influence quantities and for the user to be aware of them. Whether they are realized or not, their effects can be reduced by calibrating under conditions as close as possible to those holding for the live measurement. Influence quantities may be complicated. Thus it is not only temperature—often important—that can affect an instrument, but also rate of change of temperature and temperature differences between various items in apparatus.

One particular factor that could be thought of as an influence quantity is the direction in which the quantity to be measured is changing. Many instruments give slightly different readings according to whether, as it changes, the particular value of interest is approached from above or below. This phenomenon is called 'hysteresis'.

'Non-linearity errors' arise if it is assumed that an instrument's output is exactly proportional to some quantity and there is a discrepancy from this law. The error can be specified as the maximum departure of the true input/output curve from the idealized straight line approximating it: it may be noted that this does not cover changes in 'incremental gain', the term used for the local slope of the input/output curve. Calibration at sufficient intermediate points in the range of an instrument can cover systematic non-linearity and the advent of sophisticated data-processing facilities, which allow easy correction, has reduced the problems it introduces.

Special terms used in the discussion above are defined in BS 5233 along with numerous others.

The general approach to errors that we have outlined follows a statistical approach to a static situation. In communications theory, working frequencies and time available are emphasized, and this approach may gain importance in instrument technology. Sensors often feed to electronic amplifiers and the electronic noise in the amplifier may be an ultimate source of error. This will mean that more accurate results can be expected when a longer time is available in which to make the measurement. Other sources of error can then also be treated as noise.

There is, of course, some danger of making a highly accurate measurement of the wrong thing! This could happen from faulty system analysis throwing up the wrong quantity as relevant to process control. More directly significant for instrumentation, the operation of measurement could disturb the quantity measured. This can happen in most fields: a flow-meter can obstruct flow and reduce the velocity to be measured, an over-large temperature sensor can cool the material studied or a low-impedance voltmeter can reduce the potential it is monitoring. Part of the instrument engineer's task is to foresee and avoid errors resulting from the effect his instrument has on the system it is being used to study.

In fact a considerable part of his task is to be concerned with accuracy. He should give his mind to the question of what accuracy is really needed and may have to argue with a client, whose tendency may well be to ask for an arbitrarily high accuracy, regardless of effort and cost. Once a figure is agreed there must be constant alertness whether any factors have crept in that will increase errors. The practical man will think a lot about accuracy even if he is not steeped too deeply in the theory of errors. He may remember and sympathize with Rutherford's reported remark to one of his students: 'Do forget about the theory of errors and go back to your laboratory and do the experiment again.'

4 Environment

Instruments must always be selected in full consciousness of the environment in which they will be used. On plant there may be extremes of temperature, vibration, dust much more severe than are found in the laboratory. There are two sorts of ill effects: false readings from exceptional values of influence quantities and irreversible breakdown of equipment. Sometimes manufacturers specify limits to working conditions, sometimes these have to be estimated from a general judgement of robustness.

The reliability of equipment—the likelihood of its continuing to work satisfactorily over long periods—is always a key feature. We go into it more deeply in Volume 4 and it must be taken into account when choosing apparatus for all applications.

5 Units

Some introductory chapters have discussed the theme of what system of units is used in a book. Fortunately the question is becoming obsolete as SI units are adopted nearly everywhere, and certainly in this book. In a few areas, where other units still have some usage, we have listed the relations for the benefit of those who are still more at home with the older expressions.

6 References

British Standards Institution, *Glossary of terms used in Metrology*, BS 5233, (1975)

Dietrich, D. F., *Uncertainty, Calibration and Probability; the Statistics of Scientific and Industrial Measurement*, Adam Hilger, London, (1973)

Sydenham, P. H., (ed.), *A Working List of Books Published on Measurement Science and Technology in the Physical Sciences*, Applied Physics Dept., Technische Hogeschool, Delft, (1980)

Sydenham, P. H., 'The literature of instrument science and technology', *J. Phys. E.*, **15**, 487–491, (1982)

1 Measurement of flow

G. FOWLES

1.1 Introduction

Flow measurement is a technique used in any process requiring the transport of a material from one point to another (for example, bulk supply of oil from a road tanker to a garage holding tank). It can be used for quantifying a charge for material supplied or maintaining and controlling a specific rate of flow. In many processes, plant efficiency will depend on being able to measure and control flow accurately.

However it is applied, a flow-measurement system will need to be compatible with the process or material being measured whilst being capable of producing the desired accuracy and repeatability.

It is often said that, 'The ideal flowmeter should be non-intrusive, inexpensive, have absolute accuracy, infinite repeatability and run forever without maintenance.' Unfortunately, such a device does not yet exist, although some manufacturers may claim that it does. Over recent years, however, many improvements have been made to established systems, and new products utilizing novel techniques are continually being introduced onto the market. The 'ideal flowmeter', may not in fact be so far away and now more than ever potential users must be fully aware of the systems at their disposal.

1.2 Basic principles of flow measurement

Before a full understanding of the operational techniques of existing or new measurement systems can be gained, it is necessary to develop a knowledge of the basic theory of flow measurement and the derivation of flow formulae.

Flow can be measured as either a volumetric quantity or an instantaneous velocity (this is normally translated into a flow rate). If Figure 1.1 is examined the interdependence of these measurements can be established.

$$\text{flow rate} = \text{velocity} \times \text{area} = \frac{m}{s} . m^2 = \frac{m^3}{s}$$

$$\text{quantity} = \text{flow rate} \times \text{time} = \frac{m^3}{s} . s = m^3$$

If, as above, flow rate is recorded for a period of time, the quantity is equal to the area under the curve (shaded area). This can be established automatically by many instruments and the process is called integration. It may be carried out by an instrument's integrator either electrically or mechanically.

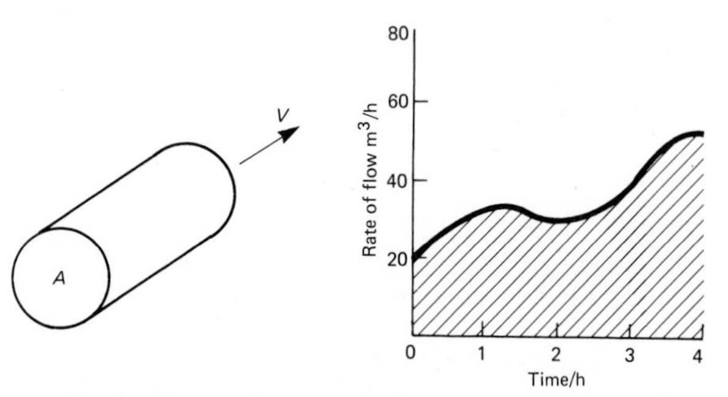

Figure 1.1 Flow–time graph.

1.2.1 Streamlined and turbulent flow

Streamlined flow in a liquid is a phenomenon best described by example. Reynolds did a considerable amount of work on this subject and Figure 1.2 illustrates the principle of streamlined flow (also called laminar flow).

A thin filament of coloured liquid is introduced into a quantity of water flowing through a smooth glass tube. The paths of all fluid particles will be parallel to the tube walls and therefore the coloured liquid travels in a straight line, almost as if it were a tube within a tube. However, this state is velocity- and viscosity-dependent and as velocity is increased, a point is

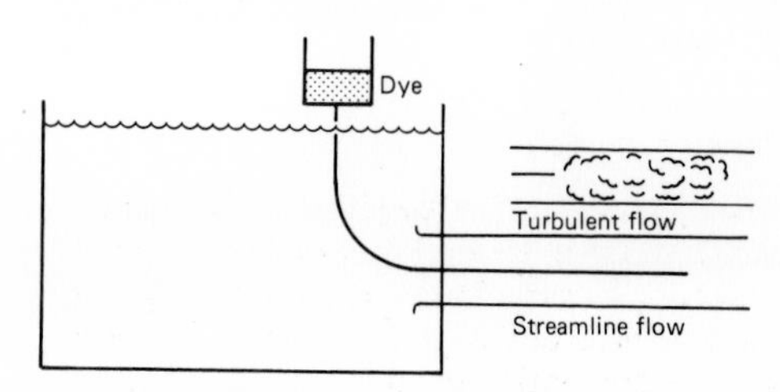

Figure 1.2 Reynolds's experiment.

reached (critical velocity) when the coloured liquid will appear to disperse and mix with the carrier liquid. At this point the motion of the particles of fluid are not all parallel to the tube walls but have a transverse velocity also. This form of flow pattern is called turbulent flow. Summarizing therefore, for velocities below the critical velocity, flow is said to be streamlined or laminar and for velocities above the critical value flow is said to be turbulent—this situation is most common in practice.

Reynolds formulated his data in a dimensionless form

$$Re=\frac{D.v.\rho}{\mu} \tag{1.1}$$

where Re is Reynolds number, D is the diameter of the throat of the installation, v is velocity, ρ is density of fluid, and μ is absolute viscosity. Flow of fluid in pipes is expected to be laminar if the Reynolds number is less than 2000 and turbulent if it is greater than 4000. Between these values is the critical zone. If systems have the same Reynolds number and are geometrically similar they are said to have dynamic similarity.

1.2.1.1 Flow profile

The velocity across the diameter of a pipe varies and the distribution is termed the velocity profile of the system. For laminar flow the profile is parabolic in nature, the velocity at the centre of the pipe being twice the mean velocity. For turbulent flow, after a sufficient straight pipe run the flow profile becomes fully developed where velocity at the centre of the pipe is only about 1.2 times the mean velocity and is the preferred situation to allow accurate flow measurement.

1.2.1.2 Energy of a fluid in motion

Before establishing the use of Reynolds number in universal flow formulae, it is worthwhile considering the forms in which energy will be represented in a fluid in motion. The basic types of energy associated with a moving fluid are:

(a) Potential energy or potential head.
(b) Kinetic energy.
(c) Pressure energy.
(d) Heat energy.

1.2.1.3 Potential energy

This is the energy the fluid has by virtue of its position or height above some fixed level. For example 1 m^3 of liquid of density ρ_1 kg/m^3 will have a mass of ρ_1 kg and would require a force of 9.81 ρ_1 N to support it at a point where the gravitational constant g is 9.81 m/s. Therefore if it is at a height of z metres above a reference plane it would have 9.81 $\rho_1 z$ joules of energy by virtue of its height.

1.2.1.4 Kinetic energy

This is the energy a fluid has, by virtue of its motion. 1 m^3 of fluid of density ρ_1 kg/m^3 with a velocity V_1 m/s would have a kinetic energy of $\frac{1}{2}\rho_1 V_1^2$ joules.

1.2.1.5 Pressure energy

This is the energy a fluid has by virtue of its pressure. For example a fluid having a volume v_1 m^3 and a pressure of p_1 N/m^2 would have a pressure energy of $p_1 v_1$ joules.

1.2.1.6 Internal energy

The fluid will also have energy by virtue of its temperature (i.e. heat energy). If there is resistance to flow in the form of friction, other forms of internal energy will be converted into heat energy.

1.2.1.7 Total energy

The total energy E of a fluid is given by the equation

$$\begin{aligned}\text{total energy } (E) = {} & \text{potential energy} \\ & + \text{kinetic energy} \\ & + \text{pressure energy} \\ & + \text{internal energy} \\ E = {} & \text{P.E.} + \text{K.E.} + \text{PR.E.} + \text{I.E.}\end{aligned} \tag{1.2}$$

1.2.2 Viscosity

The frictional resistance that exists in a flowing fluid is called viscosity and is discussed in more detail in the next chapter. Briefly, the particles of fluid actually in contact with the walls of the channel are at rest, while those at the centre of the channel move at maximum velocity. Thus, the layers of fluid near the centre which are moving at maximum velocity, will be slowed down by the slower moving layers and the slower moving layers will be speeded up by the faster moving layers.

Dynamic viscosity of a fluid is expressed in units of Ns/m^2. Thus a fluid has a dynamic viscosity of 1 Ns/m^2 if a force of 1 N is required to move a plane of 1 m^2 in area at a speed of 1 m/s parallel to a fixed plane, the moving plane being 1 m away from the fixed plane and the space between the planes being completely filled with the fluid. This is illustrated diagrammatically in Figure 1.3.

Thus for parallel flow lines

$$\text{dynamic viscosity } \mu=\frac{\text{force}(F)}{\text{area}(A)\times\text{velocity}(v)} \tag{1.3}$$

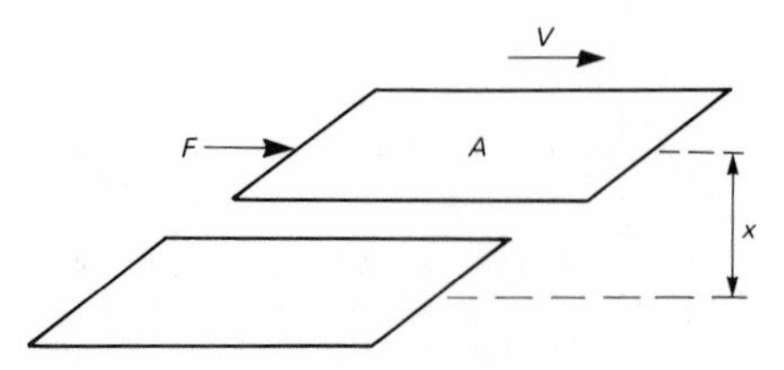

Figure 1.3 Determination of dynamic viscosity.

or, if a velocity gradient exists,

$$\mu = \frac{F}{A\,\mathrm{d}v/\mathrm{d}x} \tag{1.4}$$

It is sometimes useful to know the ratio of the dynamic viscosity of a fluid to its density at the same temperature. This is called the kinematic viscosity of the fluid.

$$\text{kinematic viscosity at } T\,^\circ\text{C} = \frac{\text{dynamic viscosity at } T\,^\circ\text{C}}{\text{density at } T\,^\circ\text{C}} \tag{1.5}$$

For liquids the viscosity decreases with increase of temperature at constant pressure whilst for gases viscosity will increase with increasing temperature, at a constant pressure.

It is viscosity that is responsible for the damping out or suppression of flow disturbances caused by bends and valves in a pipe; the energy that existed in the swirling liquid is changed into heat energy.

1.2.3 Bernoulli's theorem

All formulae for the derivation of fluid flow in a closed pipe are based on Bernoulli's theorem. This states that in a steady flow, without friction, the sum of potential energy, kinetic energy and pressure energy is a constant along any streamline.

If we now consider a closed pipe or channel (Figure 1.4) in which two sections are examined (section 1 and section 2); due to a restriction, orifice or hydraulic gradient there is a pressure or head loss in the transition from section 1 to section 2. If 1 kg of fluid enters at section 1 and there is no accumulation of fluid between section 1 and section 2 then 1 kg of fluid must leave at section 2.

The energy of the fluid at section 1

$$= \text{potential energy} + \text{kinetic energy} + \text{pressure energy} + \text{internal energy}$$

$$= 1\,.\,Z_1\,.\,g + \tfrac{1}{2}\,.\,1\,.\,V_1^2 + p_1\,.\,v_1 + I_1 \tag{1.6}$$

The energy of the fluid at section 2

$$= 1\,.\,Z_2\,.\,g + \tfrac{1}{2}\,.\,1\,.\,V_2^2 + p_2\,.\,v_2 + I_2 \tag{1.7}$$

and since energy cannot leave the channel nor be created or destroyed,

total energy at section 1 = total energy at section 2

$$Z_1\,.\,g + \frac{V_1^2}{2} + p_1\,.\,v_1 + I_1 = Z_2\,.\,g + \frac{V_2^2}{2} + p_2\,.\,v_2 + I_2 \tag{1.8}$$

Now, if the temperature of the fluid remains the same the internal energy remains the same and

$$I_1 = I_2 \tag{1.9}$$

and equation (1.8) reduces to

$$Z_1\,.\,g + \frac{V_1^2}{2} + p_1\,.\,v_1 = Z_2\,.\,g + \frac{V_2^2}{2} + p_2\,.\,v_2 \tag{1.10}$$

This equation applies to liquids and ideal gases.

Now consider liquids only. These can be regarded as being incompressible and their density and specific volume will remain constant along the channel and

$$v_1 = v_2 = \frac{1}{\rho_1} = \frac{1}{\rho_2} = \frac{1}{\rho} \tag{1.11}$$

and equation (1.10) may be rewritten as,

$$Z_1\,.\,g + \frac{V_1^2}{2} + \frac{p_1}{\rho} = Z_2\,.\,g + \frac{V_2^2}{2} + \frac{p_2}{\rho} \tag{1.12}$$

Dividing by g, this becomes,

$$Z_1 + \frac{V_1^2}{2g} + \frac{p_1}{\rho\,.\,g} = Z_2 + \frac{V_2^2}{2g} + \frac{p_2}{\rho\,.\,g} \tag{1.13}$$

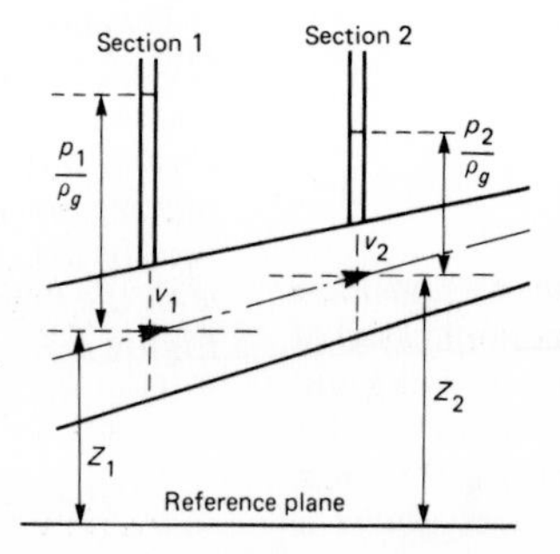

Parameter	At section 1	At section 2	Units
Area	A_1	A_2	m^2
Velocity	V_1	V_2	m/s
Pressure	p_1	p_2	N/m^2
Density	ρ_1	ρ_2	Kg/m^3
Specific volume of 1Kg	$v_1=1/\rho_1$	$v_2=1/\rho_2$	m^3
Height of centre of gravity above reference plane	Z_1	Z_2	m
Internal energy per Kg	I_1	I_2	J

Figure 1.4 Hydraulic conditions for pipe flow.

Referring back to Figure 1.4 it is obvious that there is a height differential between the upstream and downstream vertical connections representing sections 1 and 2 of the fluid. Considering first the conditions at the upstream tapping, the fluid will rise in the tube to a height $p_1/\rho.g$ above the tapping or $p_1/\rho.g+Z_1$ above the horizontal level taken as the reference plane. Similarly the fluid will rise to a height $p_2/\rho.g$ or $p_2/\rho.g+Z_2$ in the vertical tube at the downstream tapping.

The differential head will be given by

$$h=\left(\frac{p_1}{\rho.g}+Z_1\right)-\left(\frac{p_2}{\rho.g}+Z_2\right) \tag{1.14}$$

but from equation (1.13) we have

$$\left(\frac{p_1}{\rho.g}+Z_1\right)+\frac{V_1^2}{2g}=\left(\frac{p_2}{\rho.g}+Z_2\right)+\frac{V_2^2}{2g}$$

or $$\left(\frac{p_1}{\rho.g}+Z_1\right)-\left(\frac{p_2}{\rho.g}+Z_2\right)=\frac{V_2^2}{2g}-\frac{V_1^2}{2g}$$

Therefore

$$h=\frac{V_2^2}{2g}-\frac{V_1^2}{2g} \tag{1.15}$$

and

$$V_2^2-V_1^2=2gh \tag{1.16}$$

Now the volume of liquid flowing along the channel per second will be given by Q m^3 where,

$$Q=A_1.V_1=A_2.V_2$$

or $$V_1=\frac{A_2.V_2}{A_1}$$

Now substituting this value in equation (1.16):

$$V_2^2-V_2^2\frac{A_2^2}{A_1^2}=2gh$$

or $$V_2^2(1-A_2^2/A_1^2)=2gh \tag{1.17}$$

dividing by $(1-A_2^2/A_1^2)$ equation (1.17) becomes

$$V_2^2=\frac{2gh}{1-A_2^2/A_1^2} \tag{1.18}$$

and taking the square root of both sides

$$V_2=\frac{\sqrt{2gh}}{\sqrt{(1-A_2^2/A_1^2)}} \tag{1.19}$$

Now A_2/A_1 is the ratio (area of section 2)/(area of section 1) and is often represented by the symbol m. Therefore

$$\left(1-\frac{A_2^2}{A_1^2}\right)=1-m^2$$

and

$$\frac{1}{\sqrt{[1-(A_2^2/A_1^2)]}} \text{ may be written as } \frac{1}{\sqrt{(1-m^2)}}$$

This is termed the velocity of approach factor often represented by E. Equation (1.19) may be written

$$V_2=E\sqrt{2gh} \tag{1.20}$$

$$\text{and}\quad Q=A_2.V_2=A_2.E\sqrt{2gh}\ \text{m}^3/\text{s} \tag{1.21}$$

Mass of liquid flowing per second $=W=\rho.Q=A_2.\rho.E\sqrt{2gh}$ kg also since $\Delta p=hp$,

$$Q=A_2.E\sqrt{\frac{2g\,\Delta p}{\rho}}\ \text{m}^3/\text{s} \tag{1.22}$$

$$W=A_2.E\sqrt{2g\rho.\Delta p}\ \text{kg/s} \tag{1.23}$$

1.2.4 Practical realization of equations

The foregoing equations apply only to streamlined flow. To determine actual flow it is necessary to take into account various other parameters. In practice flow is rarely streamlined, but is turbulent. However, the velocities of particles across the stream will be entirely random and will not affect the rate of flow very considerably.

In developing the equations, effects of viscosity have also been neglected. In an actual fluid the loss of head between sections will be greater than that which would take place in a fluid free from viscosity.

In order to correct for these and other effects another factor is introduced into the equations for flow. This factor is the discharge coefficient C and is given by the equation

Discharge coefficient

$$C=\frac{\text{actual mass rate of flow}}{\text{theoretical mass rate of flow}}$$

or if the conditions of temperature, density, etc., are the same at both sections it may be written in terms of volume.

$$C=\frac{\text{actual volume flowing}}{\text{theoretical volume flowing}}$$

It is possible to determine C experimentally by actual tests. It is a function of pipe size, type of pressure tappings and Reynolds number.

Equation (1.22) is modified and becomes

$$Q=C.A_2.E\sqrt{\frac{2g.\Delta p}{\rho}} \tag{1.24}$$

This is true for flow systems where Reynolds number is

above a certain value (20 000 or above for orifice plates). For lower Reynolds numbers and for very small or rough pipes the basic coefficient is multiplied by a correction factor Z whose value depends on the area ratio, the Reynolds number and the size and roughness of the pipe. Values for both C and Z are listed with other relevant data in BS 1042 Part 1 1964.

We can use differential pressure to measure flow.

Consider a practical example of a device having the following dimensions:

Internal diameter of upstream pipe	D mm
Orifice or throat diameter	d mm
Pressure differential produced	h mm water gauge
Density of fluid at upstream tapping	ρ kg/m^2
Absolute pressure at upstream tapping	p bar

Then introducing the discharge coefficient C, the correction factor and the numerical constant, the equation for quantity rate of flow Q m^3/h becomes

$$Q=0.012\,52C.Z.E.d^2\sqrt{\frac{h}{\rho}} \qquad (1.25)$$

and the weight or mass rate of the flow W kg/h is given by

$$W=0.012\,52C.Z.E.d^2\sqrt{h\rho} \qquad (1.26)$$

1.2.5 Modification of flow equations to apply to gases

Gases differ from liquids in that they are compressible. If the gas under consideration can be regarded as an ideal gas (most gases are ideal when well away from their critical temperatures and pressures) then the gas obeys several very important gas laws. These laws will now be stated.

1.2.5.1 Dry gases

(a) Boyle's law This states that the volume of any given mass of gas will be inversely proportional to its absolute pressure provided temperature remains constant. Thus, if a certain mass of gas occupies a volume v_0 at an absolute pressure p_0 and a volume v_1 at an absolute pressure p then

$$p_0.v_0=p.v_1$$

$$\text{or} \quad v_1=v_0.p_0/p \qquad (1.27)$$

(b) Charles's law This states that if the volume of a given mass of gas occupies a volume v_1 at a temperature T_0 kelvin, then its volume v at T kelvin is given by

$$v_1/T_0=v/T \quad \text{or} \quad v=v_1.T/T_0 \qquad (1.28)$$

(c) The ideal gas law In the general case p, v and T change. Suppose a mass of gas at pressure p_0 and temperature T_0 kelvin has a volume v_0 and the mass of gas at pressure p and temperature T has a volume v, and that the change from the first set of conditions to the second set of conditions takes place in two stages.

(a) Change the pressure from p_0 to p at a constant temperature. Let the new volume be v_1. From Boyle's law:

$$p_0.v_0=p.v_1 \quad \text{or} \quad v_1=v_0.p_0/p$$

(b) Change the temperature from T_0 to T at constant pressure. From Charles's law:

$$v_1/T_0=v/T$$

Hence, equating the two values of v_1

$$v_0.p_0/p=v.T_0/T$$

$$p_0.v_0/T_0=pv/T=\text{constant} \qquad (1.29)$$

If the quantity of gas considered is 1 mole, i.e. the quantity of gas that contains as many molecules as there are atoms in 0.012 kg of carbon-12, this constant is represented by R, the gas constant, and equation (1.29) becomes:

$$pv=R_0.T$$

where $R_0=8.314$ J/Mol K and p is in N/m^2 and v is in m^3.

Adiabatic expansion When a gas is flowing through a primary element the change in pressure takes place too rapidly for the gas to absorb heat from its surroundings. When it expands owing to the reduction in pressure it does work, so that if it does not receive energy it must use its own heat energy, and its temperature will fall. Thus the expansion that takes place owing to the fall in pressure does not obey Boyle's law, which applies only to an expansion at constant temperature. Instead it obeys the law for adiabatic expansion of a gas:

$$p_1.v_1^\gamma=p_2.v_2^\gamma \quad \text{or} \quad p.v^\gamma=\text{constant} \qquad (1.30)$$

where γ is the ratio of the specific heats of the gas

$$\gamma=\frac{\text{specific heat of a gas at constant pressure}}{\text{specific heat of a gas at constant volume}}$$

and has a value of 1.40 for dry air and other diatomic gases, 1.66 for monatomic gases such as helium and about 1.33 for triatomic gases such as carbon dioxide.

If a fluid that is being metered cannot be regarded as being incompressible, another factor is introduced into the flow equations, to correct for the change in volume due to the expansion of the fluid while passing through the restriction. This factor is called the expansibility factor ε and has a value of unity for incompressible fluids. For ideal compressible fluids expanding without any change of state the value can be calculated from the equation

$$\varepsilon=\sqrt{\left(\frac{\gamma r^{2/\gamma}}{\gamma-1}\frac{1-m^2}{1-m^2 r^{2/\gamma}}\frac{1-r^{(\gamma-1)/\gamma}}{1-r}\right)}$$

where r is the ratio of the absolute pressures at the upstream and downstream tappings (i.e. $r=p_1/p_2$) and γ is the ratio of the specific heat of the fluid at constant pressure to that at constant volume. This is detailed in BS 1042 Part 1 1964.

In order that working fluid flow equations can be applied to both liquids and gases the factor ε is introduced and the equations become:

$$Q=0.012\,52CZ\varepsilon Ed^2\sqrt{h/\rho}\ \text{m}^3/\text{h} \qquad (1.32)$$

$$W=0.012\,52CZ\varepsilon Ed^2\sqrt{h\rho}\ \text{kg/h} \qquad (1.33)$$

$\varepsilon=1$ for liquids

1.2.5.2 Critical flow of compressible fluids

It can be shown theoretically for flow through a convergent tube such as a nozzle that the value of r at the throat cannot be less than a critical value r_c. When the pressure at the throat is equal to this critical fraction of the upstream pressure, the rate of flow is a maximum and cannot be further increased except by raising the upstream pressure. The critical pressure ratio is given by the equation

$$2r_c^{(1-\gamma)/\gamma}+(\gamma-1)m^2\,.\,r_c^{2/\gamma}=\gamma-1 \qquad (1.34)$$

The value of r is about 0.5 but it increases slightly with increase of m and with decrease of specific heat ratio. Values of r are tabulated in BS 1042 Part 1 1964.

The basic equation for critical flow is obtained by substituting $(1-r_c)\rho$ for Δp in equation (1.23) substituting r_c for r in equation (1.31) and the equation becomes

$$W=1.252U\,.\,d^2\sqrt{\rho p}\ \text{kg/h} \qquad (1.35)$$

where

$$U=C\sqrt{(\gamma/2)r_c\cdot(\gamma-1)/\gamma} \qquad (1.36)$$

The volume rate of flow (in m^3/h) is obtained by dividing the weight ratio of flow by the density (in kg/m^3) of the fluid at the reference conditions.

1.2.5.3 Departure from gas laws

At room temperature and at absolute pressures less than 10 bar most common gases except carbon dioxide behave sufficiently like an ideal gas that the error in flow calculations brought about by departure from the ideal gas laws is less than 1 per cent. In order to correct for departure from the ideal gas laws a deviation coefficient K (given in BS 1042 Part 1 1964) is used in the calculation of densities of gases where the departure is significant. For ideal gases $K=1$.

1.2.5.4 Wet gases

The above modification applies to dry gases. In practice many gases are wet, being a mixture of gas and water vapour. Partial pressure due to saturated water vapour does not obey Boyle's law.

Gas humidity is discussed in Chapter 6 of volume 2. If the temperature and absolute pressure at the upstream tapping and the state of humidity of the gas are known, a correction factor can be worked out and applied to obtain the actual mass of gas flowing.

Gas density is given by the equation

$$\rho=6.196\left[\delta\frac{(p-p_v)}{k.T}+\frac{0.622p_v}{T}\right]\text{kg/m}^3 \qquad (1.37)$$

where δ is specific gravity of dry gas relative to air, T is temperature in kelvin, p is pressure in mbar at the upstream tapping, p_v is partial pressure in mbar of the water vapour, k is the gas law deviation at temperature T, and ρ is gas density. For dry gas pv is zero and the equation becomes

$$\rho=6.196\frac{\delta p}{kT}\ \text{kg/m}^3 \qquad (1.38)$$

1.3 Fluid flow in closed pipes

1.3.1 Differential-pressure devices

By far the most common technique for measurement of fluid flow in pipes is that which utilizes the pressure drop caused by a constriction in the pipeline. As already shown in the derivation of Bernoulli's equation in the previous section, a constriction will cause an increase in fluid velocity in the area of that constriction, which in turn will result in a corresponding pressure drop across the constriction. This differential pressure (d.p.) is a function of the flow velocity and density of the fluid and is shown to be a square root relationship, see equation (1.24).

A flowmeter in this category would normally comprise a primary element to develop a differential pressure and a secondary element to measure it. The secondary element is effectively a pressure transducer, and operational techniques are discussed in Chapter 9, so no further coverage will be given here. However there are various types of primary element and these deserve further consideration. The main types of interest are: orifice plate, venturi, nozzle, Dall, rotameter, gate meter, Gilflo element, and target meter.

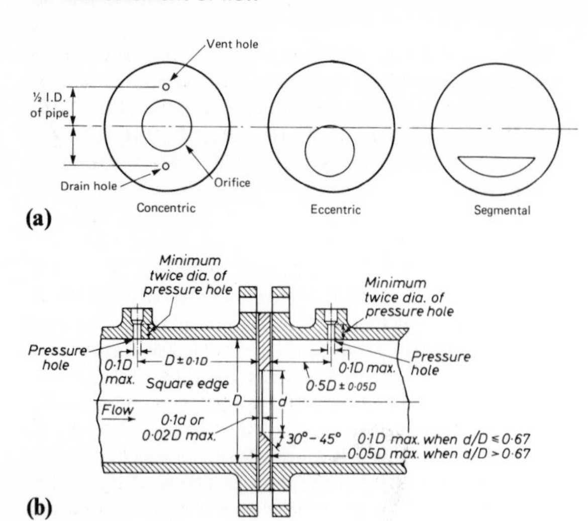

Figure 1.5 (a) Orifice plate types. (b) Concentric orifice plate with D and $D/2$ tappings mounted between flange plates. Courtesy, British Standards Institution.

1.3.1.1 Orifice plate

In its simplest form this comprises a thin steel plate with a circular orifice of known dimensions located centrally in the plate. This is termed a concentric orifice plate, see Figure 1.5(a). The plate would normally be clamped between adjacent flange fittings in a pipeline, a vent hole and drain hole being provided to prevent solids building up and gas pockets developing in the system, see Figure 1.5(b).

The differential pressure is measured by suitably located pressure tappings on the pipeline on either side of the orifice plate. These may be located in various positions depending on the application (e.g. corner, D and $D/2$, or flange tappings), and reference should be made to BS 1042 Part 1 1964 for correct application. Flow rate is determined from equation (1.24).

This type of orifice plate is inadequate to cope with difficult conditions experienced in metering dirty or viscous fluids and gives a poor disposal rate of condensate in flowing steam and vapours. Modified designs are utilized to overcome these problems in the form of segmental or eccentric orifice plates as shown in Figure 1.5(a).

The segmental orifice provides a method for measuring the flow of liquids with solids in suspension. It takes the form of a plate which covers the upper cross-section of the pipe leaving the lower portion open for the passage of solids to prevent their build-up.

The eccentric orifice is used on installations where condensed liquids are present in gas-flow measurement or where undissolved gases are present in the measurement of liquid flow. It is also useful where pipeline drainage is required.

To sum up the orifice plate:

Advantages
1. Inherently simple in operation
2. No moving parts
3. Long-term reliability
4. Inexpensive

Disadvantages
1. Square root relationship
2. Poor turn-down ratio
3. Critical installation requirements
4. High irrecoverable pressure loss

1.3.1.2 Venturi tube

The basic construction of the classical venturi tube is shown in Figure 1.6. It comprises a cylindrical inlet section followed by a convergent entrance into a cylindrical throat and a divergent outlet section. A complete specification may be found by reference to BS 1042 Part 1 1964 and relevant details are repeated here:

(a) Diameter of throat. The diameter d of the throat shall be not less than $0.224D$ and not greater than $0.742D$, where D is the entrance diameter.
(b) Length of throat. The throat shall have a length of $1.0d$.
(c) Cylindrical entrance section. This section shall have an internal diameter D and a length of not less than $1.0d$.
(d) Conical section. This shall have a taper of $10\frac{1}{2}°$. Its length is therefore $2.70(D-d)$ within $\pm 0.24(D-d)$.
(e) Divergent outlet section. The outlet section shall have an inclined angle of not less than 5° and not greater than 15°. Its length shall be such that the exit diameter is not less than $1.5d$.

In operation the fluid passes through the convergent entrance, increasing velocity as it does so, resulting in a differential pressure between the inlet and throat. This differential pressure is monitored in the same way

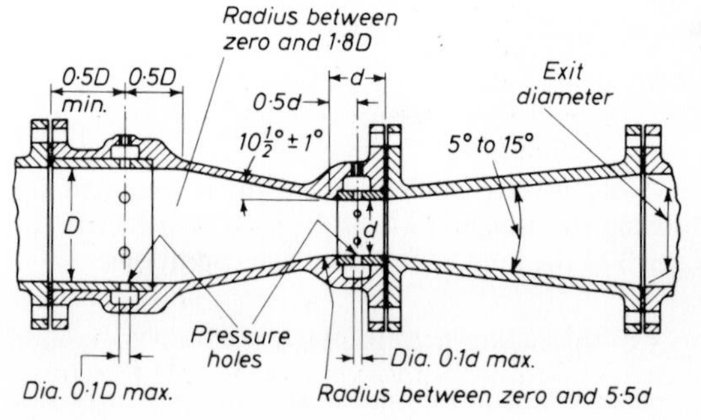

Figure 1.6 Venturi tube. Courtesy, British Standards Institution.

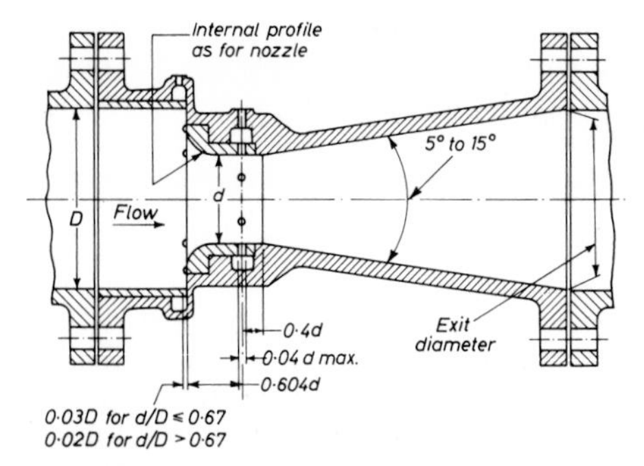

Figure 1.7 Venturi nozzle. Courtesy, British Standards Institution.

as for the orifice plate, the relationship between flow rate and differential being as defined in equation (1.24).

Location of pressure tappings The upstream pressure tapping is located in the cylindrical entrance section of the tube $0.5D$ upstream of the convergent section and the downstream pressure tapping is located in the throat at a distance $0.5D$ downstream of the convergent section. Pressure tappings should be sized so as to avoid accidental blockage.

Generally the tappings are not in the form of a single hole but several equally spaced holes connected together in the form of an annular ring sometimes called a piezometer ring. This has the advantage of giving a true mean value of pressure at the measuring section.

Application The venturi is used for applications where there is a high solids content or where high pressure recovery is desirable. The venturi is inherently a low head loss device and can result in an appreciable saving of energy.

To sum up the venturi tube:

Advantages

1. Simple in operation
2. Low head loss
3. Tolerance of high solids content
4. Long-term reliability
5. No moving parts

Disadvantages

1. Expensive
2. Square root pressure–velocity relationship
3. Poor turn-down ratio
4. Critical installation requirements

1.3.1.3 Nozzles

The venturi effect is also utilized in other more inexpensive forms, the most common being the venturi nozzle.

Venturi nozzle This is in effect a shortened venturi tube. The entrance cone is much shorter and has a curved profile. The inlet pressure tap is located at the mouth of the inlet cone and the low pressure tap in the plane of minimum section as shown in Figure 1.7. This reduction in size is taken a stage further in the flow nozzle.

Flow nozzle Overall length is again reduced greatly. The entrance cone is bell-shaped and there is no exit cone. This is illustrated in Figure 1.8. The flow nozzle is not suitable for viscous liquids but for other applications it is considerably cheaper than standard venturi tube. Also, due to the smooth entrance cone there is less resistance to fluid flow through the nozzle and a lower value of m may be used for a given rate of flow. Its main area of use therefore is in high-velocity mains where it will produce a substantially smaller pressure drop than an orifice plate of similar m number.

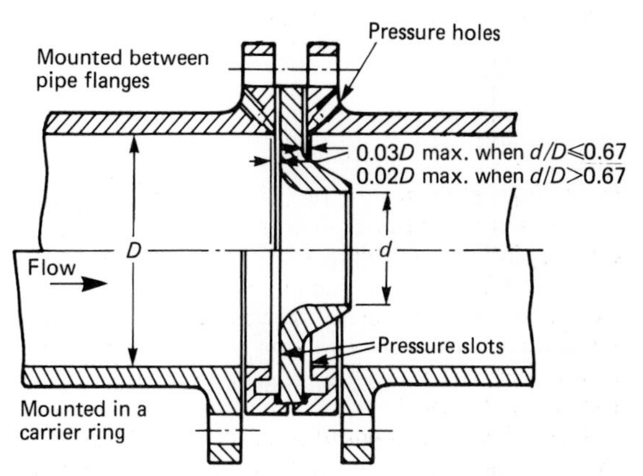

Figure 1.8 Flow nozzle. Courtesy, British Standards Institution.

1.3.1.4 Dall tube

This is another variation of the venturi tube and gives a higher differential pressure but a lower head loss than the conventional venturi tube. Figure 1.9 shows a cross-section of a typical Dall flow tube. It consists of a short straight inlet section, a convergent entrance section, a narrow throat annulus and a short divergent recovery cone. The whole device is about 2 pipe-diameters long.

A shortened version of the Dall tube, the Dall orifice or insert is also available; it is only 0.3 pipe-diameter long. All the essential Dall tube features are retained in a truncated format as shown in Figure 1.10.

Pressure loss All of the differential pressure devices discussed so far cause an irrecoverable pressure loss of varying degree. In operation it is advantageous to keep this loss as low as possible and this will often be a major factor in the selection criteria of a primary

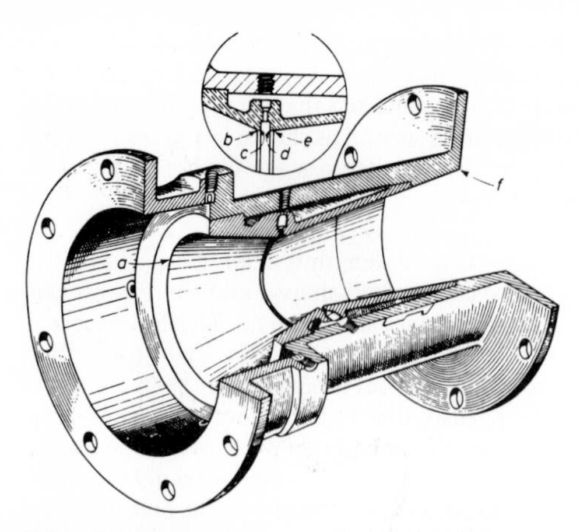

Figure 1.9 Dall tube. Courtesy, Kent Instruments Ltd.

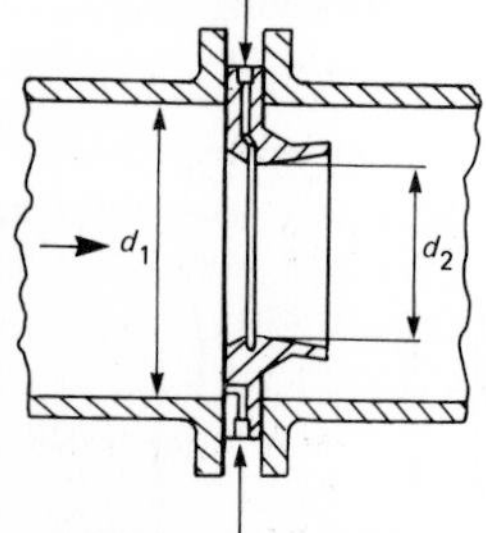

Figure 1.10 Dall insert. Courtesy, British Standards Institution.

element. The pressure loss curves for nozzles, orifices and venturi tubes are given in Figure 1.11.

Installation requirements As already indicated installation requirements for differential-pressure devices are quite critical. It is advisable to install primary elements as far downstream as possible from flow disturbances, such as bends, valves and reducers. These requirements are tabulated in considerable detail in BS 1042 Part 1 1964 and are reproduced in part in Appendix 1.1.

1.3.1.5 Variable-orifice meters

So far the devices discussed have relied on a constriction in the flowstream causing a differential pressure varying with flow rate. Another category of differential-pressure device relies on maintaining a nominally constant differential pressure by allowing effective area to increase with flow. The principal defices to be considered are: rotameter, gate meter and Gilflo.

Rotameter This is shown schematically in Figure 1.12(a). In a tapered tube the upward stream of fluid supports the float where the force on its mass due to gravity is balanced against the flow force determined by the annular area between the float and the tube and the velocity of the stream. The float's position in the tube is measured by a graduated scale and its position is taken as an indication of flow rate.

Many refinements are possible, including the use of magnetic coupling between the float and external devices to translate vertical movement into horizontal and develop either electrical transmission or alarm actuation. Tube materials can be either metal or glass depending on application. Figure 1.12(b) shows an exploded view of a typical rotameter.

Gate meter In this type of meter the area of the orifice may be varied by lowering a gate either manually or by an automatically controlled electric motor. The gate is moved so as to maintain a constant pressure drop across the orifice. The pressure drop is measured by pressure tappings located upstream and downstream of the gate as shown in Figure 1.13(a). The position of the gate is indicated by a scale. As the rate of flow through the orifice increases, the area of the orifice is increased. If all other factors in equation (1.21) except

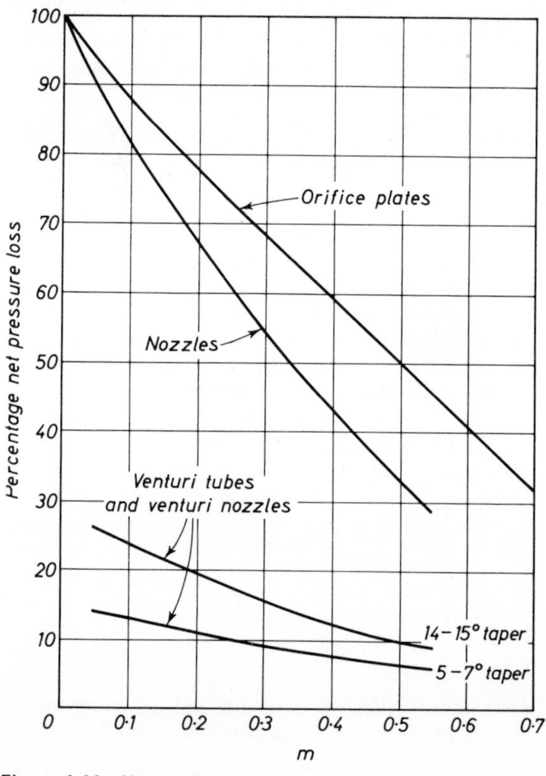

Figure 1.11 Net pressure loss as a percentage of pressure difference. Courtesy, British Standards Institution.

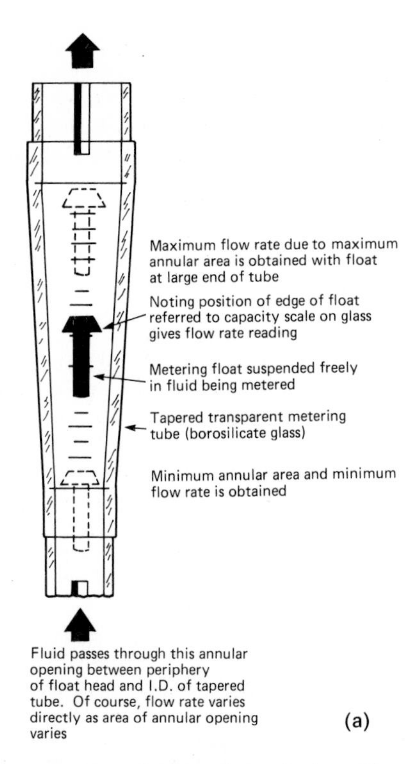

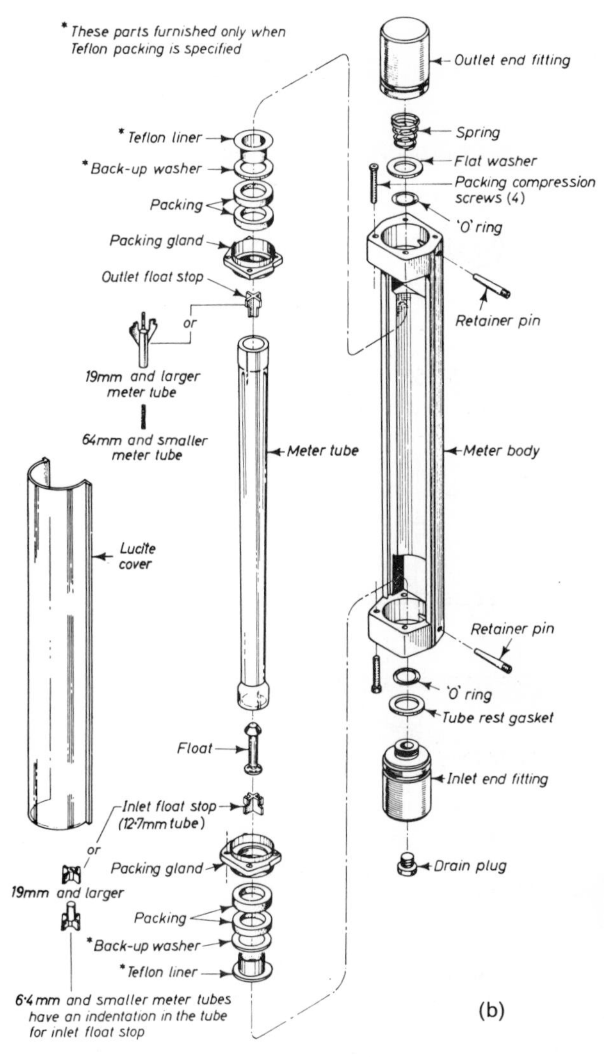

Figure 1.12 (a) Rotameter—principle of operation. Courtesy, Fischer & Porter Ltd. (b) Rotameter—exploded view. Courtesy, Fischer & Porter Ltd.

area A_2 are kept constant the flow through the orifice will depend upon the product $A_2.E$ or $A_2/\sqrt{[1-(A_2/A_1)^2]}$. As A_2 increases, $(A_2/A_1)^2$ increases and $[1-(A_2/A_1)^2]$ decreases and therefore $1/\sqrt{[1-(A_2/A_1)^2]}$ increases.

The relationship between A_2 and flow is not linear. If the vertical movement of the gate is to be directly proportional to the rate of flow, the width of the opening A_2 must decrease towards the top as shown in Figure 1.13(a).

The flow through the meter can be made to depend directly upon the area of the orifice A_2 if instead of the normal static pressure being measured at the upstream tapping the impact pressure is measured. In order to do this the upstream tap is made in the form of a tube with its open end facing directly into the flow as shown in Figure 1.13(b). It is in effect a pitot tube (see section on point-velocity measurement).

The differential pressure is given by equation (1.15), where h is the amount the pressure at the upstream tap is greater than that at the downstream tap:

$$h=\frac{V_2^2}{2g}-\frac{V_1^2}{2g} \tag{1.39}$$

Now, at the impact port, $V_2=0$

therefore $h_1=V_1^2/2g$

where h_1 is the amount the impact pressure is greater than the normal upstream static pressure. Thus the difference between impact pressure and the pressure measured at the downstream tap will be h_2 where

$$h_2=h+h_1$$

$$=\frac{V_2^2}{2g}-\frac{V_1^2}{2g}+\frac{V_1^2}{2g}=\frac{V_2^2}{2g} \tag{1.40}$$

Therefore the velocity V_2 through the section A_2 is given by $V_2=\sqrt{(2g.h_2)}$. The normal flow equations for the type of installation shown in Figure 1.13(b) will be the same for other orifices but the velocity of approach factor is 1 and flow is directly proportional to A_2. The opening of the gate may therefore be made

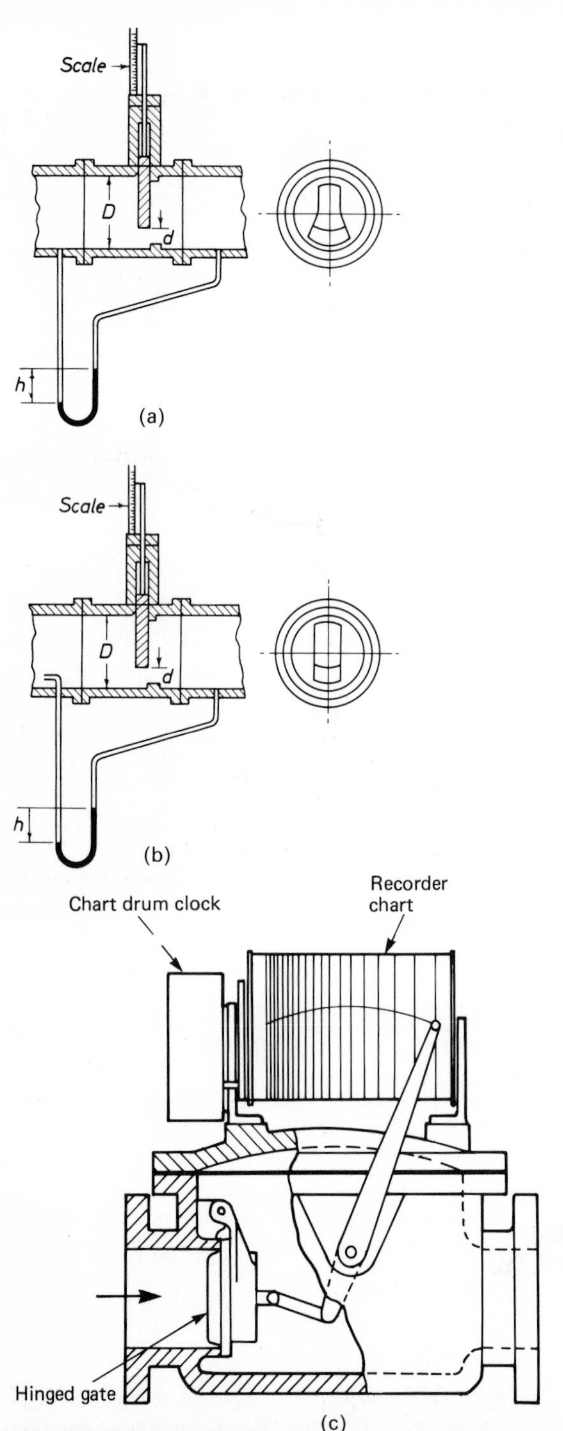

Figure 1.13 (a) Gate-type area meter. Courtesy, American Society of Mechanical Engineers. (b) Gate-type area meter corrected for velocity of approach. Courtesy, American Society of Mechanical Engineers. (c) Weight-controlled hinged-gate meter.

rectangular and the vertical movement will be directly proportional to flow.

The hinged gate meter is another version of this type of device. Here a weighted gate is placed in the flowstream, its deflection being proportional to flow. A mechanical linkage between the gate and a recorder head provides flow indication. It is primarily used for applications in water mains where the user is interested in step changes rather than absolute flow accuracy. The essential features of this device are shown in Figure 1.13(c).

The 'Gilflo' primary sensor The Gilflo metering principle was developed to overcome the limitations of the square law fixed orifice plate in the mid 1960s. Its construction is in two forms; the Gilflo 'A', Figure 1.14(a) sizes 10 to 40 mm has an orifice mounted to a strong linear bellows fixed at one end and with a shaped cone positioned concentrically in it. Under flow conditions the orifice moves axially along the cone creating a variable annulus across which the

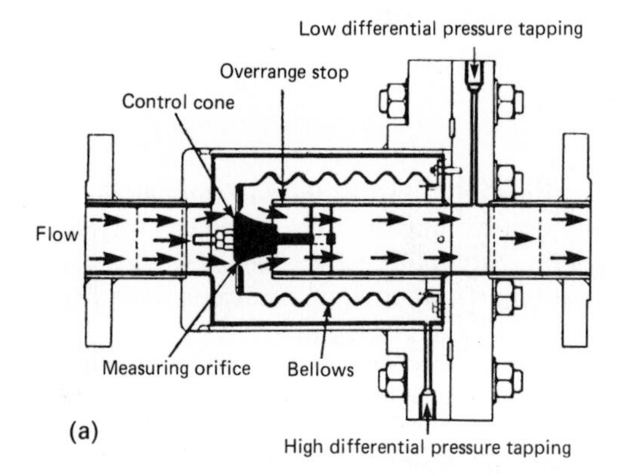

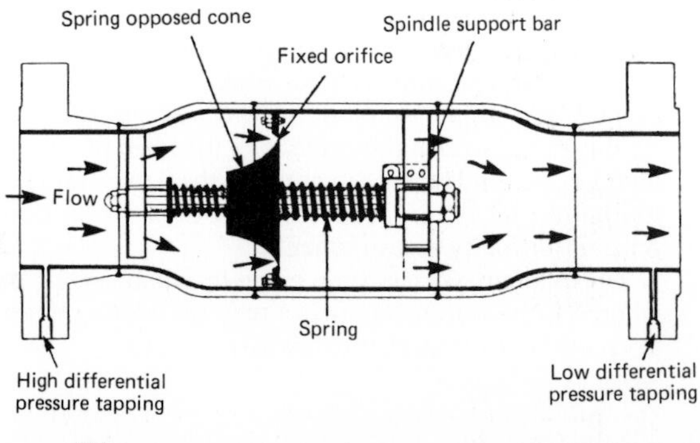

Figure 1.14 (a) The essentials of Gilflo A. As flow increases the measuring orifice moves along the control cone against the spring bellows. Courtesy, Gervase Instruments Ltd. (b) Gilflo B extends the principle to higher flows. Now the orifice is fixed and the control cone moves against the spring. Courtesy, Gervase Instruments Ltd.

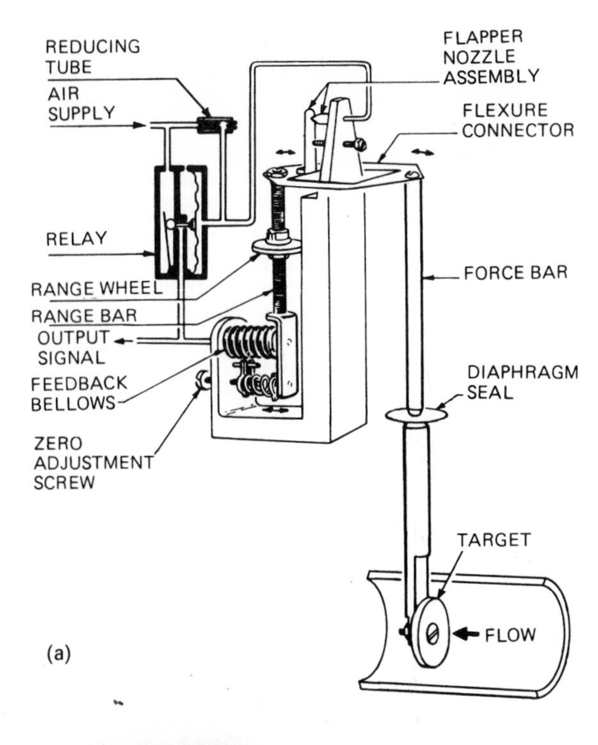

(a)

(b)

Figure 1.15 (a) Target flow transmitter working principle. Courtesy, Foxboro-Yoxall Ltd. (b) The 13 series pneumatic target flow transmitter. Courtesy, The Foxoboro Company.

differential pressure varies. Such is the relationship of change that the differential pressure is directly proportional to flowrate enabling a rangeability of up to 100:1.

The Gilflo 'B', Figure 1.14(b) sizes 40 to 300 mm standard, has a fixed orifice with a shaped cone moving axially against the resistance of a spring, again producing a linear differential pressure and a range of up to 100:1.

The Gilflo 'A' has a water equivalent range of 0–5 to 0–350 litres/minute and the Gilflo 'B' 0–100 to 0–17 500 litres/minute.

The main application for Gilflo-based systems is on saturated and superheated steam, with pressures up to 200 bar and temperatures up to +500 °C.

1.3.1.6 Target flowmeter

Although not strictly a differential-pressure device it is generally categorized under that general heading. The primary and secondary element form an integral unit and differential pressure tappings are not required. It is particularly suited for measuring the flow of high-viscosity liquids; hot asphalt, tars, oils and slurries at pressures up to 100 bar and Reynolds numbers as low as 2000. Figure 1.15 shows the meter and working principles.

The liquid impinging on the target will be brought to rest so that pressure increases by $V^2/2g$ in terms of head of liquid so that the force F on the target will be

$$F = K\gamma' V_1^2 A_t/2 \text{ N} \tag{1.41}$$

where γ' is the mass per unit volume in kg/m^3. The area of the target is A_t measured in m^3, K is a constant, and V_1 is the velocity in m/s of the liquid through the annular ring between target and pipe.

If the pipe diameter is D m, and the target diameter d m, then area A of the annular space equals $\pi(D^2 - d^2)/4$ m^2.

Therefore volume flow rate is

$$Q = A \,.\, V_1 = \frac{\pi(D^2 - d^2)}{4}\sqrt{\frac{8F}{K\gamma'\pi d^2}}$$

$$= \frac{C(D^2 - d^2)}{d^2}\sqrt{\frac{F}{\gamma'}} \text{ m}^3\text{/s} \tag{1.42}$$

where C is a new constant including the numerical factors. Mass flow rate is

$$W = Q\gamma' = \frac{C(D^2 - d^2)}{d}\sqrt{F\gamma'} \text{ kg/s} \tag{1.43}$$

The force F is balanced through the force bar, by the air pressure in the bellows so that a 0.2 to 1.0 bar signal proportional to the square root of flow is obtained.

Flow ranges available vary from 0–52.7 to 0–123 litres/minute for the 19 mm size at temperatures up to 400 °C, to from 0–682 to 0–2273 litres/minute for the 100 mm size at temperatures up to 260 °F. Meters are also available for gas flow.

The overall accuracy of the meter is ±0.5 per cent with repeatability of ±0.1 per cent.

1.3.2 Rotating mechanical meters for liquids

Rotating mechanical flowmeters derive a signal from a moving rotor which is rotated at a speed proportional to the fluid flow velocity. Most of these meters are velocity-measuring devices except for positive-displacement meters which are quantity or volumetric in operation. The principal types to be discussed are: positive-displacement, rotating vane, angled propeller meter, bypass meter, helix meter, and turbine meter.

1.3.2.1 Positive-displacement

Positive-displacement meters are widely used on applications where high accuracy and good repeatability are required. Accuracy is not affected by pulsating flow and accurate measurement is possible at higher liquid viscosities than with many other flowmeters. Positive-displacement meters are frequently used in oil and water undertakings for accounting purposes.

The principle of the measurement is that as the liquid flows through the meter, it moves a measuring element which seals off the measuring chamber into a series of measuring compartments which are successively filled and emptied. Thus, for each complete cycle of the measuring element a fixed quantity of liquid is permitted to pass from the inlet to the outlet of the meter. The seal between the measuring element and the measuring chamber is provided by a film of the measured liquid. The number of cycles of the measuring element is indicated by means of a pointer moving over a dial driven from the measuring element by suitable gearing.

The extent of error, defined as the difference between the indicated quantity and the true quantity and expressed as a percentage of the true quantity, is dependent on many factors, among them being:

(a) The amount of clearance between the rotor and the measuring chamber through which liquid can pass unmetered.
(b) The amount of torque required to drive the register. The greater the torque the greater the pressure drop across the measuring element which in turn determines the leakage rate past the rotor.
(c) The viscosity of the liquid to be measured. Increase in viscosity will also result in increased pressure drop across the measuring element, but this is compensated for by the reduction in flow through the rotor clearances for a given pressure drop.

The accuracy of measurement attained with a positive-displacement meter varies very considerably from one design to another, with the nature and condition of the liquid measured, and with the rate of flow. Great care should be taken to choose the correct meter for an application.

The most common forms of positive-displacement meters are: rotary piston, reciprocating piston, nutating disc, fluted spiral rotor, sliding vane, rotating vane, and oval gear.

Rotary piston The rotary-piston flowmeter is most common in the water industry where it is used for metering domestic supplies. It consists of a cylindrical working chamber which houses a hollow cylindrical piston of equal length. The central hub of the piston is guided in a circular motion by two short inner cylinders. The piston and cylinder are alternately filled and emptied by the fluid passing through the meter. A slot in the sidewall of the piston is removed so that a partition extending inward from the bore of the working chamber can be inserted. This has the effect of restricting the movement of the piston to a sliding motion along the partition. The rotary movement of the piston is transmitted via a permanent-magnet coupling from the drive shaft to a mechanical register. The basic design and principle of operation of this meter is shown diagrammatically in Figure 1.16.

Reciprocating piston A reciprocating meter can be either of single- or multi-piston type, this being dependent on the application. This type of meter exhibits a wide turn-down ratio (e.g. 300:1), with extreme accuracy of ± 0.1 per cent and can be used for a wide range of liquids. Figure 1.17 illustrates the operating principle of this type of meter.

Suppose the piston is at the bottom of its stroke. The valve is so arranged that inlet liquid is admitted below the piston, causing it to travel upwards and the liquid above the piston to be discharged to the outlet pipe. When the piston has reached the limit of its travel, the top of the cylinder is cut off from the outlet side, and opened to the inlet liquid supply. At the same time the bottom of the cylinder is opened to the outlet side but cut off from the inlet liquid. The pressure of the incoming liquid will therefore drive the piston downwards, discharging the liquid from below the piston to the outlet pipe. The process is then repeated.

As the piston reciprocates, a ratchet attached to the piston rod provides an actuating force for an incremental counter, each count representing a predetermined quantity of liquid.

Nutating-disc type This type of meter is similar in principle to the rotary-piston type. In this case, however, the gear train is driven not by a rotating piston but by a movable disc mounted on a concentric sphere. The basic construction is shown in Figure 1.18.

The liquid enters the left side of the meter, alternately above and below the disc, forcing it to rock (nutate) in a circular path without rotating about its own axis. The disc is contained in a spherical working chamber and is restricted from rotating about its own axis by a radial partition that extends vertically across the chamber. The disc is slotted to fit over this partition. The spindle protruding from the sphere traces a circular path and is used to drive a geared register.

This type of meter can be used for a wide variety of liquids—disc and body materials being chosen to suit.

Fluted-spiral-rotor type (*rotating-impeller type*) The principle of this type of meter is shown in Figure 1.19. The meter consists of two fluted rotors supported in sleeve-type bearings and mounted so as to rotate rather like gears in a liquid tight case. The clearance between the rotors and measuring chambers is kept to a minimum. The shape of the rotors is designed so that a uniform uninterrupted rotation is produced by the liquid. The impellers in turn rotate the index of a counter which shows the total measured quantity.

This type of meter is used mainly for measuring crude and refined petroleum products covering a range of flows up to 3000 m^3/h at pressures up to 80 bar.

Sliding-vane type The principle of this type is illustrated in Figure 1.20. It consists of an accurately machined body containing a rotor revolving on ball bearings. The rotor has four evenly spaced slots, forming guides for four vanes. The vanes are in contact with a fixed cam. The four cam-followers follow the contour of the cam, causing the vanes to move radially. This ensures that during transition through the measuring chamber the vanes are in contact with the chamber wall.

The liquid impact on the blades causes the rotor to revolve allowing a quantity of liquid to be discharged.

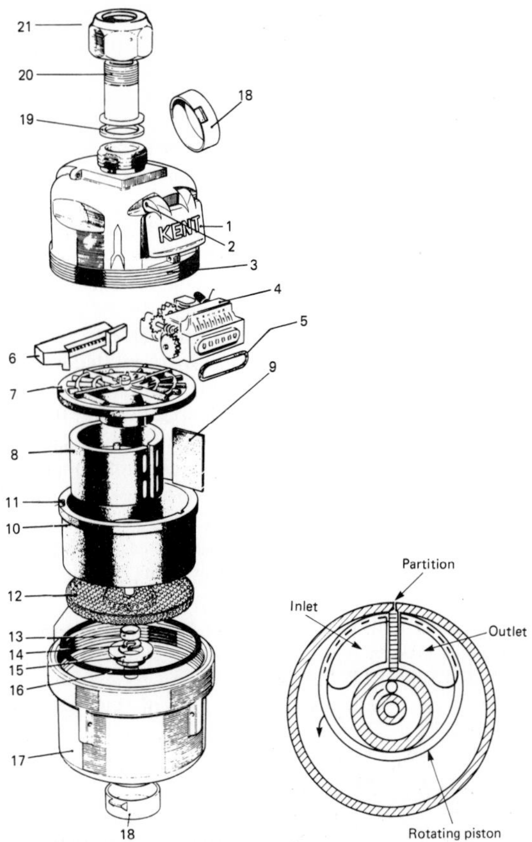

Figure 1.16 Rotary-piston positive-displacement meter. Courtesy, Kent Meters Ltd. 1. Lid. 2. Hinge pin. 3. Counter housing complete with lid and hinge pin. 4. Counter with worm reduction gear and washer. 5. Counter washer. 6. Ramp assembly. 7. Top plate assembly comprising top plate only; driving spindle; driving dog; dog retaining clip. 8. Piston. 9. Shutter. 10. Working chamber only. 11. Locating pin. 12. Strainer—plastic. Strainer—copper. 13. Strainer cap. 14. Circlip. 15. Non-return valve. 16. O ring. 17. Chamber housing. 18. Protective caps for end threads.

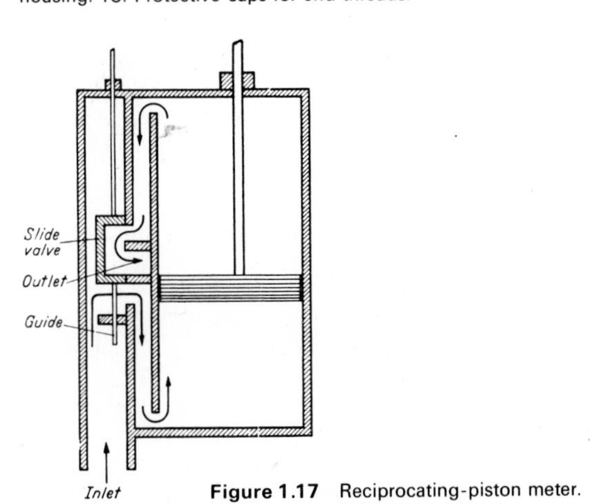

Figure 1.17 Reciprocating-piston meter.

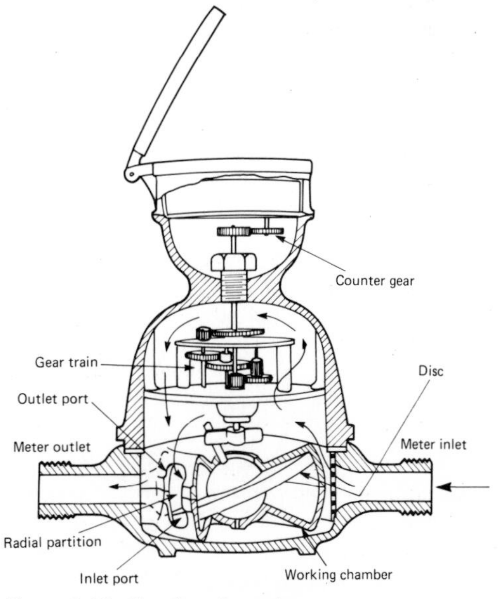

Figure 1.18 Nutating-disc meter.

The number of revolutions of the rotor is a measure of the volume of liquid passed through the meter.

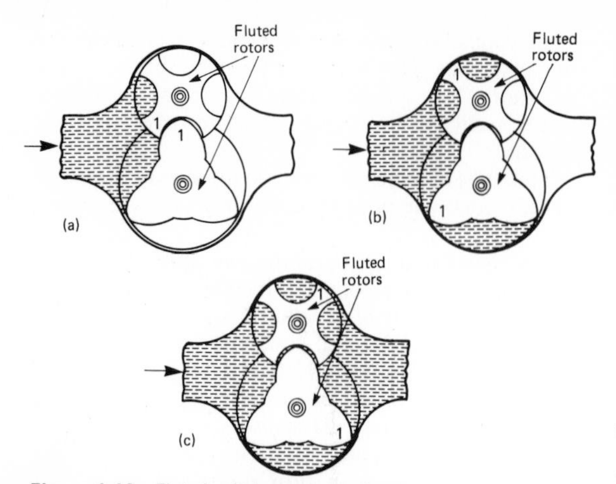

Figure 1.19 Fluted spiral rotor type of meter.

Rotating-vane type This meter is similar in principle to the sliding-vane meter but the measuring chambers are formed by four half-moon-shaped vanes spaced equidistant on the rotor circumference. As the rotor is revolved, the vanes turn to form sealed chambers between the rotor and the meter body. Accuracy of ± 0.1 per cent is possible down to 20 per cent of the rated capacity of the meter.

Oval-gear type This type of meter consists of two intermeshing oval gearwheels which are rotated by the fluid passing through it. This means that for each revolution of the pair of wheels a specific quantity of liquid is carried through the meter. This is shown diagrammatically in Figure 1.21. The number of revolutions is a precise measurement of the quantity of liquid passed. A spindle extended from one of the gears can be used to determine the number of revolutions and convert them to engineering units by suitable gearing.

Oval-gear meters are available in a wide range of materials, in sizes from 10 to 400 mm and suitable for pressures up to 60 bar and flows up to 1200 m^3/h. Accuracy of ± 0.25 per cent of rate of flow can be achieved.

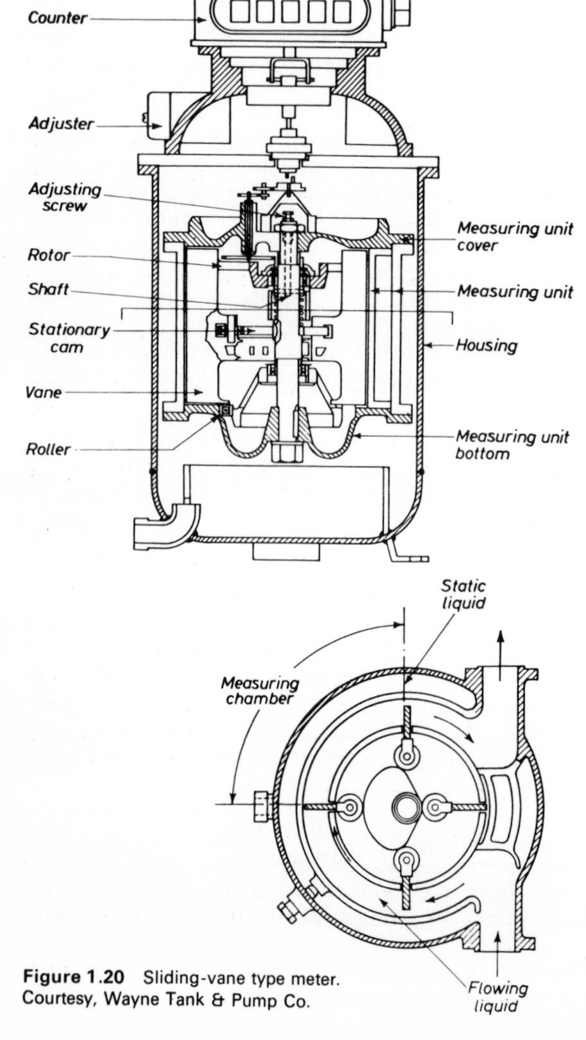

Figure 1.20 Sliding-vane type meter. Courtesy, Wayne Tank & Pump Co.

1.3.2.2 *Rotating vane*

This type of meter operates on the principle that the incoming liquid is directed to impinge tangentially on the periphery of a free spinning rotor. The rotation is monitored by magnetic, or photo-electric pick-up, the frequency of the output being proportional to flow rate, or alternatively by a mechanical register connected through gearing to the rotor assembly as shown in Figure 1.22.

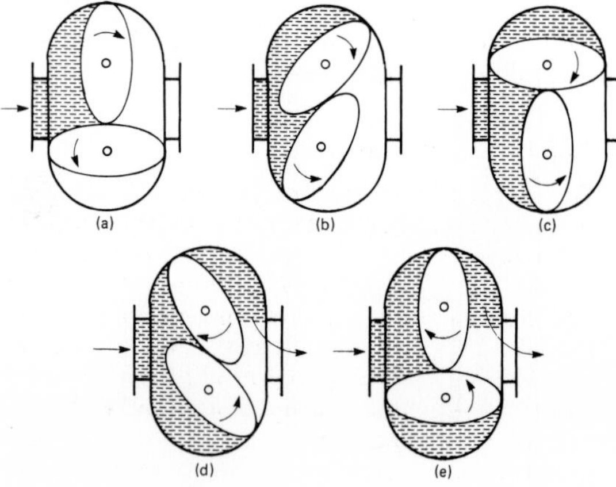

Figure 1.21 Oval-gear meter.

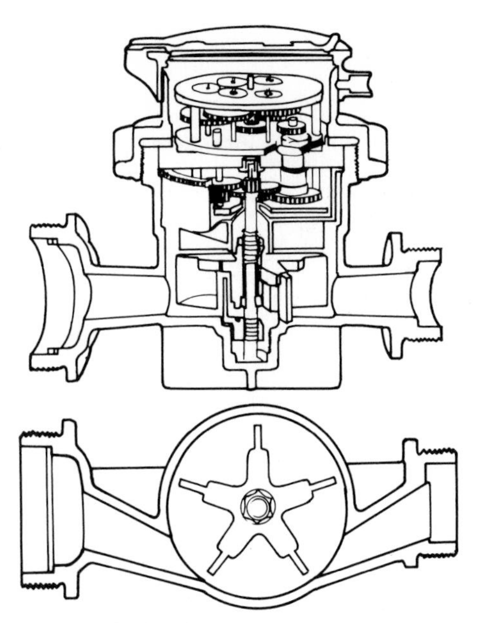

Figure 1.22 Rotating-vane type meter.

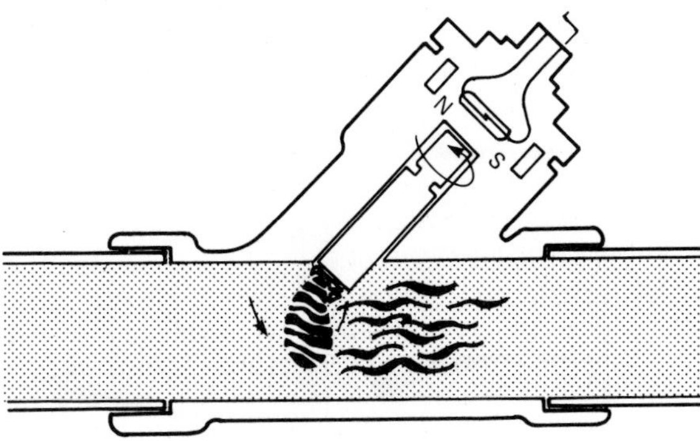

Figure 1.23 Angled-propeller meter.

Accuracy is dependent on calibration and turn-down ratios up to 20:1 can be achieved. This device is particularly suited to low flow rates.

1.3.2.3 Angled-propeller meter

The propeller flowmeter comprises of a Y-type body with all components apart from the propeller being out of the liquid stream. The construction of this type of meter is shown in Figure 1.23. The propeller has three blades and is designed to give maximum clearance in the measuring chamber, thereby allowing maximum tolerance of suspended particles. The propeller body is angled at 45° to the main flowstream and liquid passing through the meter rotates it at a speed proportional to flow rate. As the propeller goes through each revolution, encapsulated magnets generate pulses through a pick-up device, the number of pulses being proportional to flow rate.

1.3.2.4 Bypass meter

In this type of meter (also known as a shunt meter) a proportion of the liquid is diverted from the main flowstream by an orifice plate into a bypass configuration. The liquid is concentrated through nozzles to impinge on the rotors of a small turbine located in the bypass, the rotation of the turbine being proportional to flow rate.

This type of device can give moderate accuracy over a 5:1 turn-down ratio and is suitable for liquids, gases and steam.

1.3.2.5 Helix meter

In this type of meter the measuring element takes the form of a helical vane mounted centrally in the measuring chamber with its axis along the direction of flow as shown in Figure 1.24. The vane consists of a hollow cylinder with accurately formed wings. Owing to the effect of the buoyancy of the liquid on the cylinder, friction between its spindle and the sleeve bearings is small. The water is directed evenly onto the vanes by means of guides.

Transmission of the rotation from the undergear to the meter register is by means of ceramic magnetic coupling.

The body of the meter is cast iron and the mechanism and body cover is of thermoplastic injection moulding. The meter causes only small head loss in operation and is suited for use in water-distribution mains. It is available in sizes from 40 mm up to 300 mm, respective maximum flow rates being 24 m^3/h and 1540 m^3/h, with accuracy of ± 2 per cent over 20:1 turn-down ratio.

1.3.2.6 Turbine meter

This type of meter consists of a practically friction-free rotor pivoted along the axis of the meter tube and designed in such a way that rate of rotation of the rotor is proportional to the rate of flow of fluid through the meter. This rotational speed is sensed by means of an electric pick-off coil fitted to the outside of the meter housing as shown in Figure 1.25(a).

The only moving component in the meter is the rotor and the only component subject to wear is the rotor bearing assembly. However, with careful choice of materials (e.g. tungsten carbide for bearings) the meter should be capable of operating for up to 5 years without failure.

In the Kent turbine flowmeter range the rotor is designed so that the pressure distribution of the

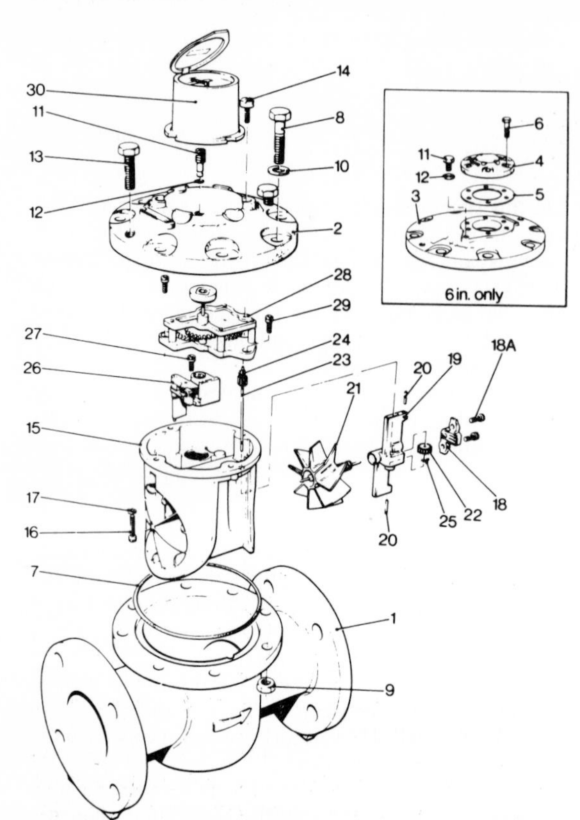

Figure 1.24 Helix meter, exploded view. 1. Body. 2. Top cover with regulator plug and regulator sealing ring. 3. Top cover plate. 4. Joint plate. 5. Joint plate gasket. 6. Joint plate screws. 7. Top cover sealing ring. 8. Body bolt. 9. Body bolt unit. 10. Body bolt washer. 11. Regulator plug. 12. Regulator plug sealing ring. 13. Joint breaking screw. 14. Counter box screw. 15. Measuring element. 16. Element securing screw. 17. Element securing screw washer. 18. Back bearing cap assembly. 19. Back vane support. 20. Tubular dowel pin. 21. Vane. 22. Worm wheel. 23. Vertical worm shaft. 24. First pinion. 25. Drive clip. 26. Regulator assembly. 27. Regulator assembly screw. 28. Undergear. 29. Undergear securing screw. 30. Register.

process liquid helps to suspend the rotor in an 'axial' floating position, thereby eliminating end-thrust and wear, improving repeatability and extending the linear flow range. This is illustrated in Figure 1.25(b).

As the liquid flows through the meter, there is a small gradual pressure loss up to point A caused by the rotor hangers and housing. At this point the area through which flow can take place reduces and velocity increases, resulting in a pressure minimum at point B. By the time the liquid reaches the downstream edge of the rotor (C), the flow pattern has re-established itself and a small pressure recovery occurs which causes the rotor to move hard upstream in opposition to the downstream forces. To counteract

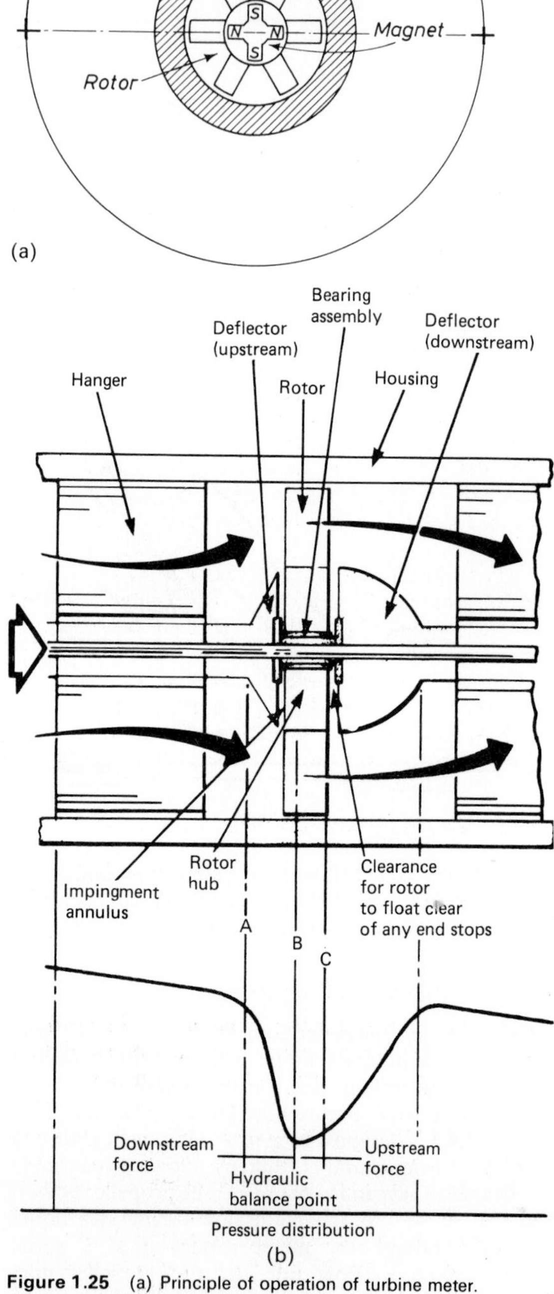

Figure 1.25 (a) Principle of operation of turbine meter. (b) Pressure distribution through turbine meter.

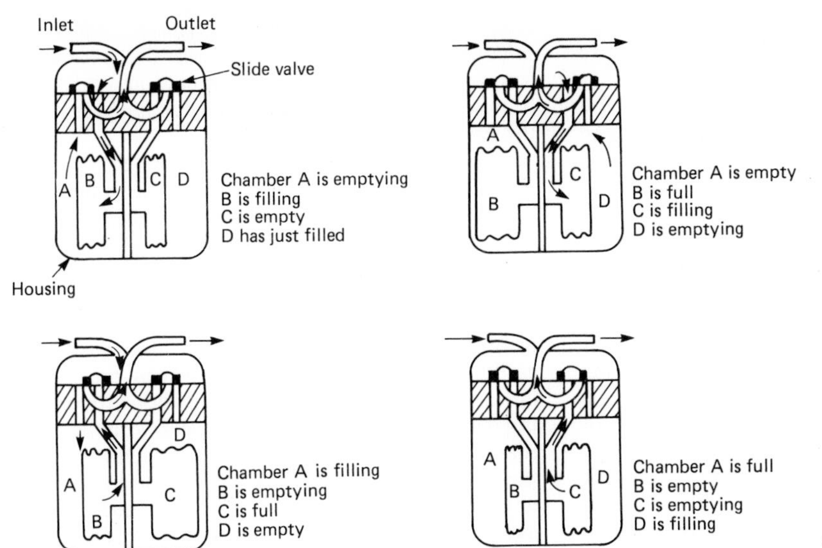

Figure 1.26 Diaphragm meter—stages of operation.

this upstream force the rotor hub is designed to be slightly larger in diameter than the outside diameter of the deflector cone to provide an additional downstream force. A hydraulic balance point is reached with the rotor floating completely clear of any end stops.

The turbine meter is available in a range of sizes up to 500 mm with linearity better than ± 0.25 per cent and repeatability better than ± 0.02 per cent and can be bi-directional in operation. To ensure optimum operation of the meter it is necessary to provide a straight pipe section of 10 pipe-diameters upstream and 5 pipe-diameters downstream of the meter. The addition of flow straighteners is sometimes necessary.

1.3.3 Rotating mechanical meters for gases

The principal types to be discussed are positive displacement, deflecting vane, rotating vane, and turbine.

1.3.3.1 Positive displacement

Three main types of meter come under this heading. They are diaphragm meter, wet gas meter (liquid sealed drum), and rotary displacement meter.

Diaphragm meter (bellows type) This type of meter has remained fundamentally the same for over 100 years and is probably the most common kind of meter in existence. It is used in the UK for metering the supply of gas to domestic and commercial users.

The meter comprises a metal case having an upper and a lower section. The lower section consists of four chambers, two of which are enclosed by flexible diaphragms that expand and contract as they are charged and discharged with the gas being metered. Figure 1.26 illustrates the meter at four stages of its operating cycle.

Mechanical readout is obtained by linking the diaphragms to suitable gearing since each cycle of the diaphragms discharges a known quantity of gas. This type of meter is of necessity highly accurate and trouble-free and the performance is governed by the regulations of the Department of Trade and Industry.

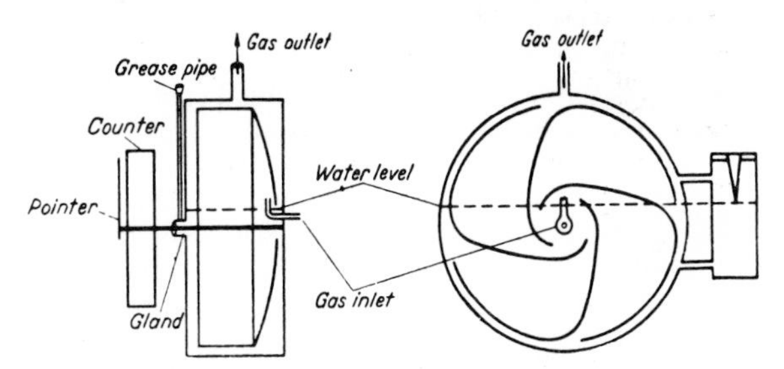

Figure 1.27 Liquid sealed drum type gas meter.

Liquid sealed drum This type of meter differs from the bellows type of meter in that the sealing medium for the measuring chambers is not solid but is water or some other suitable liquid.

The instrument is shown in section in Figure 1.27. It consists of an outer chamber of tinned brass plate or Staybrite steel sheeting containing a rotary portion. This rotating part consists of shaped partitions forming four measuring chambers made of light-gauge tinplate or Staybrite steel, balanced about a centre spindle so that it can rotate freely. Gas enters by the gas inlet near the centre and leaves by the outlet pipe at the top of the outer casing. The measuring chambers are sealed off by water or other suitable liquid which fills the outer chamber to just above the centre line. The level of the water is so arranged that when one chamber becomes unsealed to the outlet side, the partition between it and the next chamber seals it off from the inlet side. Thus, each measuring chamber will, during the course of a rotation, deliver a definite volume of gas from the inlet side to the outlet side of the instrument. The actual volume delivered will depend upon the size of the chamber and the level of the water in the instrument. The level of the water is therefore critical and is maintained at the correct value by means of a hook type of level indicator in a side chamber which is connected to the main chamber of the instrument. If the level becomes very low, the measuring chambers will become unsealed and gas can pass freely through the instrument without being measured; while if the level is too high, the volume delivered at each rotation will be too small and water may pass back down the inlet pipe. The correct calibration is obtained by adjusting the water level.

When a partition reaches a position where a small sealed chamber is formed connected to the inlet side there is a greater pressure on the inlet side than on the outlet side. There will therefore be a force that moves the partition in an anticlockwise direction, and so increases the volume of the chamber. This movement continues until the chamber is sealed off from the inlet pipe but opened up to the outlet side, while at the same time the chamber has become open to the inlet gas but sealed off from the outlet side. This produces continuous rotation. The rotation operates a counter which indicates complete rotations and fractions of rotation, and can be calibrated in actual volume units. The spindle between the rotor and the counter is usually made of brass and passes through a grease-packed gland. The friction of this gland, together with the friction in the counter gearing, will determine the pressure drop across the meter, which is found to be almost independent of the speed of rotation. This friction must be kept as low as possible, for if there is a large pressure difference between inlet and outlet sides of the meter, the level of the water in the measuring chambers will be forced down, causing errors in the volume delivered; and at low rates of flow the meter will rotate in a jerky manner.

It is very difficult to produce partitions of such a shape that the meter delivers accurate amounts for fractions of a rotation; consequently the meter is only approximately correct when fractions of a rotation are involved.

The mass of gas delivered will depend upon the temperature and pressure of the gas passing through the meter. The volume of gas is measured at the inlet pressure of the meter, so if the temperature and the density of the gas at s.t.p. are known it is not difficult to calculate the mass of gas measured. The gas will of course be saturated with water vapour and this must be taken into account in finding the partial pressure of the gas.

Rotating-impeller type This type of meter is similar in principle to the rotating-impeller type meter for liquids and could be described as a two-toothed gear pump. It is shown schematically in Figure 1.28. Although the meter is usually manufactured almost entirely from cast iron, other materials may be used if desired. The meter basically consists of two impellers housed in a casing and supported on rolling element bearings. A clearance of a few thousandths of an inch between the impellers and the casing prevents wear, with the result that the calibration of the meter remains constant throughout its life. The leakage rate is only a small fraction of 1 per cent and this is compensated for in the gearing counter ratio. Each lobe of the impellers has a scraper tip machined onto its periphery to prevent deposits forming in the measuring chamber. The impellers are timed relative to each other by gears fitted to one or both ends of the impeller shafts.

The impellers are caused to rotate by the decrease in pressure which is created at the meter outlet following the use of gas by the consumer. Each time an impeller passes through the vertical position a pocket of gas is momentarily trapped between the impeller and the casing. Four pockets of gas are therefore trapped and expelled during each complete revolution of the index shaft. The rotation of the impellers is transmitted to the meter counter by suitable gearing so that the counter reads directly in cubic metres or cubic feet. As the meter records the quantity of gas passing through it at the conditions prevailing at the inlet it is necessary to correct the volume indicated by the meter index for various factors. These are normally pressure,

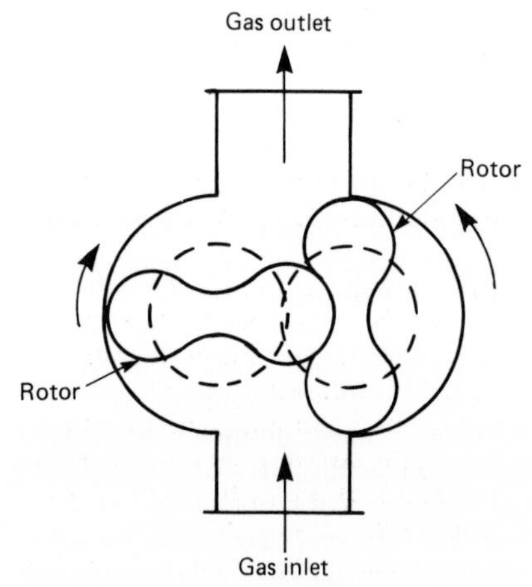

Figure 1.28 Rotary displacement meter.

temperature and compressibility. Corrections can be carried out manually if the conditions within the meter are constant. Alternatively the correction can be made continuously and automatically by small mechanical or electronic computers if conditions within the meter vary continuously and by relatively large amounts. Meters can also drive, through external gearing, various types of pressure- or temperature-recording devices as required.

Meters of this type are usually available in pressures up to 60 bar and will measure flow rates from approximately 12 m^3/h up to 10 000 m^3/h. Within these flow rates the meters will have a guaranteed accuracy of ± 1.0 per cent, over a range of from 5 to 100 per cent of maximum capacity. The pressure drop across the meter at maximum capacity is always less than 50 mm wg. These capacities and the pressure loss information are for meters operating at low pressure; the values would be subject to the effects of gas density at high pressure.

1.3.3.2 Deflecting-vane type: velometers

The principle of this type of instrument is similar to that of the same instrument for liquids. The construction however has to be different, for the density of a gas is usually considerably less than that of a liquid. As the force per unit area acting on the vane depends upon the rate of change of momentum and momentum is mass multiplied by velocity, the force will depend upon the density and upon the velocity of the impinging gas. The velocity of gas flow in a main is usually very much greater (6 to 10 times) than that of liquid flow but this is not sufficient to compensate for the greatly reduced density. (Density of dry air at 0 °C and 760 mm is 0.0013 g/ml while density of water is 1 g/ml.)

The vane must therefore be considerably larger when used for gases or be considerably reduced in weight. The restoring force must also be made small if an appreciable deflection is to be obtained.

The simple velometer consists of a light vane which travels in a shaped channel. Gas flowing through the channel deflects the vane according to the velocity and density of the gas, the shape of the channel and the restoring torque of the hairspring attached to the pivot of the vane.

The velometer is usually attached to a 'duct jet' which consists of two tubes placed so that the open end of one faces upstream while the open end of the other points downstream. The velometer then measures the rate of flow through the pair of tubes and as this depends upon the lengths and size of connecting pipes and the resistance and location of the pressure holes, each assembly needs individual calibration.

The main disadvantages of this simple velometer are the effects of hot or corrosive gases on the vane and channel. This disadvantage may be overcome by measuring the flow of air through the velometer produced by a differential air pressure equal to that produced by the 'duct jet'. In this way the hot gases do not pass through the instrument and so it is not damaged.

1.3.3.3 Rotating-vane type

Anemometers As in the case of the deflecting-vane type the force available from gases to produce the rotation of a vane is considerably less than that available in the measurement of liquids. The vanes must therefore be made light or have a large surface area. The rotor as a whole must be accurately balanced and the bearings must be as friction-free as possible and may be in the form of a multi-cap or multiple-fan blade design, the speed of rotation being proportional to air speed.

Rotary gas meter The rotary meter is a development of the air meter type of anemometer and is shown in Figure 1.29. It consists of three main assemblies: the body, the measuring element and the multi-point index driven through the intergearing. The lower casing (1) has integral in-line flanges (2) and is completed by the bonnet (3) with index glass (4) and bezel (5).

The measuring element is made up of an internal tubular body (6), which directs the flow of gas through a series of circular ports (7) onto a vaned anemometer (8). The anemometer is carried by a pivot (9) which runs in a sapphire–agate bearing assembly (10), the upper end being steadied by a bronze bush (11).

The multi-pointer index (12) is driven by an integear (13) supported between index plates (14). The index assembly is positioned by pillars (15) which are secured to the top flange of the internal tubular body.

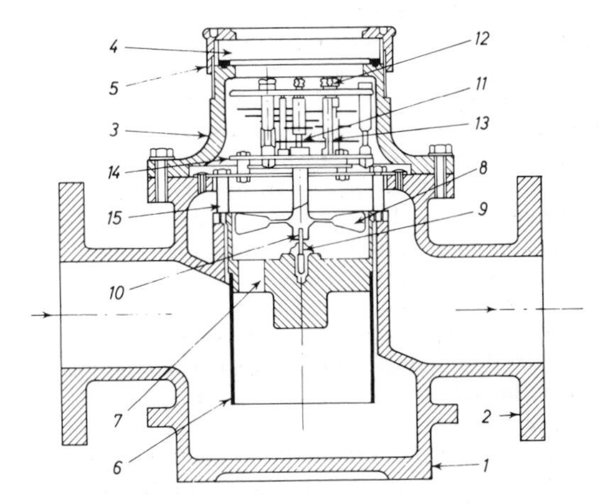

Figure 1.29 Diagrammatic section of a rotary gas meter. Courtesy, Parkinson & Cowan Compteurs.

The meter casing is made of cast iron whilst the anemometer is made from aluminium. The larger sizes have a separate internal tubular body made from cast iron, with a brass or mild steel skirt which forms part of the overall measuring element.

Its area of application is in the measurement of gas flow in industrial and commercial installations at pressures up to 1.5 bar and flows up to 200 m^3/h giving accuracy of ± 2 per cent over a flow range of 10:1.

1.3.3.4 Turbine meter

The gas turbine meter operates on the same principle as the liquid turbine meter previously described although the design is somewhat different since the densities of gases are much lower than those of liquids—high gas velocities are required to turn the rotor blades.

1.3.4 Electronic flowmeters

Either the principle of operation of flowmeters in this category is electronically based or the primary sensing is by means of an electronic device. Most of the flowmeters discussed in this section have undergone considerable development in the last 5 years and the techniques outlined are a growth area in flowmetering applications. They include electromagnetic flowmeters, ultrasonic flowmeters, oscillatory flowmeters, and cross-correlation techniques.

1.3.4.1 Electromagnetic flowmeters

The principle of operation of this type of flowmeter is based on Faraday's law of electromagnetic induction which states that if an electric conductor moves in a magnetic field, an electromotive force (e.m.f.) is induced whose amplitude is dependent on the force of the magnetic field, the velocity of the movement and the length of the conductor such that,

$$E \propto BlV \tag{1.44}$$

where E is e.m.f., B is magnetic field density, l is length of conductor, and V is rate at which the conductor is cutting the magnetic field. The direction of the e.m.f. with respect to the movement and the magnetic field is given by Fleming's right-hand generator rule.

If the conductor now takes the form of a conductive liquid an e.m.f. is generated in accordance with Faraday's law. It is useful at this time to refer to BS 5792 1980 which states: 'If the magnetic field is perpendicular to an electrically insulating tube through which a conductive liquid is flowing, a maximum potential difference may be measured between two electrodes positioned on the wall of the tube such that the diameter joining the electrodes is orthogonal to the magnetic field. The potential difference is proportional to the magnetic field strength, the axial velocity and the distance between the electrodes'. Hence the axial velocity and rate of flow can be determined. This principle is illustrated in Figure 1.30(a).

Figure 1.30(b) shows the basic construction of an electromagnetic flowmeter. It consists of a primary device, which contains the pipe through which the liquid passes, the measurement electrodes and the magnetic field coils and a secondary device, which provides the field-coil excitation and amplifies the output of the primary device and converts it to a form suitable for display, transmission and totalization.

The flow tube, which is effectively a pipe section, is lined with some suitable insulating material (dependent on liquid type) to prevent short circuiting of the electrodes which are normally button-type mounted flush with the liner. The field coils wound around the outside of the flow tube are usually epoxy-resin-encapsulated to prevent damage by damp or liquid submersion.

Field-coil excitation To develop a suitable magnetic field across the pipeline it is necessary to drive the field coil with some form of electrical excitation. It is not possible to use pure d.c. excitation due to the resulting polarization effect on electrodes and subsequent electrochemical action, so some form of a.c. excitation is employed. The most common techniques are: sinusoidal and non-sinusoidal (square wave, pulsed d.c., or trapezoidal).

Sinusoidal a.c. excitation Most early electromagnetic flowmeters used standard 50 Hz mains voltage as an excitation source for the field coils and in fact most systems in use today operate on this principle. The signal voltage will also be a.c. and is normally capacitively coupled to the secondary electronics to avoid any d.c. interfering potentials. This type of system has several disadvantages. Due to a.c. excitation the transformer effect produces interfering voltages. These are caused by stray pick-up by the signal cables from the varying magnetic field. It has a high power consumption and suffers from zero drift caused by the above interfering voltages and electrode contamination. This necessitates manual zero control adjustment.

These problems have now been largely overcome by the use of non-sinusoidal excitation.

Non-sinusoidal excitation Here it is possible to arrange that rate of change of flux density $dB/dt = 0$ for part of the excitation cycle and therefore there is no transformer action during this period. The flow signal is sampled during these periods and is effectively free from induced error voltages.

Square-wave, pulsed and trapezoidal excitations

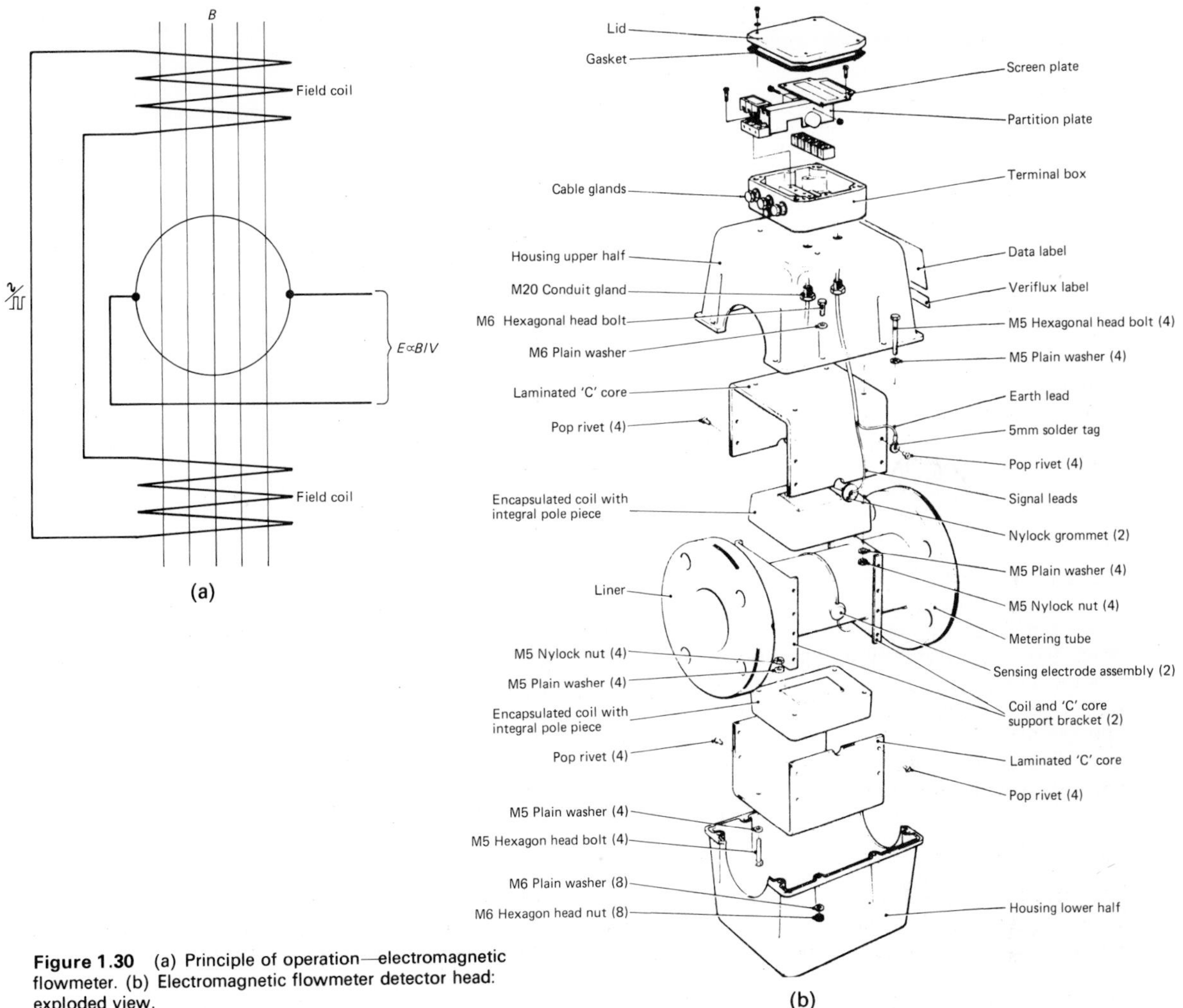

Figure 1.30 (a) Principle of operation—electromagnetic flowmeter. (b) Electromagnetic flowmeter detector head: exploded view.

have all been employed initially at frequencies around 50 Hz but most manufacturers have now opted for low-frequency systems (2–7 Hz) offering the benefits of minimum power consumption (i.e. only 20 per cent of the power used by a comparative 50 Hz system), automatic compensation for interfering voltages, automatic zero adjustment and tolerance of light build-up of material on electrode surfaces.

An example of this type of technique is illustrated in Figure 1.31 where square-wave excitation is used. The d.c. supply to the coils is switched on and off at approximately 2.6 Hz with polarity reversal every cycle. Figure 1.31(a) shows the ideal current waveform for pulsed d.c. excitation but, because of the inductance of the coils, this waveform cannot be entirely achieved. The solution as shown in Figure 1.31(b) is to power the field coils from a constant-current source giving a near square-wave excitation. The signal produced at the measuring electrodes is shown in Figure 1.31(c). The signal is sampled at five points during each measurement cycle as shown, microprocessor techniques being utilized to evaluate and separate the true flow signal from the combined flow and zero signals as shown in the equation in Figure 1.31(c).

Area of application Electromagnetic flowmeters are suitable for measuring a wide variety of liquids such as dirty liquids, pastes, acids, slurries and alkalis; accuracy is largely unaffected by changes in temperature, pressure, viscosity, density or conductivity. Although in the case of the latter conductivities must be greater than 1 microhm/cm.

Installation The primary element can be mounted in any attitude in the pipework although care should be taken to ensure that when the flowmeter is mounted

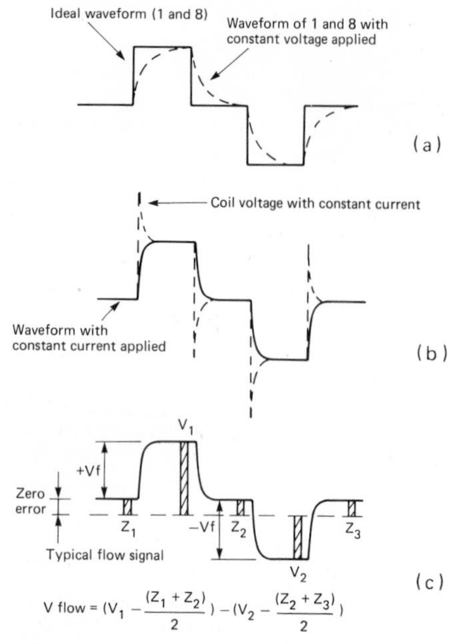

Figure 1.31 Electromagnetic flowmeter—pulsed d.c. excitation. Courtesy, Flowmetering Instruments Ltd.

horizontally, the axis of the electrodes be in the horizontal plane.

Where build-up of deposits on the electrodes is a recurring problem there exist two alternatives for consideration:

(a) Ultrasonic cleaning of electrodes.
(b) Utilize capacitive electrodes which do not come into contact with the flowstream and therefore insulating coatings have no effect.

It should be noted that on insulated pipelines earthing rings will normally be required to ensure that the flowmeter body is at the same potential as that of the flowing liquid to prevent circulating current and interfering voltages occurring.

The accuracy of the flowmeter can be affected by flow profile and the user should allow at least 10 straight pipe-diameters upstream and 5 straight pipe-diameters downstream of the primary element to ensure optimum conditions. Also to ensure system accuracy it is essential that the primary element should remain filled with the liquid being metered at all times. Entrained gases will cause similar inaccuracy.

For further information on installation requirements the reader is referred to the relevant sections of BS 5792 1980.

Flowmeters are available in sizes from 32 mm to 1200 mm nominal bore to handle flow velocities from 0–0.5 m/s to 0–10 m/s with accuracy of ±1 per cent over a 10:1 turn-down ratio.

1.3.4.2 Ultrasonic flowmeters

Ultrasonic flowmeters measure the velocity of a flowing medium by monitoring interaction between the flowstream and an ultrasonic sound wave transmitted into or through it. Many techniques exist, the two most commonly applied being Doppler and transmissive (time of flight). These will now be dealt with separately.

Doppler flowmeters These make use of the well-known Doppler effect which states that the frequency of sound changes if its source or reflector moves relative to the listener or monitor. The magnitude of the frequency change is an indication of the speed of the sound source or sound reflector.

In practice the Doppler flowmeter comprises a housing in which two piezo-electric crystals are potted, one being a transmitter and the other a receiver, the whole assembly being located on the pipe wall as shown in Figure 1.32. The transmitter transmits ultrasonic waves of frequency F_1 at an angle θ to the flowstream. If the flowstream contains particles, entrained gas or other discontinuities, some of the transmitted energy will be reflected back to the receiver. If the fluid is travelling at velocity V, the frequency of the reflected sound as monitored by the receiver can be shown to be F_2 such that

$$F_2 = F_1 \pm 2V.\cos\theta.\frac{F_1}{C}$$

where C is the velocity of sound in the fluid. Rearranging:

$$V = \frac{C(F_2 - F_1)}{2.F_1.\cos\theta}$$

which shows that velocity is proportional to the frequency change.

The Doppler meter is normally used as an inexpensive clamp-on flowmeter, the only operational constraints being that the flowstream must contain discontinuities of some kind (the device will not monitor clear liquids) and the pipeline must be acoustically transmissive.

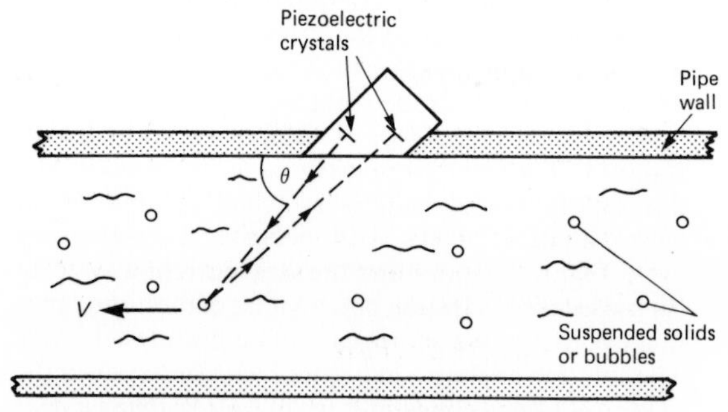

Figure 1.32 Principle of operation—Doppler meter.

Accuracy and repeatability of the Doppler meter are somewhat suspect and difficult to quantify since its operation is dependent on flow profile, particle size and suspended solids concentration. However, under ideal conditions and given the facility to calibrate *in situ* accuracies of ± 5 per cent should be attainable. This type of flowmeter is most suitable for use as a flow switch or for flow indication where absolute accuracy is not required.

Transmissive flowmeters Transmissive devices differ from Doppler flowmeters in that they rely on transmission of an ultrasonic pulse through the flowstream and therefore do not depend on discontinuities or entrained particles in the flowstream for operation.

The principle of operation is based on the transmission of an ultrasonic sound wave between two points, first in the direction of flow and then opposing flow. In each case the time of flight of the sound wave between the two points will have been modified by the velocity of the flowing medium and the difference between the flight times can be shown to be directly proportional to flow velocity.

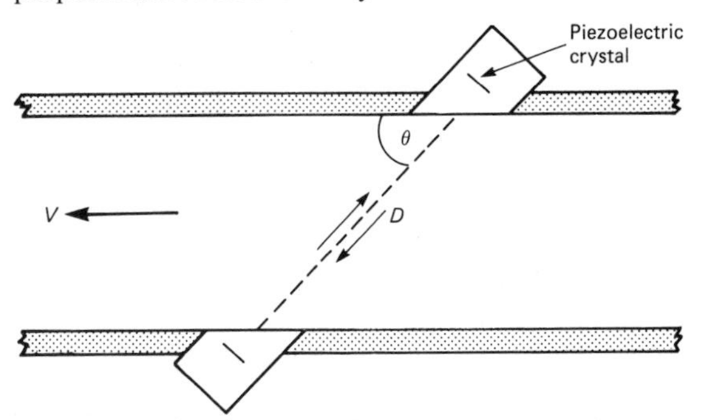

Figure 1.33 Principle of operation—time-of-flight ultrasonic flowmeter.

In practice the sound waves are not generated in the direction of flow but at an angle across it as shown in Figure 1.33. Pulse transit times downstream T_1 and upstream T_2 along a path length D can be expressed as: $T_1 = D/(C+V)$ and $T_2 = D/(C-V)$, where C is the velocity of sound in the fluid and V is the fluid velocity. Now

$$T = T_1 - T_2 = 2DV/(C^2 - V^2) \tag{1.44}$$

Since V^2 is very small compared to C^2 it can be ignored. It is convenient to develop the expression in relation to frequency and remove the dependency on the velocity of sound (C). Since $F_1 = 1/T_1$ and $F_2 = 1/T_2$ and average fluid velocity $\bar{V} = V/\cos\theta$ equation (1.44) is developed to:

$$F_1 - F_2 = (2\bar{V}\cos\theta)/D$$

The frequency difference is calculated by an electronic converter which gives an analogue output proportional to average fluid velocity. A practical realization of this technique operates in the following manner.

A voltage-controlled oscillator generates electronic pulses from which two consecutive pulses are selected. The first of these is used to operate a piezo-electric ceramic crystal transducer which projects an ultrasonic beam across the liquid flowing in a pipe. This ultrasonic pulse is then received on the other side of the pipe, where it is converted back to an electronic pulse. The latter is then received by the 'first-arrival' electronics, comparing its arrival time with the second pulse received directly. If the two pulses are received at the same time, the period of time between them equates to the time taken for the first pulse to travel to its transducer and be converted to ultra-sound, to travel across the flowstream, to be reconverted back to an electronic pulse and travel back to the first-arrival position.

Should the second pulse arrive before the first one, then the time between pulses is too short. Then the first-arrival electronics will step down the voltage to the voltage-controlled oscillator (VCO), reducing the resulting frequency. The electronics will continue to reduce voltage to the VCO in steps, until the first and second pulses are received at the first-arrival electronics at the same time. At this point, the periodic time of the frequency will be the same as the ultrasonic flight time, plus the electronic delay time.

If, now, a similar electronic circuit is used to project an ultrasonic pulse in the opposite direction to that shown, another frequency will be obtained which, when subtracted from the first, will give a direct measure of the velocity of the fluid in the pipe, since the electronic delays will cancel out.

In practice, the piezo-electric ceramic transducers used act as both transmitters and receivers of the ultrasonic signals and thus only one is required on each side of the pipe.

Typically the flowmeter will consist of a flowtube containing a pair of externally mounted, ultrasonic transducers and a separate electronic converter/transmitter as shown in Figure 1.34(a). Transducers may be wetted or non-wetted and consist of a piezo-electric crystal sized to give the desired frequency (typically 1–5 MHz for liquids and 0.2–0.5 MHz for gases). Figure 1.34(b) shows a typical transducer assembly.

Due to the fact that the flowmeter measures velocity across the centre of the pipe it is susceptible to flow profile effects and care should be taken to ensure sufficient length of straight pipe upstream and downstream of the flowtube to minimize such effects. To overcome this problem, some manufacturers use multiple-beam techniques where several chordal velocities are measured and the average computed. However, it is still good practice to allow for approximately 10 upstream and 5 downstream

(a)

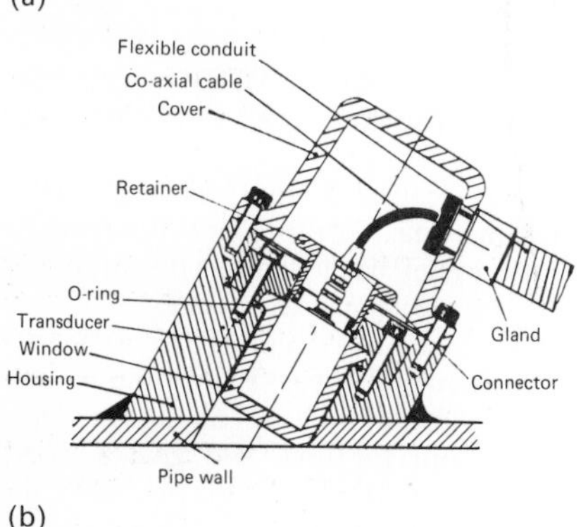

(b)

Figure 1.34 (a) Ultrasonic flowmeter. Courtesy, Bestobell Sparling Ltd. (b) Transducer assembly.

diameters of straight pipe. Also since this type of flowmeter relies on transmission through the flowing medium, fluids with a high solids or gas-bubble content cannot be metered.

This type of flowmeter can be obtained for use on liquids or gases for pipe sizes from 75 mm nominal bore up to 1500 mm or more for special applications and it is bi-directional in operation. Accuracy of better than ±1 per cent of flow rate can be achieved over a flow range of 0.2 to 12 metres per second.

This technique has also been successfully applied to open channel and river flow and is also now readily available as a clamp-on flowmeter for closed pipes, but accuracy is dependent on knowledge of each installation and *in situ* calibration is desirable.

1.3.4.3 Oscillatory flowmeters

The operating principle of flowmeters in this category is based on the fact that if an obstruction of known geometry is placed in the flowstream the fluid will start to oscillate in predictable manner. The degree of oscillation is related to fluid flow rate. The two main types of flowmeter in this category are: vortex-shedding flowmeter and swirl flowmeter.

The vortex flowmeter This type of flowmeter operates on the principle that if a bluff (i.e. non-streamlined) body is placed in a flowstream vortices will be detached or shed from the body. The principle is illustrated in Figure 1.35.

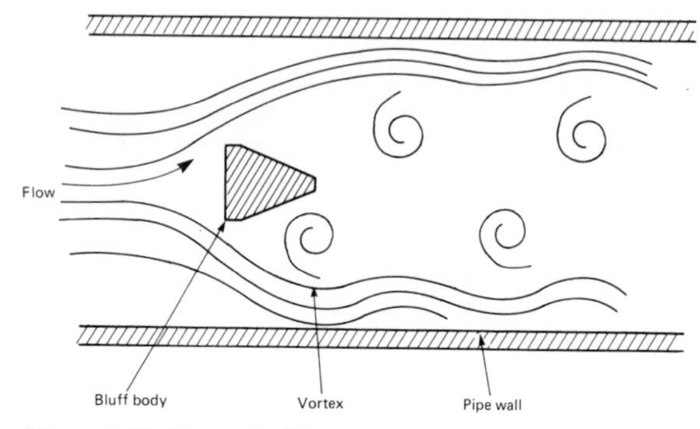

Figure 1.35 Vortex shedding.

The vortices are shed alternately to each side of the bluff body, the rate of shedding being directly proportional to flow velocity. If this body is fitted centrally into a pipeline the vortex-shedding frequency is a measure of the flow rate.

Any bluff body can be used to generate vortices in a flowstream, but for these vortices to be regular and well defined requires careful design. Essentially, the body must be non-streamlined, symmetrical and capable of generating vortices for a wide Reynolds number range. The most commonly adopted bluff body designs are shown in Figure 1.36.

These designs all attempt to enhance the vortex-shedding effect to ensure regularity or simplify the detection technique. If the design (d) is considered it will be noted that a second non-streamlined body is placed just downstream of the vortex-shedding body. Its effect is to reinforce and stabilize the shedding. The width of the bluff body is determined by pipe size and a rule-of-thumb guide is that the ratio of body width to pipe diameter should not be less than 0.2.

Sensing methods Once the bluff-body type has been selected we must adopt a technique to detect the vortices. Various methods exist, the more popular techniques being as follows:

(a) Ultrasonic. Where the vortices pass through an ultrasonic beam and cause refraction of this beam resulting in modulation of the beam amplitude.

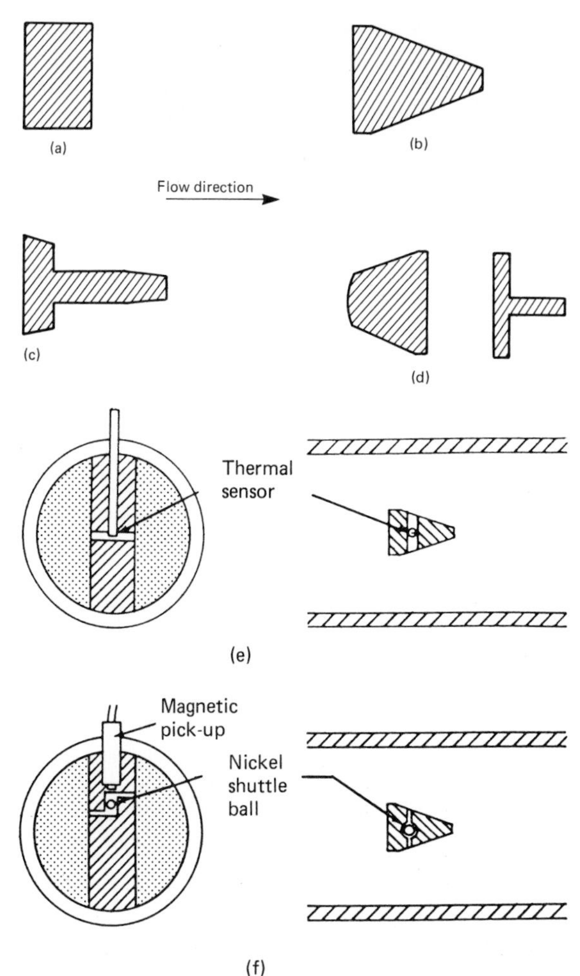

Figure 1.36 (a)–(d) Bluff body shapes. (e) Thermal sensor, Courtesy, Neptune Measurement Ltd. (f) Shuttle ball sensor. Courtesy, Neptune Measurement Ltd.

(b) Thermal (Figure 1.36(e)). Where a thermistor-type sensor is located in a through passage across the bluff body and behind its face. The heated thermistor will sense alternating vortices due to the cooling effect caused by their passage and an electrical pulse output is obtained.

(c) Oscillating disc. Sensing ports on both sides of the flow element cause a small disc to oscillate. A variable-reluctance pick-up detects the disc's oscillation. This type is particularly suited to steam or wet-gas flow.

(d) Capacitance. Metal diaphragms are welded on opposite sides of the bluff body, the small gaps between the diaphragms and the body being filled with oil. Interconnecting ports allow transfer of oil between the two sides. An electrode is placed close to each plate and the oil used as a dielectric. The vortices alternately deform the diaphragm plates causing a capacitance change between the diaphragm and electrode. The frequency of changes in capacitance is equal to the shedding frequency.

(e) Strain. Here the bluff body is designed such that the alternating pressures associated with vortex shedding are applied to a cantilevered section to the rear of the body. The alternating vortices create a cyclic strain on the rear of the body which is monitored by an internal strain gauge.

(f) Shuttle ball (Figure 1.36(f)). The shuttle technique uses the alternating pressures caused by vortex shedding to drive a magnetic shuttle up and down the axis of a flow element. The motion of the shuttle is detected by a magnetic pick-up.

The output derived from the primary sensor is a low-frequency signal dependent on flow; this is then applied to conditioning electronics to provide either analogue or digital output for display and transmission. The calibration factor (pulses per m^3) for the vortex meter is determined by the dimensions and geometry of the bluff body and will not change.

Installation parameters for vortex flowmeters are quite critical. Pipe flange gaskets upstream and at the transmitter should not protrude into the flow and to ensure a uniform velocity profile there should be 20 diameters of straight pipe upstream and 5 diameters downstream. Flow-straighteners can be used to reduce this requirement if necessary.

The vortex flowmeter has wide-ranging applications in both gas and liquid measurement providing the Reynolds number lies between 2×10^3 and 1×10^5 for gases and 4×10^3 and 1.4×10^5 for liquids. The output of the meter is independent of the density, temperature and pressure of the flowing fluid and represents the flow rate to better than ± 1 per cent of full scale giving turn-down ratios in excess of 20:1.

The swirlmeter Another meter that depends on the oscillatory nature of fluids is the swirlmeter shown in Figure 1.37. A swirl is imparted to the body of flowing fluid by the curved inlet blades which give a tangential component to the fluid flow. Initially the axis of the fluid rotation is the centre line of the meter, but a change in the direction of the rotational axis (precession) takes place when the rotating liquid enters the enlargement, causing the region of highest velocity to rotate about the meter axis. This produces an oscillation or precession, the frequency of which is proportional to the volumetric flow rate. The sensor, which is a bead thermistor heated by a constant-current source, converts the instantaneous velocity changes into a proportional electrical pulse output. The number of pulses generated is directly proportional to the volumetric flow.

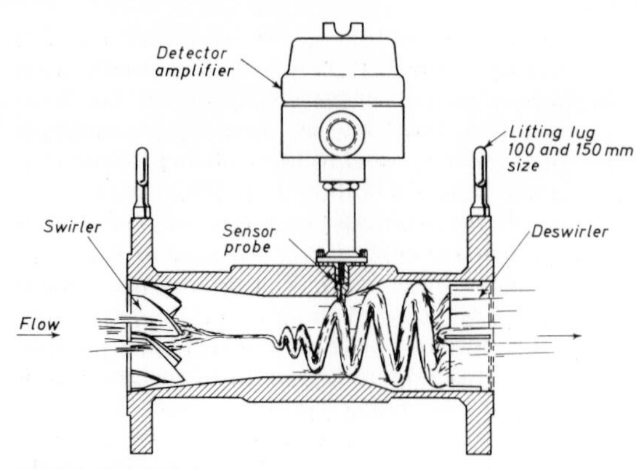

Figure 1.37 Cutaway view of the Swirlmeter. Courtesy, Fischer & Porter Ltd.

The operating range of the swirlmeter depends upon the specific application, but typical for liquids are 3.5 to 4.0 litres per minute for the 25 mm size to 1700 to 13 000 litres per minute for the 300 mm size. Typical gas flow ranges are 3 to 35 m^3/h for the 25 mm size to 300 to 9000 m^3/h for the 300 mm size. Accuracy of ± 1 per cent of rate is possible with repeatability of ± 0.25 per cent of rate.

1.3.4.4 Cross-correlation

In most flowing fluids there exist naturally occurring random fluctuations such as density, turbulence and temperature which can be detected by suitably located transducers. If two such transducers are installed in a pipeline separated by a distance L as shown in Figure 1.38, the upstream transducer will pick up a random fluctuation t seconds before the downstream transducer and the distance between the transducers divided by the transit time t will yield flow velocity. In practice the random fluctuations will not be stable and are compared in a cross-correlator which has a peak response at transit time T_p and correlation velocity $V = L/T_p$ metres per second.

This is effectively a non-intrusive measurement and could in principle be developed to measure flow of most fluids. Very few commercial cross-correlation systems are in use for flow measurement because of the slow response time of such systems. However with the use of microprocessor techniques processing speed has been increased significantly and several manufacturers are now producing commercial systems for industrial use. Techniques for effecting the cross-correlation operation are discussed in Volume 4.

1.3.5 Mass flowmeters

The measurement of mass flow rate can have certain advantages over volume flow rate, i.e. pressure, temperature and specific gravity do not have to be considered. The main interfering parameter to be avoided is that of two-phase flow where gas/liquid, gas/solid or liquid/solid mixtures are flowing together in the same pipe. The two phases may be travelling at different velocities and even in different directions. This problem is beyond the scope of this book but the user should be aware of the problem and ensure where possible that the flow is as near homogeneous as possible (by pipe-sizing or meter-positioning) or that the two phases are separately metered.

Methods of measurement can be categorized under two main headings: true mass-flow measurement in which the measured parameter is directly related to mass flow rate, and inferential mass-flow measurement in which volume flow rate and fluid density are measured and combined to give mass flow rate. Since volume flow rate and density measurement are discussed elsewhere only true mass-flow measurement will be dealt with here.

1.3.5.1 True mass-flow measurement methods

Fluid-momentum methods (a) Angular momentum. This type of device consists of two turbines on separate axial shafts in the meter body. The upstream turbine is rotated at constant speed and imparts a swirling motion to the fluid passing through it. On reaching the downstream turbine, the swirling fluid attempts to impart motion onto it; however, this turbine is constrained from rotating by a calibrated spring. The meter is designed such that on leaving the downstream turbine all angular velocity will have been removed from the fluid and the torque produced on it is proportional to mass flow.

This type of device can be used for both gases and liquids with accuracies of ± 1 per cent.

(b) Gyroscopic/Coriolis mass flowmeter. Mass flowmeters in this category use the measurement of torque developed when subjecting the fluid stream to a Coriolis acceleration,* as a measure of mass flow rate.

* On a rotating surface there is an inertial force acting on a body at right angles to its direction of motion in addition to the ordinary effects of motion of the body. This force is known as a Coriolis force.

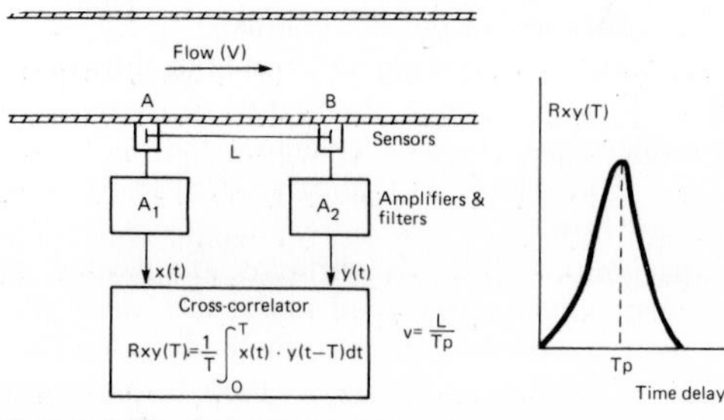

Figure 1.38 Cross correlation meter.

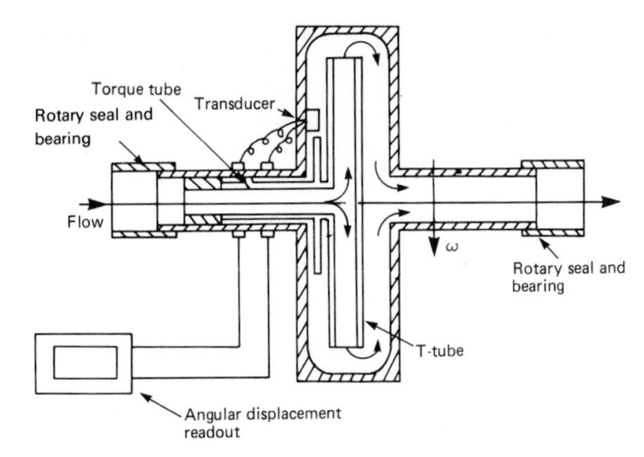

Figure 1.39 Early form of Coriolis mass flowmeter.

An early application of this technique is illustrated in Figure 1.39.

The fluid enters a T-shaped tube, flow being equally divided down each side of the T, and then recombines into a main flowstream at the outlet from the meter. The whole assembly is rotated at constant speed causing an angular displacement of the T-tube which is attached to the meter casing through a torque tube. The torque produced is proportional to mass flow rate.

This design suffered from various problems mainly due to poor sealing of rotating joints or inadequate speed control. However recent developments have overcome these problems as shown in Figure 1.40.

The mass flowmeter consists of a U-tube and a T-shaped leaf spring as opposite legs of a tuning fork. An electromagnet is used to excite the tuning fork, thereby subjecting each particle within the pipe to a Coriolis-type acceleration. The resulting forces cause an angular deflection in the U-tube inversely proportional to the stiffness of the pipe and proportional to the mass flow rate. This movement is picked up by optical transducers mounted on opposite sides of the U-tube, the output being a pulse that is width-modulated proportional to mass flow rate. An oscillator/counter digitizes the pulse width and provides an output suitable for display purposes.

This system can be used to measure the flow of liquids or gases and accuracies better than ± 0.5 per cent of full scale are possible.

Pressure-differential methods In its classical form the meter consists of four matched orifice plates installed in a Wheatstone bridge arrangement. A pump is used to transfer fluid at a known rate from one branch of the bridge into another to create a reference flow. The resultant differential pressure measured across the bridge is proportional to mass flow rate.

Thermal mass flowmeter This version of a mass flowmeter consists of a flowtube, an upstream and downstream temperature sensor and a heat source as illustrated in Figure 1.41. The temperature sensors are effectively active arms of a Wheatstone bridge. They are mounted equidistant from the constant-temperature heat source such that for no flow conditions, heat received by each sensor is the same and the bridge remains in balance. However, with increasing flow, the downstream sensor receives progressively more heat than the upstream sensor causing an imbalance to occur in the bridge circuit. The temperature difference is proportional to mass flow rate and an electrical output representing this is developed by the bridge circuit.

This type of mass flowmeter is most commonly applied to the measurement of gas flows within the ranges 2.5×10^{-10} to 5×10^{-3} kg/s and accuracy of ± 1 per cent of full scale is attainable.

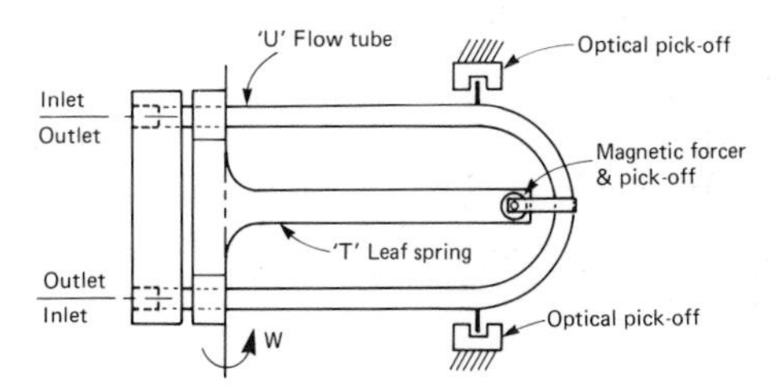

Figure 1.40 Gyroscopic/Coriolis mass flowmeter.

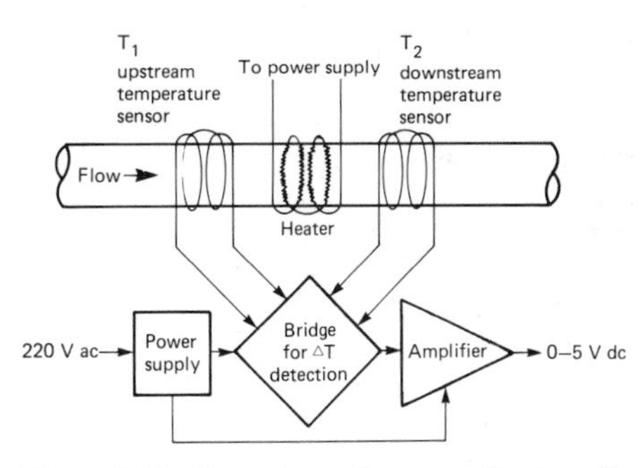

Figure 1.41 Thermal mass flowmeter. Courtesy, Emerson Electric Co.

1.4 Flow in open channels

Flow measurement in open channels is a requirement normally associated with the water industry. Flow in rivers, sewers (part-filled pipes) and regular-shaped channels may be measured by the following methods:

(a) Head/area method. Where a structure is built into the flowstream to develop a unique head/flow relationship as in,

(i) The weir which is merely a dam over which liquid is allowed to flow, the depth of liquid over the sill of the weir being a measure of the rate of flow.

(ii) The hydraulic flume, an example being the venturi flume in which the channel is given the same form in the horizontal plane as a section of a venturi tube while the bottom of the channel is given a gentle slope up the throat.

(b) Velocity/area method. Where measurement of both variables, i.e. head and velocity, is combined with the known geometry of a structure to determine flow.

(c) Dilution gauging.

1.4.1 Head/area method

1.4.1.1 Weirs

Weirs may have a variety of forms and are classified according to the shape of the notch or opening.

The simplest is the rectangular notch, or in certain cases the square notch.

The V or triangular notch is a V-shaped notch with the apex downwards. It is used to measure rates of flow which may become very small. Owing to the shape of the notch the head is greater at small rates of flow with this type than it would be for the rectangular notch.

Notches of other forms, which may be trapezoidal or parabolic, are designed so that they have a constant discharge coefficient, or a head that is directly proportional to the rate of flow.

The velocity of the liquid increases as it passes over the weir because the centre of gravity of the liquid falls. Liquid that was originally at the level of the surface above the weir can be regarded as having fallen to the level of the centre of pressure of the issuing stream. The head of liquid producing the flow is therefore equal to the vertical distance from the centre of pressure of the issuing stream to the level of the surface of the liquid upstream.

If the height of the centre of pressure above the sill can be regarded as being a constant fraction of the height of the surface of the liquid above the sill of the weir, then the height of the surface above the sill will give a measure of the differential pressure producing the flow. If single particles are considered, some will have fallen a distance greater than the average but this is compensated for by the fact that others have fallen a smaller distance.

The term 'head of a weir' is usually taken to mean the same as the depth of the weir, and is measured by the height of the liquid above the level of the sill of the weir just upstream of where it begins to curve over the weir, and is denoted by H and usually expressed in metres.

Rectangular notch Consider the flow over the weir in exactly the same way as the flow through other primary differential-pressure elements. If the cross-section of the stream approaching the weir is large in comparison with the area of the stream over the weir, then the velocity V_1 at section 1 upstream can be neglected in comparison with the velocity V_2 over the weir, and in equation (1.16) $V_1=0$ and the equation becomes:

$$V_2^2=2gh \quad \text{or} \quad V_2=\sqrt{(2gh)}$$

The quantity of liquid flowing over the weir will be given by:

$$Q=A_2V_2$$

But the area of the stream is BH, where H is the depth over the weir and B the breadth of the weir, and h is a definite fraction of H.

By calculus it can be shown that for a rectangular notch

$$Q=\tfrac{2}{3}BH\sqrt{(2gH)} \tag{1.45}$$

$$=\tfrac{2}{3}B\sqrt{(2gH^3)}\ \text{m}^3/\text{s} \tag{1.46}$$

The actual flow over the weir is less than that given by equation (1.45) for the following reasons:

(a) The area of the stream is not BH but something less, for the stream contracts at both the top and bottom as it flows over the weir as shown in Figure 1.42 making the effective depth at the weir less than H.

(b) Owing to friction between the liquid and the sides of the channel, the velocity at the sides of the channel will be less than that at the middle. This effect may be reduced by making the notch narrower than the width of the stream as shown in Figure 1.43. This, however, produces side-contraction of the stream. Therefore $B_1=B$ should be at least equal to $4H$ when the side-contraction is equal to $0.1H$ on both sides, so that the effective width becomes $B-0.2H$.

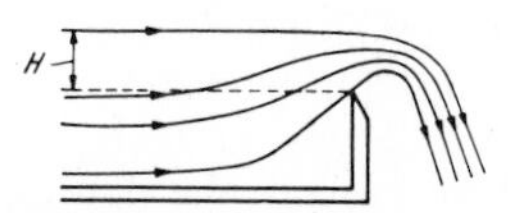

Figure 1.42 Rectangular notch, showing top and bottom of contraction.

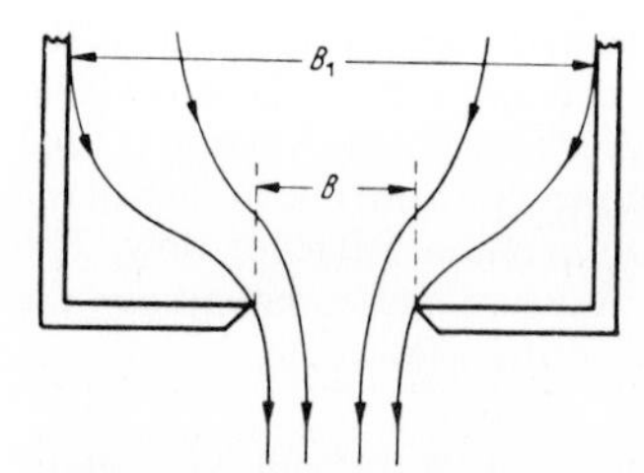

Figure 1.43 Rectangular notch, showing side-contraction.

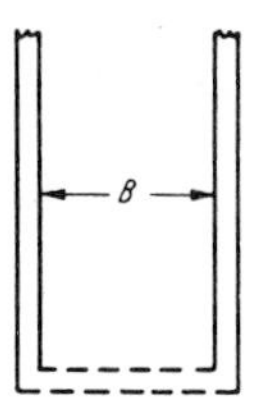

Figure 1.44 Rectangular notch, showing side plates.

When it is required to suppress side-contraction and make the measurement more reliable, plates may be fitted as shown in Figure 1.44 so as to make the stream move parallel to the plates as it approaches the weir.

To allow for the difference between the actual rate of flow and the theoretical rate of flow, the discharge coefficient C, defined as before, is introduced and equation (1.46) becomes:

$$Q=\tfrac{2}{3}CB\sqrt{(2gH^3)}\ \text{m}^3/\text{s} \qquad (1.47)$$

The value of C will vary with H and will be influenced by the following factors, which must remain constant in any installation if its accuracy is to be maintained: (a) the relative sharpness of the upstream edge of the weir crest, (b) the width of the weir sill. Both these factors influence the bottom-contraction and influence C, so the weir sill should be inspected from time to time to see that it is free from damage.

In developing the above equations it was assumed that the velocity of the liquid upstream of the weir could be neglected. As the rate of flow increases, this is no longer possible and a velocity of approach factor must be introduced. This will influence the value of C, and as the velocity of approach increases it will cause the observed head to become less than the true or total head so that a correcting factor must be introduced.

Triangular notch If the angle of the triangular notch is θ as shown in Figure 1.45, $B=2H\tan(\theta/2)$. The position of the centre of pressure of the issuing stream will now be at a different height above the bottom of the notch from what it was for the rectangular notch. It can be shown by calculus that the numerical factor involved in the equation is now $\frac{4}{15}$. Substituting this factor and the new value of A_2 in equation (1.47):

$$Q=\frac{4}{15}CB\sqrt{(2gH^3)}\ \text{m}^3/\text{s}$$

$$=\frac{4}{15}C2H\tan\frac{\theta}{2}\sqrt{(2gH^3)}$$

$$=\frac{8}{15}C\tan\frac{\theta}{2}\sqrt{(2gH^5)} \qquad (1.48)$$

Experiments have shown that θ should have a value between 35° and 120° for satisfactory operation of this type of installation.

While the cross-section of the stream from a triangular weir remains geometrically similar for all values of H, the value of C is influenced by H. The variation of C is from 0.57 to 0.64, and takes into account the contraction of the stream.

If the velocity of approach is not negligible the value of H must be suitably corrected as in the case of the rectangular weir.

Installation and operation of weirs

(a) Upstream of a weir there should be a wide, deep, and straight channel of uniform cross-section, long enough to ensure that the velocity distribution in the stream is uniform. This approach channel may be made shorter if baffle plates are placed across it at the inlet end to break up currents in the stream.
(b) Where debris is likely to be brought down by the stream, a screen should be placed across the approach channel to prevent the debris reaching the weir. This screen should be cleaned as often as necessary.
(c) The upstream edge of the notch should be maintained square or sharp-edged according to the type of installation.
(d) The weir crest should be level from end to end.
(e) The channel end wall on which the notch plate is mounted should be cut away so that the stream may fall freely and not adhere to the wall. To ensure this happens a vent may be arranged in the side wall of the channel so that the space under the falling water is open to the atmosphere.
(f) Neither the bed, nor the sides of the channel downstream from the weir should be nearer the weir than 150 mm and the water level downstream should be at least 75 mm below the weir sill.
(g) The head H may be measured by measuring the height of the level of the stream above the level of the weir sill, sufficiently far back from the weir to ensure the surface is unaffected by the flow. This measurement is usually made at a distance of at least $6H$ upstream of the weir. It may be made by any appropriate method for liquids as described in the section on level measurement: for example, the hook gauge, float-operated mechanisms, air purge systems or ultrasonic techniques. It is often more convenient to measure the level of the liquid in a 'stilling well' alongside the channel at the appropriate distance above the notch. This well is

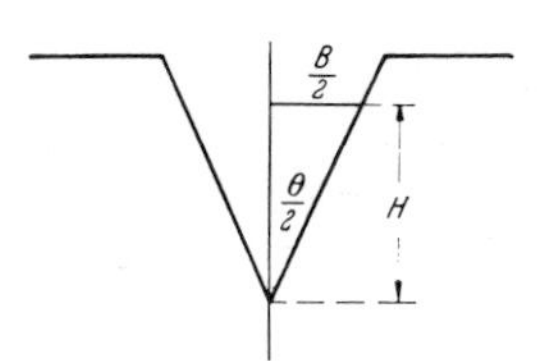

Figure 1.45 Triangular notch (V-notch).

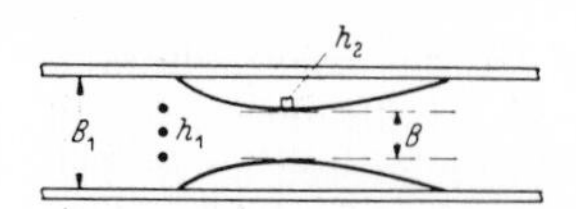

Figure 1.46 Hydraulic flume (venturi type).

connected to the weir chamber by a small pipe or opening near the bottom. Liquid will rise in the well to the same height as in the weir chamber and will be practically undisturbed by currents in the stream.

1.4.1.2 Hydraulic flumes

Where the rate of fall of a stream is so slight that there is very little head available for operating a measuring device or where the stream carries a large quantity of silt or debris, a flume is often much more satisfactory than a weir. Several flumes have been designed, but the only one we shall consider here is the venturi flume. This may have more than one form, but where it is flat-bottomed and of the form shown in Figure 1.46 the volume rate of flow is given by the equation

$$Q = CBh_2\sqrt{\frac{2g(h_1 - h_2)}{1-(Bh_2/B_1h_1)^2}}\ \text{m}^3/\text{s} \qquad (1.49)$$

where B_1 is width of channel, B is width of the throat, h_1 is depth of water measured immediately upstream of the entrance to the converging section, and h_2 is minimum depth of water in the throat. C is discharge coefficient whose value will depend upon the particular outline of the channel and the pattern of the flow. Tests on a model of the flume may be used to determine the coefficient provided that the flow in the model and in the full-sized flume are dynamically similar.

The depths of water h_1 and h_2 are measured as in the case of the weir by measuring the level in wells at the side of the main channel. These wells are connected to the channel by small pipes opening into the channel near or at the bottom.

As in the case of the closed venturi tube a certain minimum uninterrupted length of channel is required before the venturi is reached, in order that the stream may be free from waves and vortices.

By carefully designing the flume, it is possible to simplify the actual instrument required to indicate the flow. If the channel is designed in such a manner that the depth in the exit channel at all rates of flow is less than a certain percentage of the depth in the entrance channel, the flume will function as a free-discharge outlet. Under these conditions, the upstream depth is independent of the downstream conditions, and the depth of water in the throat will maintain itself at a certain critical value, at which the energy of the water is at the minimum whatever the rate of flow. When this is so, the quantity of water flowing through the channel is a function of the upstream depth h_1 only, and may be expressed by the equation:

$$Q = kh_1^{3/2}$$

where k is a constant for a particular installation and can be determined.

It is now necessary to measure h_1 only, and this may be done by means of a float in a well, connected to the upstream portion of the channel. This float operates an indicated recording and integrating instrument.

The channel is usually constructed of concrete, the surface on the inside of the channel being made smooth to reduce the friction between water and channel. Flumes of this kind are used largely for measuring flow of water or sewerage and may be made in a very large variety of sizes to measure anything from the flow of a small stream to that of a large river.

1.4.2 Velocity/area methods

In these methods volume flow rate is determined by measurement of the two variables concerned (mean velocity and head), since the rate of flow is given by the equation

$$Q = V.A\ \text{m}^3/\text{s}$$

where area A is proportional to head or level.

The head/level measurement can be made by many of the conventional level devices described in Chapter 5 and will not therefore be dealt with here. Three general techniques are used for velocity measurement, these being turbine current meter, electromagnetic, and ultrasonic. The techniques have already been discussed in the section on closed pipe flow and application only will be described here.

1.4.2.1 Turbine current meter

In a current-meter gauging, the meter is used to give point velocity. The meter is sited in a predetermined cross-section in the flowstream and the velocity obtained. Since the meter only measures point velocity it is necessary to sample throughout the cross-section to obtain mean velocity.

The velocities that can be measured in this way range from 0.03 to 3.0 m/s for a turbine meter with a propeller of 50 mm diameter. The disadvantage of a current-meter gauging is that it is a point and not a continuous measurement of discharge.

1.4.2.2 Electromagnetic method

In this technique Faraday's law of electromagnetic induction is utilized in the same way as for closed-pipe flow measurement (Section 1.3.4.1). That is, $E \propto BlV$, where E is e.m.f. generated, B is magnetic field strength,

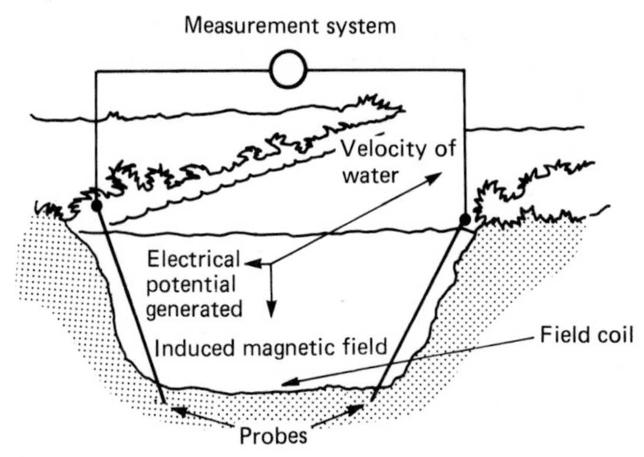

Figure 1.47 Principle of electromagnetic gauge. Courtesy, Plessey Electronic Systems Ltd.

l is width of river or channel in metres, and V is average velocity of the flowstream.

This equation only applies if the bed of the channel is insulated, similar to the requirement for pipe flowmeters. In practice it is costly to insulate a riverbed and where this cannot be done, riverbed conductivity has to be measured to compensate for the resultant signal attenuation.

In an operational system a large coil buried under the channel is used to produce a vertical magnetic field. The flow of water through the magnetic field causes an e.m.f. to be set up between the banks of the river. This potential is sensed by a pick-up electrode at each bank. This is shown diagrammatically in Figure 1.47.

1.4.2.3 Ultrasonic method

As for closed-pipe flow two techniques are available, single-path and multi-path, both relying on time-of-flight techniques as described in Section 1.3.4.2. Transducers capable of transmitting and receiving acoustic pulses are staggered along either bank of the river or channel. In practice the acoustic path is approximately 60° to the direction of flow, but angles between 30° and 60° could be utilized. The smaller the angle the longer the acoustic path. Path lengths up to 400 metres can be achieved.

1.4.3 Dilution gauging

This technique is covered in detail in the section on flow calibration but basically the principle involves injecting a tracer element such as brine, salt or radioactive solution and estimating the degree of dilution caused by the flowing liquid.

1.5 Point velocity measurement

It is often desirable in flow studies and survey work to be able to measure the velocity of liquids at points within the flow pattern inside both pipes and open channels to determine either mean velocity or flow profile. The following techniques are most common: laser Doppler anemometer, hot-wire anemometer, pitot tube, insertion electromagnetic, insertion turbine, propeller-type current meter, insertion vortex, and Doppler velocity probe.

1.5.1 Laser Doppler anemometer

This uses the Doppler shift of light scattered by moving particles in the flowstream to determine particle velocity and hence fluid flow velocity. It can be used for both gas and liquid flow studies and is used in both research and industrial applications.

Laser Doppler is a non-contact technique and is particularly suited to velocity studies in systems that would not allow the installation of a more conventional system; for example, around propellers and in turbines.

1.5.2 Hot-wire anemometer

The hot-wire anemometer is widely used for flow studies in both gas and liquid systems. Its principle of operation is that a small electrically heated element is placed within the flowstream; the wire sensor is typically 5 μm diamerer and approximately 5 mm long. As flow velocity increases it tends to cool the heated element. This change in temperature causes a change in resistance of the element proportional to flow velocity.

1.5.3 Pitot tube

The pitot tube is a device for measuring the total pressure in a flowstream (i.e. impact/velocity pressure and static pressure) and the principle of operation is as follows.

If a tube is placed with its open end facing into the flowstream (Figure 1.48) then the fluid impinging on the open end will be brought to rest and its kinetic energy converted into pressure energy. The pressure build-up in the tube will be greater than that in the free

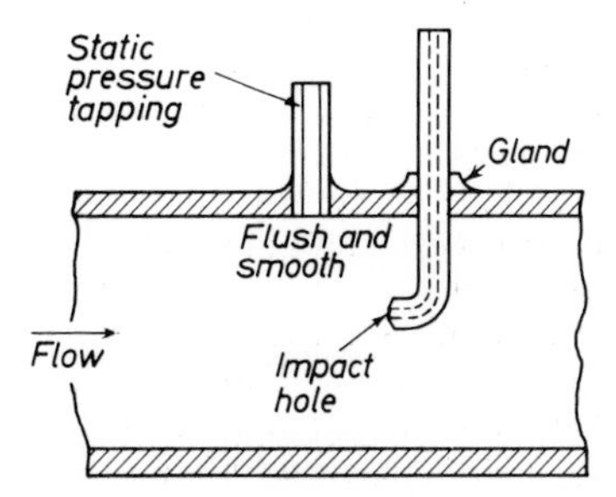

Figure 1.48 Single hole pitot tube.

stream by an amount termed the 'impact pressure'. If the static pressure is also measured, the differential pressure between that measured by the pitot tube and the static pressure will be a measure of the impact pressure and therefore the velocity of the stream. In equation (1.15) h the pressure differential or impact pressure developed is given by $h=(V_2^2/2g)-(V_1^2/2g)$ where $V_2=0$. Therefore, $h=-V_1^2/2g$, i.e. the pressure increases by $V_1^2/2g$. The negative sign indicates that it is an increase in pressure and not a decrease.

Increase in head:

$$h=V_1^2/2g \quad \text{or} \quad V_1^2=2gh \quad \text{i.e.} \quad V_1=\sqrt{(2gh)} \tag{1.50}$$

However, since this is an intrusive device not all of the flowstream will be brought to rest on the impact post; some will be deflected round it. A coefficient C is introduced to compensate for this and equation (1.50) becomes:

$$V_1=C\sqrt{(2gh)} \tag{1.51}$$

If the pitot tube is to be used as a permanent device for measuring the flow in a pipeline the relationship between the velocity at the point of its location to the mean velocity must be determined. This is achieved by traversing the pipe and sampling velocity at several points in the pipe, thereby determining flow profile and mean velocity.

For more permanent types of pitot-tube installation an Annubar may be used as shown in Figure 1.49. The pressure holes are located in such a way that they measure the representative dynamic pressure of equal annuli. The dynamic pressure obtained at the four holes facing into the stream is then averaged by means of the 'interpolating' inner tube (Figure 1.49(b)), which is connected to the high-pressure side of the manometer.

The low-pressure side of the manometer is connected to the downstream element which measures the static pressure less the suction pressure. In this way a differential pressure representing the mean velocity along the tube is obtained enabling the flow to be obtained with an accuracy of ± 1 per cent of actual flow.

1.5.4 Electromagnetic velocity probe

This type of device is basically an inside-out version of the electromagnetic pipeline flowmeter discussed earlier, the operating principle being the same. The velocity probe consists of either a cylindrical or an ellipsoidal sensor shape which houses the field coil and two diametrically opposed pick-up electrodes.

The field coil develops an electromagnetic field in the region of the sensor and the electrodes pick up a voltage generated which is proportional to the point velocity. The probe system can be used for either open-channel or closed-pipe flow of conducting liquids.

1.5.5 Insertion turbine

The operating principle for this device is the same as for a full-bore pipeline flowmeter.

It is used normally for pipe-flow velocity measurement in liquids and consists of a small turbine

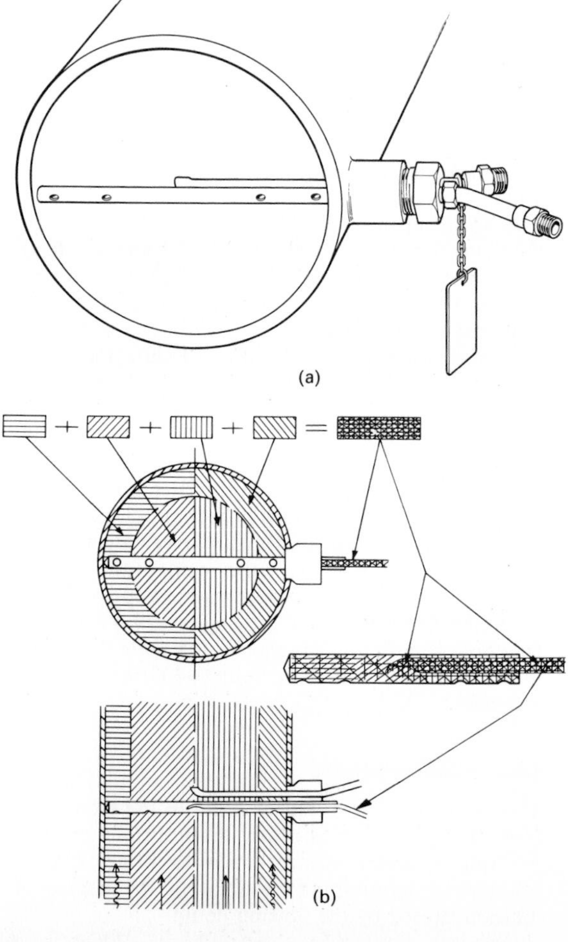

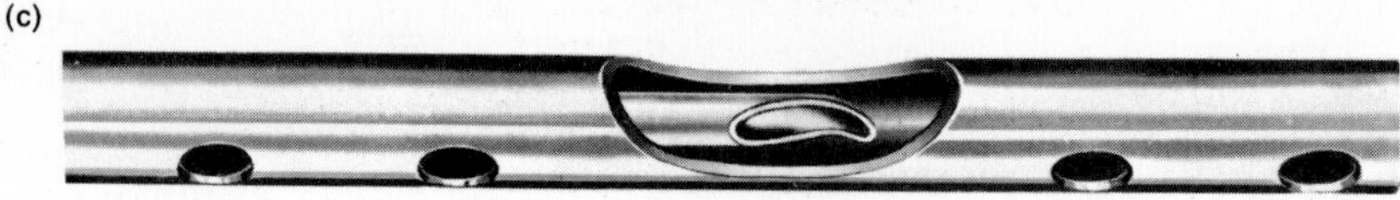

Figure 1.49 The Annubar. Courtesy, A.E.D. International Ltd.

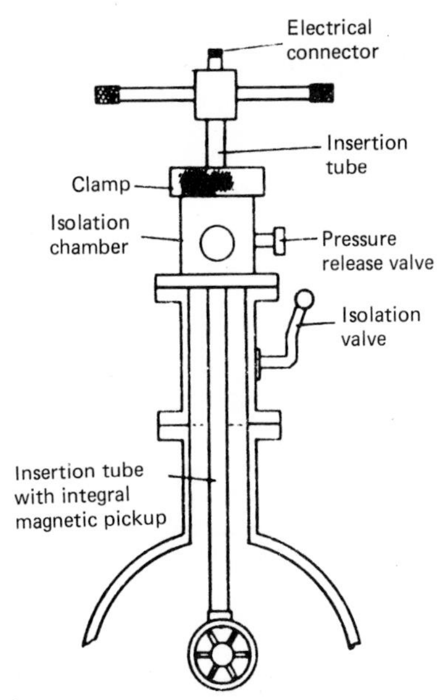

Figure 1.50 Insertion turbine flowmeter.

housed in a protective rotor cage as shown in Figure 1.50. In normal application the turbine meter is inserted through a gate valve assembly on the pipeline; hence it can be installed under pressure and can be precisely located for carrying out a flow traverse. Also, given suitable conditions it can be used as a permanent flowmetering device in the same way as the pitot tube. The velocity of the turbine is proportional to liquid velocity but a correction factor is introduced to compensate for errors caused by blockage in the flowstream caused by the turbine assembly.

1.5.6 Propeller-type current meter

Similar to the turbine in operation, this type of velocity probe typically consists of a five-bladed PVC rotor (Figure 1.51) mounted in a shrouded frame. This device is most commonly used for river or stream gauging and has the ability to measure flow velocities as low as 2.5 cm/s.

1.5.7 Insertion vortex

Operating on the same principle as the full-bore vortex meter previously described, the insertion-vortex meter consists of a short length of stainless-steel tube surrounding a centrally situated bluff body. Fluid flow through the tube causes vortex shedding. The device is normally inserted into a main pipeline via a flanged T-piece and is suitable for pipelines of 200 mm bore and above. It is capable of measuring flow velocities from 0.1 m/s up to 20 m/s for liquids and from 1 m/s to 40 m/s for gases.

1.5.8 Ultrasonic Doppler velocity probe

This device again is more commonly used for open-channel velocity measurement and consists of a streamlined housing for the Doppler meter already described.

1.6 Flowmeter calibration methods

There are various methods available for the calibration of flowmeters and the requirement can be split into two distinct categories: *in situ* and laboratory. Calibration of liquid flowmeters is generally somewhat more straightforward than that of gas flowmeters since liquids can be stored in open vessels and water can often be utilized as the calibrating liquid.

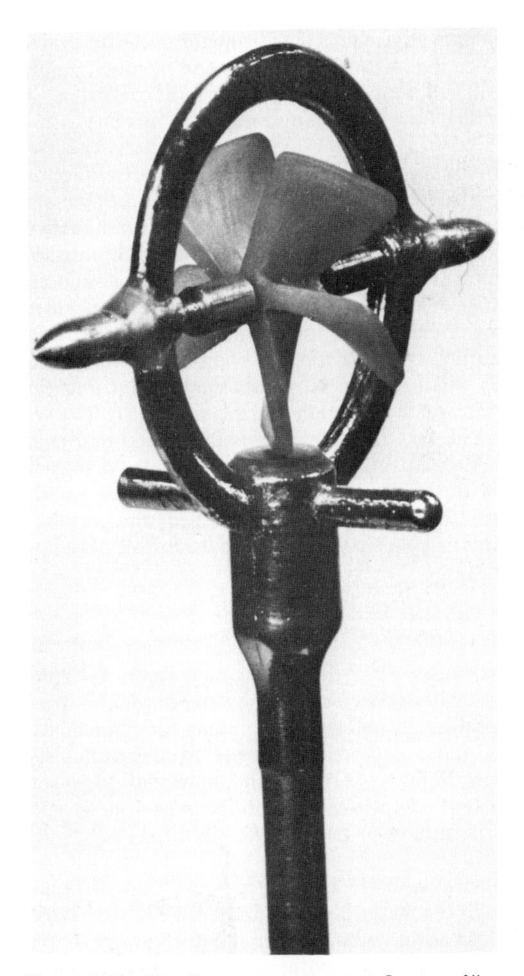

Figure 1.51 Propeller-type current meter. Courtesy, Nixon Instrumentation Ltd.

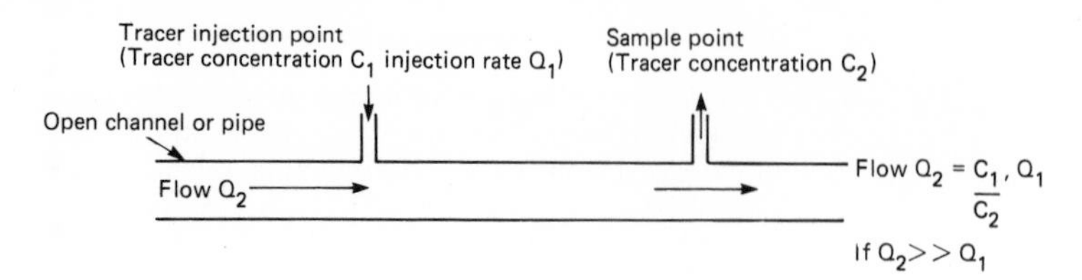

Figure 1.52 Dilution gauging by tracer injection.

1.6.1 Flowmeter calibration methods for liquids

The main principles used for liquid flowmeter calibration are *in situ*: insertion-point velocity and dilution gauging/tracer method; laboratory: master meter, volumetric, gravimetric, and pipe prover.

1.6.1.1 In-situ calibration methods

Insertion-point velocity One of the simpler methods of *in situ* flowmeter calibration utilizes point-velocity measuring devices (see Section 1.5) where the calibration device chosen is positioned in the flowstream adjacent to the flowmeter being calibrated and such that mean flow velocity can be measured. In difficult situations a flow traverse can be carried out to determine flow profile and mean flow velocity.

Dilution gauging/tracer method This technique can be applied to closed-pipe and open-channel flowmeter calibration. A suitable tracer (chemical or radioactive) is injected at an accurately measured constant rate and samples are taken from the flowstream at a point downstream of the injection point where complete mixing of the injected tracer will have taken place. By measuring the tracer concentration in the samples the tracer dilution can be established and from this dilution and the injection rate the volumetric flow can be calculated. This principle is illustrated in Figure 1.52. Alternatively a pulse of tracer material may be added to the flowstream and the time taken for the tracer to travel a known distance and reach a maximum concentration is a measure of the flow velocity.

1.6.1.2 Laboratory calibration methods

Master meter For this technique a meter of known accuracy is used as a calibration standard. The meter to be calibrated and the master meter are connected in series and are therefore subject to the same flow regime. It must be borne in mind that to ensure consistent accurate calibration the master meter itself must be subject to periodic recalibration.

Volumetric method In this technique, flow of liquid through the meter being calibrated is diverted into a tank of known volume. When full this known volume can be compared with the integrated quantity registered by the flowmeter being calibrated.

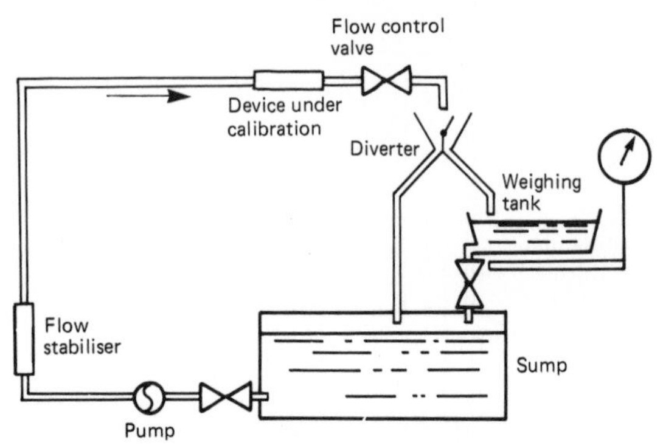

Figure 1.53 Flowmeter calibration by weighing. Courtesy, British Standards Institution.

Gravimetric method Where the flow of liquid through the meter being calibrated is diverted into a vessel that can be weighed either continuously or after a predetermined time, the weight of the liquid is compared with the registered reading of the flowmeter being calibrated, (see Figure 1.53).

Pipe prover This device sometimes known as a 'meter prover' consists of a U-shaped length of pipe and a piston or elastic sphere. The flowmeter to be calibrated is installed on the inlet to the prover and the sphere is forced to travel the length of the pipe by the flowing liquid. Switches are inserted near both ends of the pipe and operate when the sphere passes them. The swept volume of the pipe between the two switches is determined by initial calibration and this known volume is compared with that registered by the flowmeter during calibration. A typical pipe-prover loop is shown in Figure 1.54.

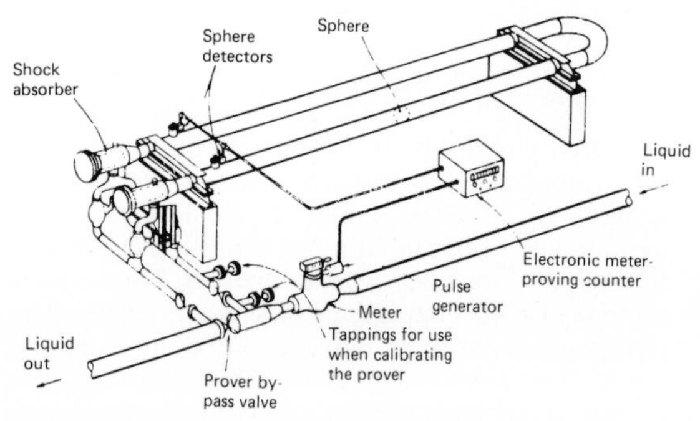

Figure 1.54 Pipe prover.

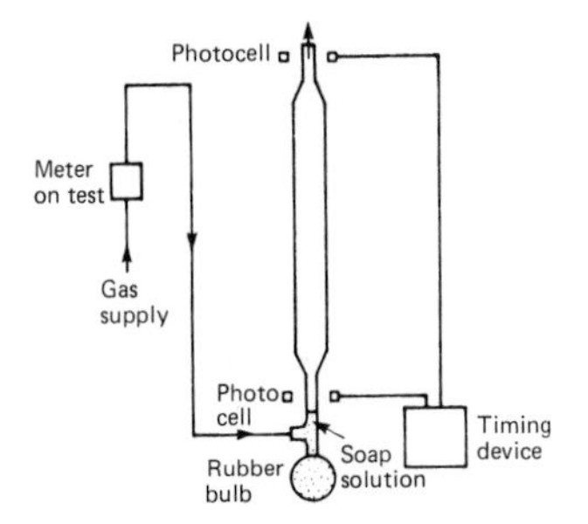

Figure 1.55 Gas flowmeter calibration—soap-film burette.

1.6.2 Flowmeter calibration methods for gases

Methods suitable for gas flowmeter calibration are *in situ* as for liquids; and laboratory: soap-film burette, water-displacement method, and gravimetric.

1.6.2.1 Laboratory calibration methods

Soap-film burette This method is used to calibrate measurement systems with gas flows in the range of 10^{-7} to 10^{-4} m^3/s. Gas flow from the meter on test is passed through a burette mounted in the vertical plane. As the gas enters the burette a soap film is formed across the tube and travels up it at the same velocity as the gas. By measuring the time of transit of the soap film between graduations of the burette it is possible to determine flow rate. A typical calibration system is illustrated in Figure 1.55.

Water-displacement method In this method a cylinder closed at one end is inverted over a water bath as shown in Figure 1.56. As the cylinder is lowered into the bath a trapped volume of gas is developed. This gas can escape via a pipe connected to the cylinder out through the flowmeter being calibrated. The time of the fall of the cylinder combined with the knowledge of the volume/length relationship leads to a determination of the amount of gas displaced which can be compared with that measured by the flowmeter under calibration.

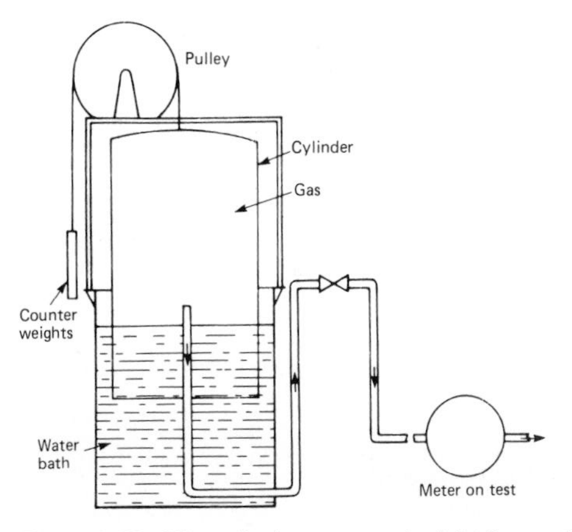

Figure 1.56 Water displacement method (bell prover).

Gravimetric method Here gas is diverted via the meter under test into a gas-collecting vessel over a measured period of time. By weighing the collecting vessel before diversion and again after diversion the difference will be due to the enclosed gas, and flow can be determined. This flow can then be compared with that measured by the flowmeter.

It should be noted that the cost of developing laboratory flow calibration systems as outlined can be quite prohibitive and it may be somewhat more cost-effective to have systems calibrated by the various national standards laboratories (such as NEL and SIRA) or by manufacturers, rather than committing capital to what may be an infrequently used system.

1.7 References

BS 1042, *Methods for the Measurement of Fluid Flow in Pipes, Part 1 Orifice Plates, Nozzles & Venturi Tubes, Part 2a Pitot Tubes*, (1964)

BS 3680, *Methods of Measurement of Liquid Flow in Open Channels*, (1969–1983)

BS 5781, *Specification for Measurement & Calibration Systems*, (1979)

BS 5792, *Specification for Electromagnetic Flowmeters*, (1980)

BS 6199, *Measurement of Liquid Flow in Closed Conduits Using Weighting and Volumetric Methods*, (1981)

Cheremisinoff, N. P., *Applied Fluid Flow Measurement*, Dekker, (1979)

Durrani, T. S. and Greated, C. A., *Laser Systems in Flow Measurement*, Plenum, (1977)

Haywood, A. T. J., *Flowmeters—A Basic Guide and Sourcebook for Users*, Macmillan, (1979)

Henderson, F. M., *Open Channel Flow*, Macmillan, (1966)

Holland, F. A., *Fluid Flow for Chemical Engineers*, Arnold, (1973)

International Organization for Standardization, ISO 3354, (1975) *Measurement of Clean Water Flow in Closed Conduits (Velocity Area Method Using Current Meters)*

Linford, A., *Flow Measurement and Meters*, E. & F.N. Spon

Miller, R. W., *Flow Measurement Engineering Handbook*, McGraw-Hill, (1982)

Shercliff, J. A., *The Theory of Electromagnetic Flow Measurement*, Cambridge University Press, (1962)

Watrasiewisy, B. M. and Rudd, M. J., *Laser Doppler Measurements*, Butterworth, (1975)

Appendix 1.1 Minimum lengths of straight pipeline upstream of device*

	Minimum number of pipe diameters for Cases A to F listed below								
	(a) Minimum length of straight pipe immediately upstream of device								*(b) Minimum length between first upstream fitting and next upstream fitting*
Diameter ratio d/D less than:	*0.22*	*0.32*	*0.45*	*0.55*	*0.63*	*0.7*	*0.77*	*0.84*	
Area ratio m less than:	*0.05*†	*0.1*	*0.2*	*0.3*	*0.4*	*0.5*	*0.6*	*0.7*	
Fittings producing symmetrical disturbances									
Case A. Reducer (reducing not more than 0.5*D* over a length of 3*D*) Enlarger (enlarging not more than 2*D* over a length of 1.5*D*) Any pressure difference device having an area ratio *m* not less than 0.3	16	16	18	20	23	26	29	33	13
Case B. Gate valve fully open (for ¾ closed see Case H)	12	12	12	13	16	20	27	38	10
Case C. Globe valve fully open (for ¾ closed see Case J)	18	18	20	23	27	32	40	49	16
Case D. Reducer (any reduction including from a large space)	25	25	25	25	25	26	29	33	13
Fittings producing asymmetrical disturbances in one plane									
Case E. Single bend up to 90°, elbow, Y-junction, T-junction (flow in either but not both branches)	10	10	13	16	22	29	41	56	15
Case F. Two or more bends in the same plane, single bend of more than 90°, swan	14	15	18	22	28	36	46	57	18
Fittings producing asymmetrical disturbances and swirling motion									
Case G‡. Two or more bends, elbows, loops or Y-junctions in different planes, T-junction with flow in both branches	34	35	38	44	52	63	76	89	32
Case H‡. Gate valve up to ¾ closed§ (for fully open see Case B)	40	40	40	41	46	52	60	70	26
Case J‡. Globe valve up to ¾ closed§ (for fully open see Case C)	12	14	19	26	36	60	80	100	30
Other fittings									
Case K. All other fittings (provided there is no swirling motion)	100	100	100	100	100	100	100	100	50

* See Subclauses 47*b* and 47*c*.
† For area ratios less than 0.015, or diameter ratios less than 0.125 see Subclause 47*b*.
‡ If swirling motion is eliminated by a flow straightener (Appendix F) installed downstream of these fittings they may be treated as Class F, B and C respectively.
§ The valve is regarded as three quarters closed when the area of the opening is one quarter of that when fully open.

2 Measurement of viscosity

K. WALTERS and W. M. JONES

2.1 Introduction

In the *Principia* published in 1687, Sir Isaac Newton postulated that 'the resistance which arises from the lack of slipperiness of the parts of the liquid, other things being equal, is proportional to the velocity with which parts of the liquid are separated from one another' (see Figure 2.1). This 'lack of slipperiness' is what we now call *viscosity*. The motion in Figure 2.1 is referred to as steady simple shear flow and if τ is the relevant shear stress producing the motion and γ is the velocity gradient ($\gamma = U/d$), we have

$$\tau = \eta\gamma \tag{2.1}$$

η is sometimes called the coefficient of viscosity, but it is now more commonly referred to simply as the viscosity. An instrument designed to measure viscosity is called a *viscometer*. A viscometer is a special type of *rheometer* (defined as an instrument for measuring rheological properties) which is limited to the measurement of viscosity.

The SI units of viscosity are the pascal second $= 1\ \mathrm{Nsm^{-2}}$ ($= 1\ \mathrm{kg\ m^{-1}\ s^{-1}}$) and $\mathrm{Nsm^{-2}}$. The c.g.s. unit is the poise ($= 0.1\ \mathrm{kg\ m^{-1}\ s^{-1}}$) or the poiseuille ($= 1\ \mathrm{Nsm^{-2}}$). The units of kinematic viscosity ν ($= \eta/\rho$, where ρ is the density) are $\mathrm{m^2\ s^{-1}}$. The c.g.s. unit is the stokes (St) and $1\ \mathrm{cSt} = 10^{-6}\ \mathrm{m^2\ s^{-1}}$.

For simple liquids like water, the viscosity can depend on the pressure and temperature, but not on the velocity gradient (i.e. shear rate). If such materials satisfy certain further formal requirements (e.g. that they are inelastic), they are referred to as *Newtonian* viscous fluids. Most viscometers were originally designed to study these simple Newtonian fluids. It is now common knowledge, however, that most fluid-like materials one meets in practice have a much more complex behaviour and this is characterized by the adjective 'non-Newtonian'. The most common expression of non-Newtonian behaviour is that the viscosity is now dependent on the shear rate γ and it is usual to refer to the *apparent viscosity* $\eta(\gamma)$ of such fluids, where, for the motion of Figure 2.1,

$$\tau = \eta(\gamma)\gamma \tag{2.2}$$

In the next section, we shall argue that the concept of viscosity is intimately related to the flow field under investigation (e.g. whether it is steady simple shear flow or not) and in many cases it is more appropriate and convenient to define an *extensional viscosity* η_ε corresponding to a steady uniaxial extensional flow. Now, although there is a simple relation between the (extensional) viscosity η_ε and the (shear) viscosity η in the case of Newtonian liquids (in fact, $\eta_\varepsilon = 3\eta$ for Newtonian liquids) such is not the case in general for non-Newtonian liquids, and this has been one of the motivations behind the emergence of a number of *extensional viscometers* in the last decade (see Section 2.5).

Most fluids of industrial importance can be classified as non-Newtonian: liquid detergents, multi-grade oils, paints, printing inks and molten plastics are obvious examples (see, for example, Walters (1980)), and no chapter on 'the measurement of viscosity' would be complete without a full discussion of the application of viscometry to these complex fluids. This will necessitate an initial discussion of such important concepts as yield stress and thixotropy (which are intimately related to the concept of viscosity) and this is undertaken in the next section.

2.2 Newtonian and non-Newtonian behaviour

We have already indicated that for Newtonian liquids, there is a linear relation between shear stress τ and shear rate γ. For most non-Newtonian materials, the *shear-thinning* behaviour shown schematically in Figure 2.2 pertains. Such behaviour can be represented by the viscosity/shear-rate rheogram of Figure 2.3,

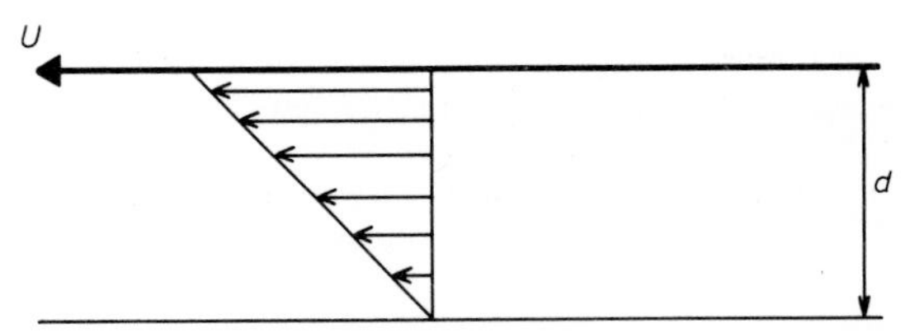

Figure 2.1 Newton's postulate.

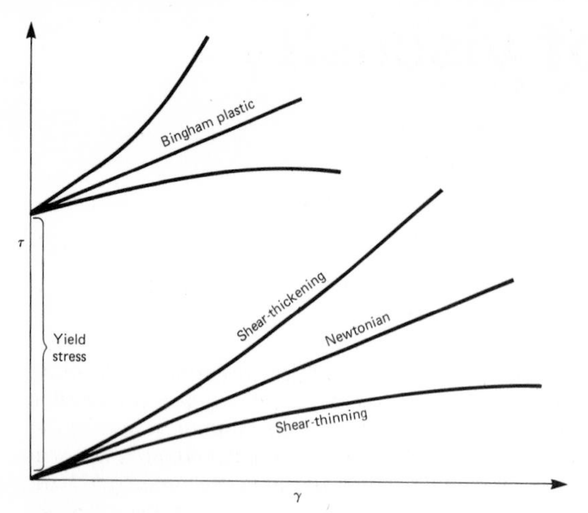

Figure 2.2 Representative (τ, γ) rheograms.

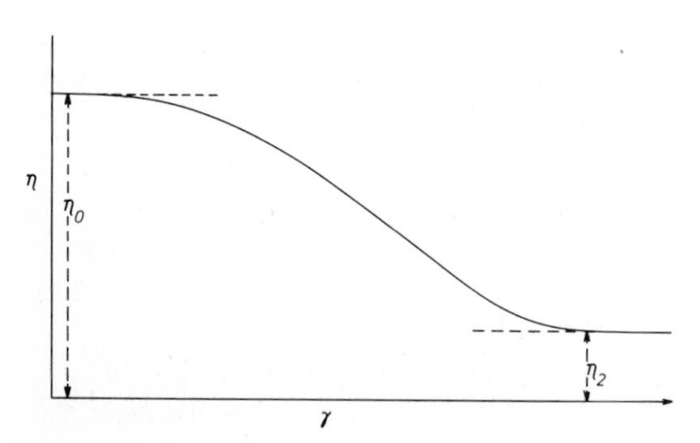

Figure 2.3 Schematic diagram of typical shear-thinning behaviour.

where we see that the viscosity falls from a 'zero-shear' value η_0 to a lower (second-Newtonian) value η_2. The term 'pseudo-plasticity' was once used extensively to describe such behaviour but this terminology is now less popular. In the lubrication literature, shear thinning is often referred to as 'temporary viscosity loss'.

Some non-Newtonian fluids, cornflour suspensions for example, show the opposite type of behaviour in which the viscosity increases with shear rate (Figure 2.2). This is called 'shear thickening'. In old-fashioned texts, the term 'dilatancy' was often used to describe such behaviour.

For many materials over a limited shear-rate range a logarithmic plot of τ against γ is linear, so that

$$\tau = K\gamma^n \tag{2.3}$$

When $n > 1$, these so-called 'power-law fluids' are shear-thickening and when $n < 1$, they are shear-thinning.

An important class of materials will not flow until a critical stress, called the 'yield stress', is exceeded. These 'plastic' materials can exhibit various kinds of behaviour above the yield stress as shown in Figure 2.2. If the rheogram above the yield stress is a straight line, we have what is commonly referred to as a Bingham plastic material.

In addition to the various possibilities shown in Figure 2.2, there are also important 'time-dependent' effects exhibited by some materials; these can be grouped under the headings 'thixotropy' and 'anti-thixotropy'. The shearing of some materials at a *constant* rate can result in a substantial lowering of the viscosity with time, with a gradual return to the initial viscosity when the shearing is stopped. This is called thixotropy. Paints are the most obvious examples of thixotropic materials. As the name suggests, anti-thixotropy involves an *increase* in viscosity with time at a constant rate-of-shear.

Clearly, the measurement of the shear viscosity within an industrial context is a non-trivial task and requires an initial appreciation of material behaviour. Is the material Newtonian or non-Newtonian? Is thixotropy important? And so on.

As if to complicate an already complex situation, it has recently been realized that many industrial processes involve more extensional deformation than shear flow, and this has been the motivation behind the search for extensional viscometers, which are constructed to estimate a material's resistance to a stretching motion of the sort shown schematically in Figure 2.4. In this case, it is again necessary to define an appropriate stress T and rate of strain κ, and to define the extensional viscosity η_ε by

$$T = \eta_\varepsilon \kappa \tag{2.4}$$

For a Newtonian liquid, η_ε is a constant $(\equiv 3\eta)$. For some non-Newtonian liquids, the extensional viscosity can take very high values indeed, and it is this exceptional resistance to stretching in some materials, together with the practical importance of extensional flow, which makes the study of extensional viscosity so important. The reader is referred to the book *Elongational Flows* by Petrie (1979) for a detailed treatise on the subject. The recent text by Dealy (1982) on polymer-melt rheometry is also recommended in this context.

A detailed assessment of the importance of non-Newtonian effects is given in the text *Rheometry: Industrial Applications* (Walters, 1980) which contains a general discussion of basic principles in addition to

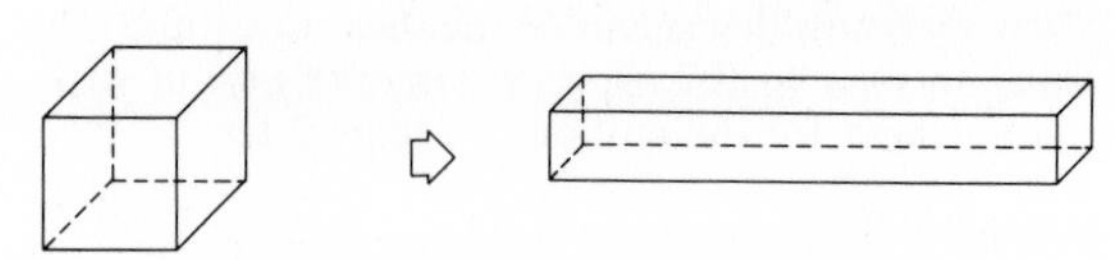

Figure 2.4 Uniaxial extensional deformation.

an in-depth study of various industrial applications.

The popular book on viscometry by Van Wazer *et al.* (1963) and that of Wilkinson (1960) on non-Newtonian flow are now out of date in some limited respects, but they have stood the test of time remarkably well and are recommended to readers, provided the dates of publication of the books are appreciated. More modern treatments, developed from different but complementary viewpoints, are given in the books by Lodge (1974), Walters (1975) and Whorlow (1980). The text by Dealy (1982) already referred to is limited to polymer-melt rheometry, but much of the book is of general interest to those concerned with the measurement of viscosity.

2.3 Measurement of the shear viscosity

It is clearly impracticable to construct viscometers with the infinite planar geometry associated with Newton's postulate (Figure 2.1), especially in the case of mobile liquid systems, and this has led to the search for convenient geometries and flows which have the same basic steady simple shear flow structure. This problem has now been resolved and a number of the so-called 'viscometric flows' have been used as the basis for viscometer design. (The basic mathematics is non-trivial and may be found in the texts by Coleman *et al.* (1966), Lodge (1974) and Walters (1975).) Most popular have been (i) capillary (or Poiseuille) flow, (ii) circular Couette flow, and (iii) cone-and-plate flow. For convenience, we shall briefly describe each of these flows and give the simple operating formulae for Newtonian liquids, referring the reader to detailed texts for the extensions to non-Newtonian liquids. We also include in Section 2.3.4 a discussion of the parallel-plate rheometer, which approximates closely the flow associated with Newton's postulate.

2.3.1 Capillary viscometer

Consider a long capillary with a circular cross-section of radius a. Fluid is forced through the capillary by the application of an axial pressure drop. This pressure drop P is measured over a length L of the capillary, far enough away from both entrance and exit for the flow to be regarded as 'fully-developed' steady simple shear flow. The volume rate of flow Q through the capillary is measured for each pressure gradient P/L and the viscosity η for a Newtonian liquid can then be determined from the so-called Hagen–Poiseuille law:

$$Q=\frac{\pi P a^4}{8\eta L} \tag{2.5}$$

The non-trivial extensions to (2.5) when the fluid is non-Newtonian may be found in Walters (1975), Whorlow (1980) and Coleman *et al.* (1966). For example, in the case of the power-law fluid (2.3), the formula is given by

$$Q=\frac{\pi n a^3}{(3n+1)}\left(\frac{aP}{2KL}\right)^{1/n} \tag{2.6}$$

One of the major advantages of the capillary viscometer is that relatively high shear-rates can be attained.

Often, it is not possible to determine the pressure gradient over a restricted section of the capillary and it is then necessary, especially in the case of non-Newtonian liquids, to study carefully the pressure losses in the entry and exit regions before the results can be interpreted correctly (see, for example, Dealy (1982) and Whorlow (1980)). Other possible sources of error include viscous heating and flow instabilities. These and other potential problems are discussed in detail by Dealy (1982), Walters (1975) and Whorlow (1980).

The so-called 'kinetic-energy correction' is important when it is not possible to limit the pressure drop measurement to the steady simple shear flow region and when this is taken over the complete length L of the capillary. For a *Newtonian* fluid, the kinetic energy correction is given (approximately) by

$$P=P_0-\frac{1.1\rho Q^2}{\pi^2 a^4} \tag{2.7}$$

where P is the pressure drop required in (2.5), P_0 is the measured pressure drop and ρ is the density of the fluid.

Since a gas is highly compressible, it is more convenient to measure the *mass* rate of flow $\dot{m}$. Equation (2.5) has then to be replaced by (see, for example, Massey (1968))

$$\eta=\frac{\pi a^4 \bar{p} M P}{8\dot{m} R T L} \tag{2.8}$$

where $\bar{p}$ is the mean pressure in the pipe, M is the molecular weight of the gas, R is the gas constant per mole and T is the Kelvin temperature. The kinetic-energy correction (2.7) is still valid and must be borne in mind, but in the case of a gas, this correction is usually very small. A 'slip correction' is also potentially important in the case of gases, but only at low pressures.

In commercial capillary viscometers for non-gaseous materials, the liquids usually flow through the capillaries under gravity. A good example is the Ostwald viscometer (Figure 2.5). In this b, c and d are fixed marks and there are reservoirs at D and E. The amount of liquid must be such that at equilibrium one meniscus is at d. To operate, the liquid is sucked or blown so that the other meniscus is now a few millimetres above b. The time t for the level to fall from

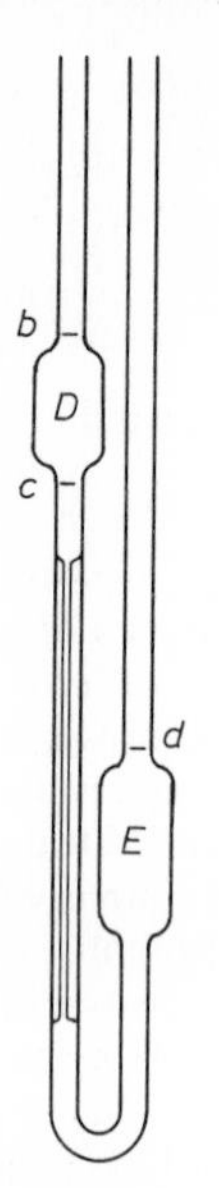

Figure 2.5 Schematic diagram of an Ostwald viscometer.

b to c is measured. The operating formula is of the form

$$v = At - B/t \tag{2.9}$$

where v is the kinematic viscosity ($\equiv \eta/\rho$). The second term on the right-hand side of equation (2.9) is a correction factor for end effects. For any particular viscometer, A and B are given as calibration constants. Viscometers with pipes of different radii are supplied according to British Standards specifications and a 'recommended procedure' is also given in B.S. Publication 188: 1957.

Relying on gravity flow alone limits the range of measurable stress to between 1 and 15 $\mathrm{Nm^{-2}}$. The upper limit can be increased to 50 $\mathrm{Nm^{-2}}$ by applying a known steady pressure of inert gas over the left-hand side of the U-tube during operation.

2.3.2 Couette viscometer

The most popular rotational viscometer is the Couette concentric-cylinder viscometer. Fluid is placed in the annulus between two concentric cylinders (regarded as infinite in the interpretation of data) which are in relative rotation about their common axis. It is usual for the outer cylinder to rotate and for the torque required to keep the inner cylinder stationary to be measured, but there are variants, as in the Brookfield viscometer, for example, where a cylindrical bob (or sometimes a disc) is rotated in an expanse of test liquid and the torque on this same bob is recorded, see Section 2.4.

If the outer cylinder of radius r_0 rotates with angular velocity Ω_0 and the inner cylinder of radius r_I is stationary, the torque C per unit length of cylinder on the inner cylinder for a Newtonian liquid is given by

$$C = \frac{4\pi\Omega_0 r_I^2 r_0^2 \eta}{(r_0^2 - r_I^2)} \tag{2.10}$$

so that measurement of C at each rotational speed Ω_0 can be used to determine the viscosity η. The extensions to (2.10) when the fluid is non-Newtonian are again non-trivial (unless the annular gap is very small) but the relevant analysis is contained in many texts (see, for example Walters (1975) and Whorlow (1980)). With reference to possible sources of error, end effects are obvious candidates as are flow instabilities, misalignment of axes and viscous heating. A detailed discussion of possible sources of error is to be found in Dealy (1982), Walters (1975) and Whorlow (1980).

2.3.3 Cone-and-plate viscometer*

Consider the cone-and-plate arrangement shown schematically in Figure 2.6. The cone rotates with angular velocity Ω_0 and the torque C required to keep the plate stationary is measured. The gap angle θ_0 is usually very small (<4°) and, in the interpretation of results, edge effects are neglected. It is then easy to show that for a Newtonian liquid, the operating formula is

$$C = \frac{2\pi a^3 \Omega_0}{3\theta_0}\eta \tag{2.11}$$

where a is the radius of the cone.

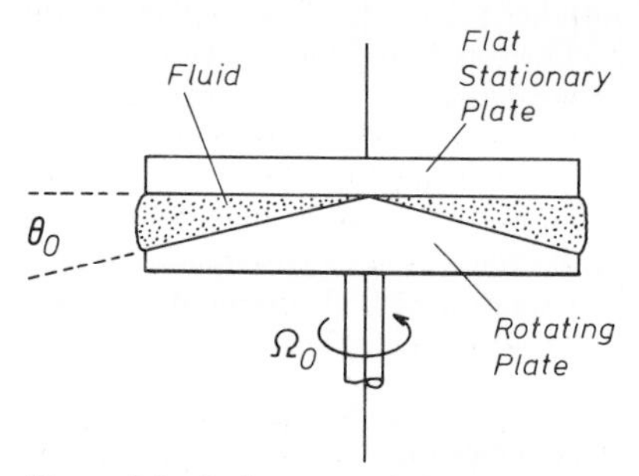

Figure 2.6 Basic cone-and-plate geometry.

In contrast to the capillary-flow and Couette-flow situations, the operating formula for non-Newtonian fluids is very similar to (2.11) and is in fact given by

$$C = \tfrac{2}{3}\pi a^3 \gamma \eta(\gamma) \tag{2.12}$$

where the shear rate γ is given by

$$\gamma = \Omega_0/\theta_0 \tag{2.13}$$

which is (approximately) constant throughout the test

* The torsional-flow rheometer in which the test fluid is contained between parallel plates is similar in operation to the cone-and-plate rheometer, but the data interpretation is less straightforward, except in the Newtonian case (see, for example, Walters (1975)).

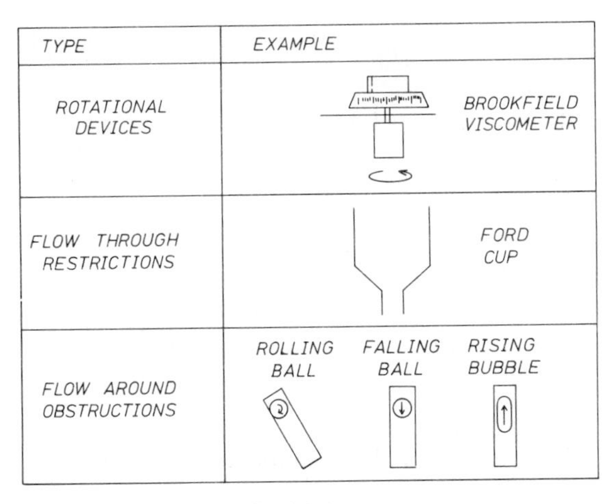

Figure 2.7 Classes of industrial viscometers.

fluid, provided θ_0 is small ($<4°$ say). This is an important factor in explaining the popularity of cone-and-plate flow in non-Newtonian viscometry. Indeed, it is apparent from (2.12) and (2.13) that measurements of the torque C as a function of rotational speed Ω_0 immediately yield apparent viscosity/shear-rate data.

Sources of error in the cone-and-plate viscometer have been discussed in detail by Walters (1975) and Whorlow (1980). Measurements on all fluids are limited to modest shear rates ($<100\ \mathrm{s}^{-1}$) and this upper bound is significantly lower for some fluids like polymer melts.

Time-dependent effects such as thixotropy are notoriously difficult to study in a systematic way and the constant shear rate in the gap of a cone-and-plate viscometer at least removes one of the complicating factors. The cone-and-plate geometry is therefore recommended for the study of time-dependent effects.

For the rotational viscometer designs discussed thus far, the shear rate is fixed and the corresponding stress is measured. For plastic materials with a yield stress this may not be the most convenient procedure and the last decade has seen the emergence of constant-stress devices, in which the shear *stress* is controlled and the resulting motion (i.e. shear rate) recorded. The Deer rheometer is the best known of the constant-stress devices and at least three versions of such an instrument are now commercially available. The cone-and-plate geometry is basic in current instruments.

2.3.4 Parallel-plate viscometer

In the parallel-plate rheometer, the test fluid is contained between two parallel plates mounted vertically; one plate is free to move in the vertical direction, so that the flow is of the plane-Couette type and approximates that associated with Newton's postulate.

A mass M is attached to the moving plate (of area A) and this produces a displacement x of the plate in a time t. If the plates are separated by a distance h, the relevant shear stress τ is given by

$$\tau = Mg/A \tag{2.14}$$

and the shear rate γ by

$$\gamma = x/th \tag{2.15}$$

so that the viscosity η is determined from

$$\eta = Mgth/xA \tag{2.16}$$

Clearly, this technique is only applicable to 'stiff' systems, i.e. liquids of very high viscosity.

2.4 Shop-floor viscometers

A number of *ad hoc* industrial viscometers are very popular at the shop-floor level of industrial practice and these usually provide a very simple and convenient method of determining the viscosity of *Newtonian* liquids. The emphasis on the 'Newtonian' is important since their application to non-Newtonian systems is far less straightforward (see, for example, Walters and Barnes (1980)). Three broad types of industrial viscometer can be identified (see Figure 2.7). The first type comprises simple rotational devices such as the Brookfield viscometer, which can be adapted in favourable circumstances to provide the apparent viscosity of non-Newtonian systems (see, for example, Williams (1979)). The instrument is shown schematically in Figure 2.8. The pointer and the dial rotate together. When the disc is immersed, the test fluid exerts a torque on the disc. This twists the spring and the pointer is displaced relative to the dial. For Newtonian liquids (and for non-Newtonian liquids in

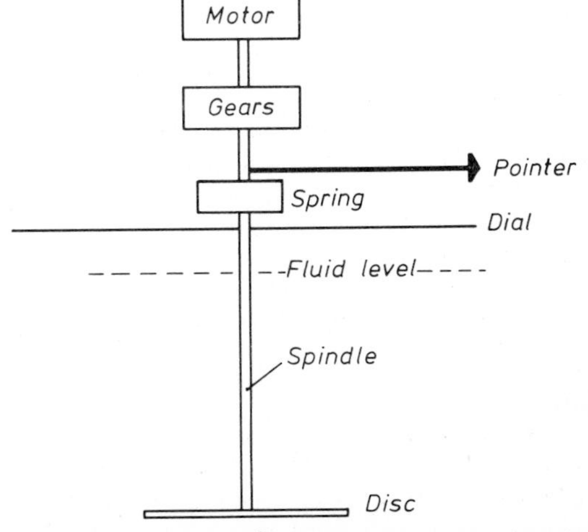

Figure 2.8 Schematic diagram of the Brookfield viscometer.

favourable circumstances) the pointer displacement can be directly related to the viscosity of the test sample.

The second type of industrial viscometer involves what we might loosely call 'flow through constrictions' and is typified by the Ford-cup arrangement. The idea of measuring the viscosity of a liquid by timing its efflux through a hole at the bottom of a cup is very attractive. It is simple to operate, inexpensive, and the apparatus can be made very robust. Historically, the cup device was probably one of the first forms of viscometer ever used and today there are over 50 versions of the so-called flow cups.

Often, results from flow cups are simply expressed as 'time in seconds' (e.g. 'Redwood seconds') but for Newtonian liquids these can be converted to kinematic viscosity ν through an (approximate) formula of the form

$$\nu = At - B/t \tag{2.17}$$

where A and B are constants which depend on the cup geometry (see, for example, Walters and Barnes (1980)).

The second term on the right-hand side of (2.17) is essentially a kinetic-energy correction. For Newtonian liquids, A and B can be determined by carrying out standard experiments on liquids of known kinematic viscosity.

A major disadvantage of the standard Ford cup so far as *non*-Newtonian liquids is concerned is that only one time can be taken, i.e. the time taken for the cup to empty. Such a measurement leads to a single (averaged) viscosity for a complicated deformation regime and this is difficult to interpret consistently for rheologically complex fluids. Indeed, liquids with different rheologies as regards shear viscosity, extensional viscosity and elasticity may behave in an identical fashion in a Ford-cup experiment (Walters and Barnes, 1980) so that shop-floor instruments of this sort should be used with extreme caution when dealing with *non*-Newtonian liquids. The same applies to the 'flow-around-obstacle' viscometers of Figure 2.7. Typical examples of this type of viscometer are the Glen Creston falling-ball viscometer and the Hoeppler rolling-ball instrument (see, for example, Van Wazer *et al.* (1963) and Cheng (1979). Rising-bubble techniques may also be included in this category.

2.5 Measurement of the extensional viscosity

Many industrial processes, especially in the polymer industries, involve a high extensional-flow component and there is an acknowledged need for *extensional viscometers.* The construction of such devices is, however, fraught with difficulties. For example, it is difficult to generate an extensional deformation over a sufficient deformation-rate range. Indeed, many of the most popular and sophisticated devices for work on polymer melts (such as those constructed at B.A.S.F. in Germany) cannot reach the steady state required to determine the extensional viscosity η_ε defined in (2.4). Therefore, they are, as yet, of unproven utility. A full discussion of the subject of extensional viscometry within the context of polymer-melt rheology is provided by Dealy (1982).

In the case of more mobile liquid systems, it is difficult to generate flows which approximate to steady uniaxial extension and the most that can reasonably be hoped for is that instruments will provide an *estimate* of a fluid's resistance to stretching flows (see, for example, Chapter 1 of Walters (1980)). With this important proviso, the Ferguson Spin-Line Rheometer is a commercially-available instrument which can be used on mobile liquids to provide extensional viscosity information.

2.6 Measurement of viscosity under extremes of temperature and pressure

Any of the techniques discussed above can be adapted to study the effect of temperature and pressure on viscosity, provided the apparatus can accommodate the extremes prevailing.

It is important to emphasize that viscosity is very sensitive to temperature. For example, the viscosity of water changes by 3 per cent per kelvin. It is therefore essential to control the temperature and to measure it accurately.

Pressure is also an important variable in some studies. In the case of lubricating oils, for example, high pressures are experienced during use and it is necessary to know the pressure-dependence of viscosity for these fluids.

At temperatures near absolute zero measurements have been concerned with the viscosity of liquid helium. Recently, special techniques have been developed. Webeler and Allen (1972) measured the attenuation of torsional vibrations initiated by a cylindrical quartz crystal. Vibrating-wire viscometers have also been used. The resonant frequency and damping of the oscillations of a wire vibrating transversely in a fluid depend on the viscosity and density of the fluid. References to this and other work are given in Bennemann and Ketterson (1976).

To study the effect of high pressure, Abbot *et al.* (1981) and Dandridge and Jackson (1981) have observed the rate of fall of a sphere in lubricants exposed to high pressures (~ 3 GPa). Galvin, Hutton and Jones (1981) used a capillary viscometer at high pressure to study liquids over a range of temperatures (0 to 150 °C) and shear rates (0 to 3×10^5 sec^{-1}) with pressures up to 0.2 GPa. Kamal and Nyun (1980) have also adapted a capillary viscometer for high-pressure work.

2.7 On-line measurements

It is frequently necessary to monitor the viscosity of a fluid 'on line' in a number of applications, particularly when the constitution or temperature of the fluid is likely to change. Of the viscometers described in this chapter, the capillary viscometer and the concentric-cylinder viscometer are those most conveniently adapted for such a purpose. For the former, for example, the capillary can be installed directly in series with the flow and the pressure difference recorded using suitably placed transducers and recorders. The corresponding flow rate can be obtained from a metering pump.

Care must be taken with the on-line concentric-cylinder apparatus as the interpretation of data from the resulting *helical* flow is not easy.

Other on-line methods involve obstacles in the flow channel; for example, a float in a conical tube will arrive at an equilibrium position in the tube depending on the rate of flow and the kinematic viscosity of the fluid. The parallel-plate viscometer has also been adapted for on-line measurement. These and other on-line techniques are considered in detail in *The Instrument Manual* (1975).

2.8 Accuracy and range

The ultimate absolute accuracy obtained in any one instrument cannot be categorically stated in a general way. For example, using the Ostwald viscometer, reproducible measurements of time can be made to 0.3 per cent. But to achieve this absolutely, the viscometer and the fluid must be scrupulously clean and the precise amount of fluid must be used. The temperature within the viscometer must also be uniform and be known to within 0.1 °C. Obviously, this can be achieved, but an operator might well settle for 1 to 2 per cent accuracy and find this satisfactory for his purpose with less restriction on temperature measurement and thermostating. Similar arguments apply to the Couette viscometer but here, even with precise research instruments, an accuracy of 1 per cent requires very careful experimentation.

The range of viscosities and rates of shear attainable in any type of viscometer depend on the dimensions of the viscometer, e.g. the radius of the capillary in the capillary viscometer and the gap in a Couette viscometer.

By way of illustration, we conclude with a table of values claimed by manufacturers of instruments within each type, but we emphasize that no one instrument will achieve the entire range quoted.

Table 2.1

Viscometer type	*Lowest viscosity (poise)*	*Highest viscosity (poise)*	*Shear-rate range* (s^{-1})
Capillary	2×10^{-3}	10^3	1 to 1.5×10^4
Couette	5×10^{-3}	4×10^7	10^{-2} to 10^4
Cone-and-plate	10^{-3}	10^{10}	10^{-4} to 10^3
Brookfield type	10^{-2}	5×10^5	10^{-3} to 5×10^6
Falling-ball, rolling-ball	10^{-4}	10^4	indeterminate

2.9 References

Abbott, L. H., Newhall, D. H., Zibberstein, V. A. and Dill, J. F., *A.S.L.E. Trans.*, **24**, 125, (1981)

Bennemann, K. H. and Ketterson, J. B. (eds), *The Physics of Liquid and Solid Helium*, Wiley, (Part 1, 1976; Part 2, 1978)

Cheng, D. C.-H., 'A comparison of 14 commercial viscometers and a home-made instrument', Warren Spring Laboratory LR 282 (MH), (1979)

Coleman, B. D., Markovitz, H. and Noll, W., *Viscometric Flows of Non-Newtonian Fluids*, Springer-Verlag, (1966)

Dandridge, A. and Jackson, D. A., *J. Phys. D*, **14**, 829, (1981)

Dealy, J. M., *Rheometers for Molten Plastics*, Van Nostrand, (1982)

Galvin, G. D., Hutton, J. F. and Jones, B. J., *Non-Newtonian Fluid Mechanics*, **8**, 11, (1981)

The Instrument Manual, United Trade Press, p. 62, (5th edn, 1975)

Kamal, M. R. and Nyun, H., *Polymer Eng. and Science*, **20**, 109, (1980)

Lodge, A. S., *Body Tensor Fields in Continuum Mechanics*, Academic Press, (1974)

Massey, R. S., *Mechanics of Fluids*, Van Nostrand, (1968)

Petrie, C. J. S., *Elongational Flows*, Pitman, (1979)

Van Wazer, J. R., Lyon, J. W., Kim, K. Y. and Colwell, R. E., *Viscosity and Flow Measurement*, Wiley-Interscience, (1963)

Walters, K., *Rheometry*, Chapman & Hall, (1975)

Walters, K. (ed.), *Rheometry: Industrial Applications*, Wiley, (1980)

Walters, K. and Barnes, H. A., *Proc. 8th Int. Cong. on Rheology, Naples, Italy*, p. 45, Plenum Press, (1980)

Webeler, R. W. H. and Allen, G., *Phys. Rev.*, **A5**, 1820, (1972)

Whorlow, R. W., *Rheological Techniques*, Wiley, (1980)

Wilkinson, W. L., *Non-Newtonian Fluids*, Pergamon Press, (1960)

Williams, R. W., *Rheol. Acta*, **18**, 345, (1979)

3 Measurement of length

P. H. SYDENHAM

3.1 Introduction

Length is probably the most measured physical parameter. This measurand (the term used here for the parameter that is to be measured) is known under many alternative names—displacement, movement, motion.

Length is often the intermediate stage of systems used to measure other parameters. For example, a common method of measuring fluid pressure is to use the force of the pressure to elongate a metal element, a length sensor then being used to give an electrical output related to pressure.

Older methods were largely mechanical giving readout suited to an observer's eyes. The possibility of using electrical and radiation techniques to give electronic outputs is now much wider. Pneumatic techniques are also quite widely used and these are discussed in Volume 4.

Length can now be measured through over thirty decadic orders. Figure 3.1 is a chart of some common methods and their ranges of use. In most cases only two to three decades can be covered with a specific geometrical scaling of a sensor's configuration.

This chapter introduces the reader to the commonly used methods that are used in the micrometre to sub-kilometre range.

For further reading, it may be noted that most instrumentation books contain one chapter, or more, on length measurement of the modern forms, examples being Mansfield (1973), Norton (1969), Oliver (1971) and Sydenham (1984, 1983). Mechanical methodology is more generally reported in the earlier literature on the subjects of mechanical measurements, tool-room gauging and optical tooling. Some such books are Batson and Hyde (1931), Hume (1970), Kissam (1962), Rolt (1929) and Sharp (1970). In this aspect of length measurement the value of the older books should not be overlooked for they provide basic understanding of technique that is still relevant today in proper application of modern electronic methods.

For the microdisplacement range see Garratt (1979), Sydenham (1969; 1972) and Woltring (1975); for larger ranges see Sydenham (1968) and Sydenham (1971). Neubert (1975) has written an excellent analysis of transducers, including those used for length measurement.

3.2 The nature of length

Efficient and faithful measurement requires an appreciation of the nature of the measurand and of the pitfalls that can arise for that particular physical system domain.

Length, as a measured parameter, is generally so self-evident that very little is ever written about it at the philosophical level. Measurement of length is apparently simple to conceptualize and it appears easy to devise methods for converting the measurand into an appropriate signal.

It is an experimental finding that space can be described in terms of three length parameters. Three coordinate numbers suffice to describe the position of a point in space regardless of the kind of coordinate framework used to define that point's coordinates. Where some of the mechanical degrees of freedom are constrained the number of measurement coordinates can be reduced in order to define position. Thus to measure position along a defined straight line only requires one length-sensing system channel; to plot position in a defined plane requires two sensors.

Length measurements fall into two kinds, those requiring determination of the absolute value in terms of the defined international standard and those that determine a change in length of a gauge length interval (relative length). In the latter case the measurement problem is usually greatly simplified for there is no need to determine the gauge interval length to high accuracy. Thus, to measure the length of a structure in absolute terms is a different kind of problem from measuring strains induced in the structure.

Descriptive terminology is needed to simplify general description of the measuring range of a length sensor and a classification into microdisplacement, industrial, surveying, navigation and celestial is included in Figure 3.1.

The actual range of a length sensor is not necessarily that of the size of the task. For example, to measure strain over a long test interval may make use of a long-

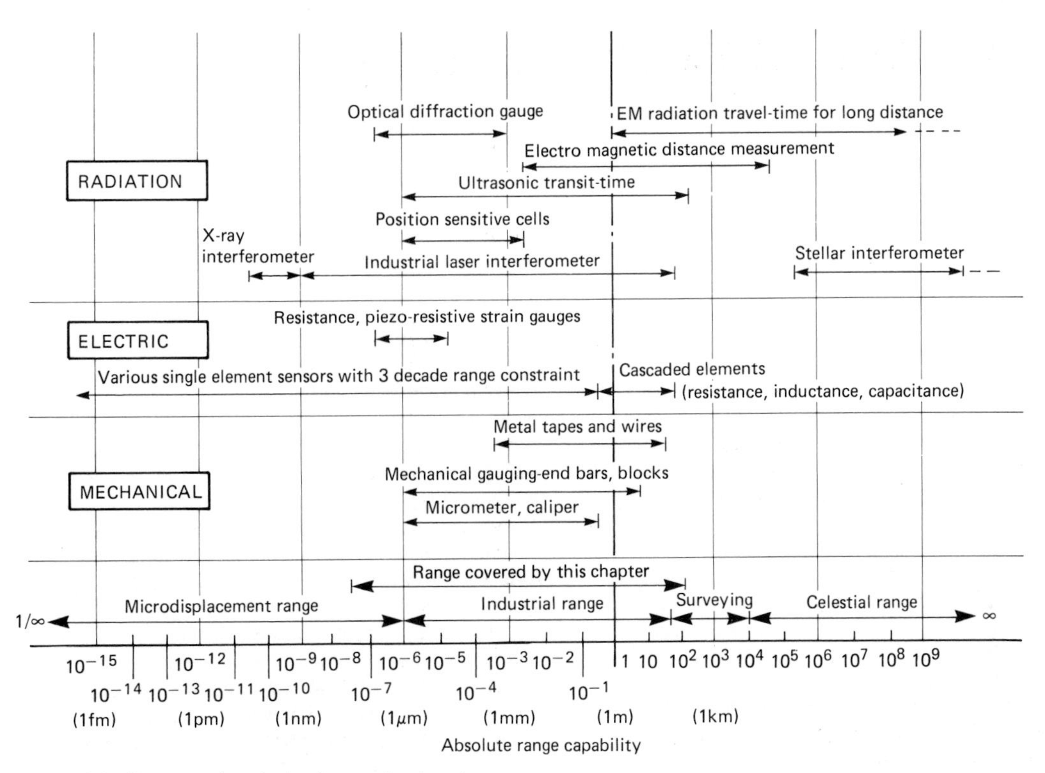

Figure 3.1 Ranges and methods of measuring length.

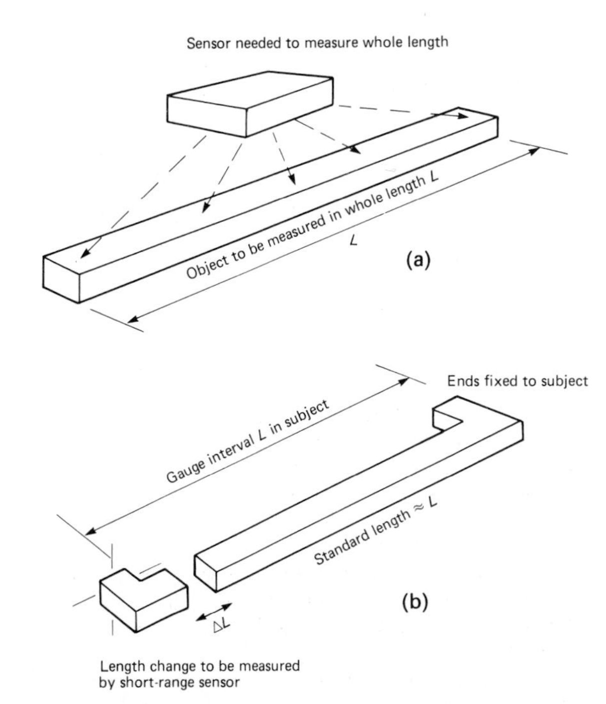

Figure 3.2 Absolute (a) and relative (b) length-measurement situations.

range, fixed-length, standard structure which is compared with the object of interest using a short-range sensor to detect the small differences that occur (see Figure 3.2(b)). Absolute whole length measurement, Figure 3.2(a), requires a sensor of longer range.

It is often possible to measure a large length by adding together successive intervals. This is obvious when using a single ruler to span a length greater than itself. The same concept is often applied using multiple electronic sensors placed in line or by stepping a fixed interval along the whole distance counting the number of coarse intervals and subdividing the last partial interval by some other sensor that has finer sensing detail.

Some mention is appropriate on the choice of use of non-contact or contacting methods. In the former (see Figure 3.3), the length measurement is made by a method that does not mechanically contact the subject. An example is the use of an optical interferometer to monitor position of a machine slide. It does not impose significant force on the slide and, as such, does not alter the measurand value by its presence.

Contacting methods must be used with some caution lest they alter the measurement value due to the mechanical forces imposed by their presence.

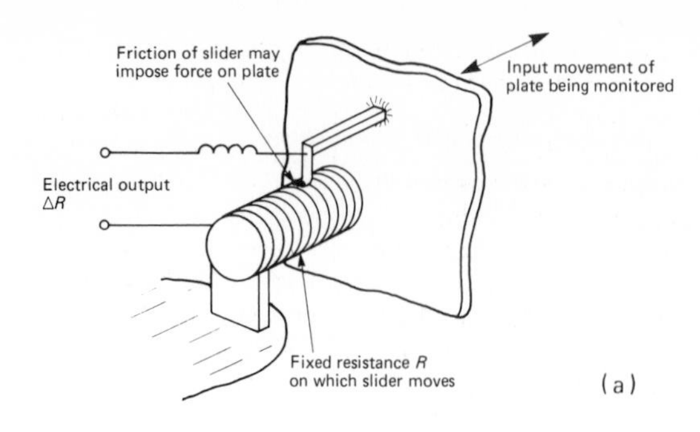

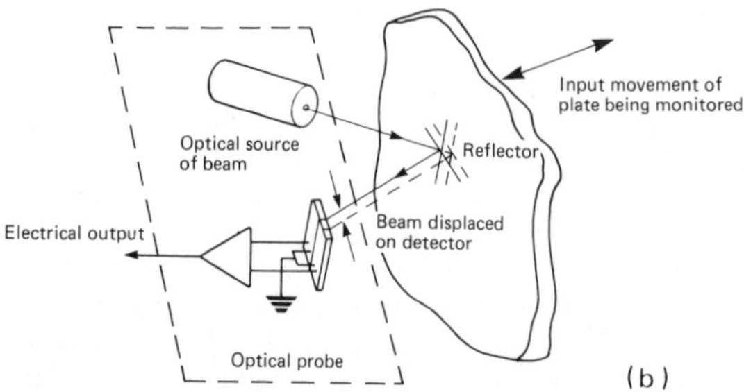

Figure 3.3 Examples of contacting and non-contacting length measurements. (a) Contacting, using variable resistance. (b) Non-contacting, using an optical probe.

3.3 Derived measurements

3.3.1 Derived from length measurement alone

Length (m) comes into other measurement parameters, including relative length change (m/m), area (m^2), volume (m^3), angle (m/m), velocity ($m\,s^{-1}$) and acceleration ($m\,s^{-2}$). To measure position, several coordinate systems can be adopted. Figure 3.4 shows those commonly used. In each instance the general position of a point P will need three measurement numbers, each being measured by separate sensing channels.

The cartesian (or rectangular) system shown in Figure 3.4(a), is that most adopted for ranges less than a few tens of metres. Beyond that absolute size it becomes very difficult to establish an adequately stable and calibratable framework. Errors can arise from lack of right angles between axes, from errors of length sensing along an axis and from the imperfection of projection out from an axis to the point.

The polar system of Figure 3.4(b) avoids the need for an all-encompassing framework, replacing that problem with the practical need for a reference base from which two angles and a length are determined. Errors arise here in definition of the two angles and in the length measurement which, now, is not restricted to a slide-way. Practical angle measurement reaches practical and cost barriers at around one arc second of discrimination. This method is well suited to such applications as radar tracking of aircraft or plotting of location under the sea.

The above two systems of coordinate framework are those mostly adopted. A third alternative which is less used, has in principle, the least error sources. This is the triangular system shown as Figure 3.4(c). In this method three lengths are measured from a triangle formed of three fixed lengths. Errors arise only in the three length measurements with respect to the base triangle and in their definition in space. Where two or more points in space are to be monitored, then their relative position can be obtained accurately even if the base triangle moves in space. The major practical problem in adopting this method is that the three length measurements each require tracking arrangements to keep them following the point. The accuracy of pointing, however, is only subject to easily tolerated cosine forms of error which allow relatively poor following ability to give quite reasonable values.

The three alternatives can also be combined to provide other arrangements but in each case there will always be the need to measure three variables (as combinations of at least one length with length and/or angle) to define point position in a general manner. Where a translational freedom is constrained the need to measure reduces to a simpler arrangement needing less sensing channels.

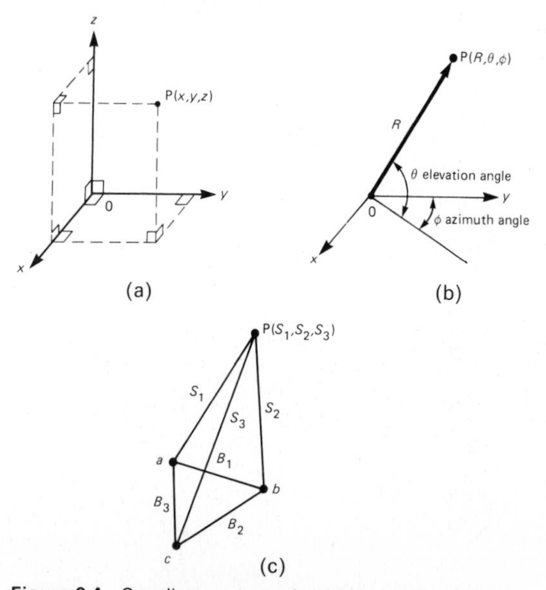

Figure 3.4 Coordinate systems that can be used to locate position in space. (a) Cartesian, rectangular, frame for three lengths. (b) Two polar directions and a length. (c) Triangulated lengths from a base triangle.

3.4 Standards and calibration of length

With very little exception length measurements are now standardized according to SI measurement unit definitions, length being one of the seven base units. It is defined in terms of the unit called the metre.

Until early 1982 the metre was defined in terms of a given number of wavelengths of krypton-86 radiation. Over the 1970 decade, however, it was becoming clear that there were improved methods available that would enable definition with reduced uncertainty.

The first was to make use, in the manner already adopted, of the radiation available from a suitable wavelength-stabilized laser source for this is easier to produce and is more reproducible than krypton radiation. At first sight this might be an obvious choice to adopt but a quite different approach was also available, that which was recommended in 1982.

The numerical value of the speed of light c ($c = 299\,792\,458\ \mathrm{m\,s^{-1}}$) is the result of numerical standards chosen for the standards of time and of length. Thus the speed of light, as a numerical value, is not a fundamental constant.

Time standards (parts in 10^{14} uncertainty) are more reproducible in terms of uncertainty than length (parts in 10^{8} uncertainty) so if the speed of light is defined as a fixed number then, in principle, the time standard will serve as the length standard provided suitable apparatus exists to make the conversion from time to length via the constant c.

Suitable equipment and experimental procedures have now been proven as workable. By choosing a convenient value for c that suited measurement needs (that given above) it was, in 1982, agreed by the signatories of the committee responsible for standardization of the metre that the new definition should be 'The metre is the length of the path travelled by light in vacuum during the fraction (1/299 792 458) of a second.'

This new definition takes reproducibility of length definition from parts in 10^{8} to parts in 10^{10}. In common industrial practice, few people require the full capability of the standard but adequate margin is needed to provide for loss of uncertainty each time the standards are transferred to a more suitable apparatus.

To establish the base standard takes many months of careful experimental work using very expensive apparatus. This method is not applicable to the industrial workplace due to reasons of cost, time and

Figure 3.5 Laser interferometer being used to measure length in an industrial application. Courtesy, Hewlett-Packard Inc.

apparatus complexity. The next level of uncertainty down is, however, relatively easily provided in the form of the industrial laser interferometer that has been on the market for several years. Figure 3.5 is such an equipment in an industrial application. The nature of the laser system shown is such that it has been given approval by the National Bureau of Standards (NBS) for use without traceable calibration for, provided the lengths concerned are not too small, it can give an uncertainty of around 1 part in 10^8 which is adequate for most industrial measurements.

Optical interferometer systems operate with wavelengths of the order of 600 nm. Subdivision of the wavelength becomes difficult at around 1/1000 of the wavelength making calibration of sub-micrometre displacements very much less certain than parts in 10^8. In practice, lengths of a micrometre cannot be calibrated to much better than 1 per cent of the range.

Laser interferometers are easy to use and very precise, but they too are often not applicable due to high cost and unsuitability of equipment. A less expensive calibration method that sits below the interferometer in the traceable chain uses the mechanical slip and gauge block family. These are specially treated and finished pieces of steel whose lengths between defined surfaces are measured using a more certain method, such as an interferometer. The length values are recorded on calibration certificates. In turn the blocks are used as standards to calibrate micrometers, go/no-go gauges and electronic transducers. Mechanical gauges can provide of the order of 1 in 10^6 uncertainties.

For lengths over a few metres, solid mechanical bars are less suitable as standard lengths due to handling reasons. Flexible tapes are used which are calibrated against the laser interferometer in standards facilities such as that shown in Figure 3.6. Tapes are relatively cheap and easy to use in the field compared with the laser interferometer. They can be calibrated to the order of a part in 10^6.

For industrial use little difficulty will be experienced in obtaining calibration of a length measuring device. Probably the most serious problem to be faced is that good calibration requires considerable time: the standard under calibration must be observed for a time in order to ensure that it does have the long-term stability needed to hold the calibration.

3.5 Practice of length measurement for industrial use

3.5.1 General remarks

A large proportion of industrial range measurements can be performed quite adequately using simple mechanical gauging and measuring instruments. If, however, the requirement is for automatic measurement such as is needed in automatic inspection, or in closed-loop control, then the manual methods must be replaced by transducer forms of length sensor.

Figure 3.6 Tape-calibration facility at the National Measurement Laboratory New South Wales, Australia. Courtesy, CSIRO.

In many applications the speed of response needed is far greater than the traditional mechanical methods can yield. Numerically controlled mills, for instance, could not function without the use of electronic sensors that transduce the various axial dimensions into control signals.

Initially, that is in the 1950s, the cost of electronic sensors greatly exceeded that of the traditional mechanical measuring tools and their servicing required a new breed of technician. Most of these earlier shortcomings are now removed and today the use of electronic sensing can be more productive than the use of manually-read micrometers and scales because of the reduced cost of the electronic part of the sensing system and the need for more automatic data processing. There can be little doubt that solely mechanical instruments will gradually become less attractive in many uses.

3.5.2 Mechanical length-measuring equipment

Measurement of length from a micrometre to fractional metres can be performed inexpensively using an appropriate mechanical instrument. These group into the familiar range of internal and external micrometers, sliding-jaw calipers and dial gauges. Accuracy obtained with these depends much upon the quality of manufacture.

Modern improvements, which have been incorporated into the more expensive units, include addition of electronic transduction to give direct digital readout of the value making them easier to read and suitable for automatic recording.

Another improvement, for the larger throat micrometers, has been the use of carbon-fibre for throat construction. This has enabled the frame to be lighter for a given size allowing larger units and increased precision.

For the very best accuracy and precision work, use is made of measuring machines incorporating manually or automatically read, optical scales. Figure 3.7 shows the modern form of such measuring machines. This is capable of a guaranteed accuracy of around 1 μm in length measurements up to its full range capability of 300 mm. Larger machines are also made covering the range of around 4 m: these machines have also been adapted to provide electronic readout, see Section 3.6.

Where measurement of complex shapes is important, the use of measuring machines can be quite tedious; more speedy, direct methods can be used when the accuracy needed is not to the highest limits. In this aspect of tool-room measurement the optical profile projector may be applicable.

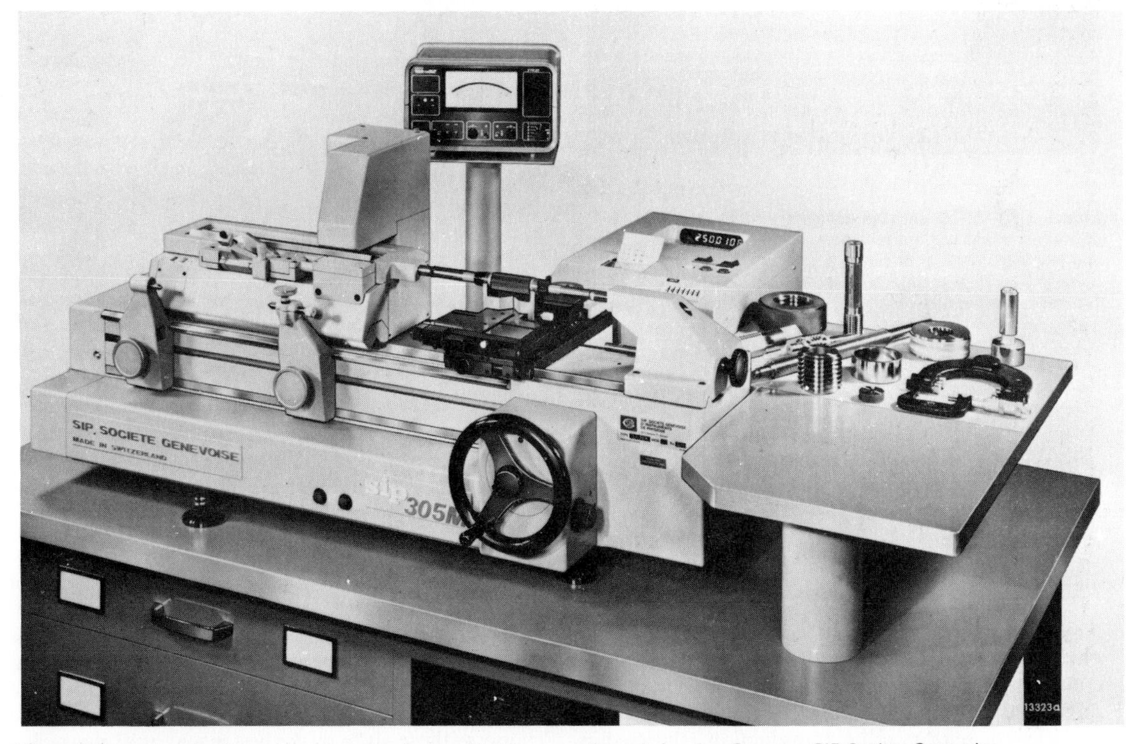

Figure 3.7 Automatically-read length-measuring machine incorporating ruled scales. Courtesy, SIP Society Genevoise d'Instruments de Physique.

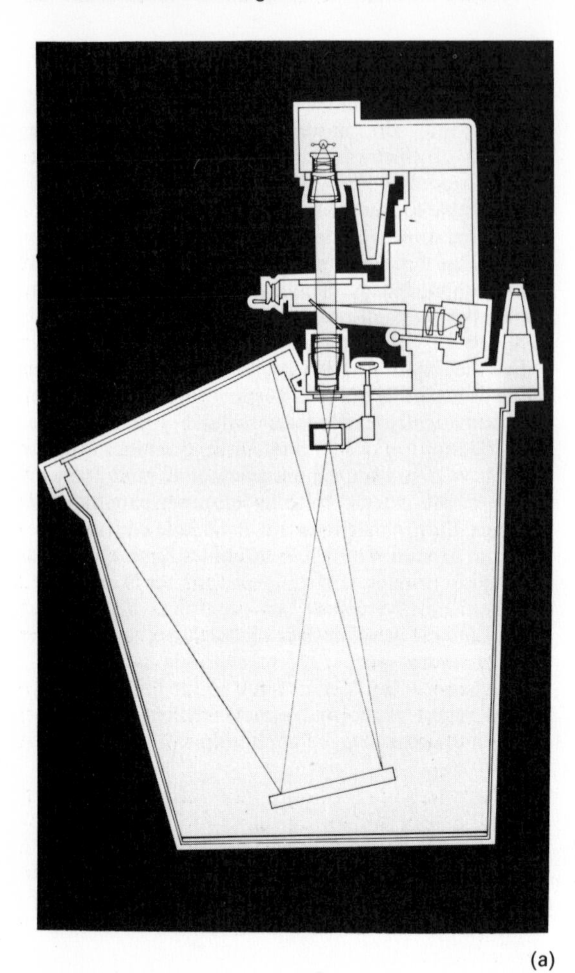

(a)

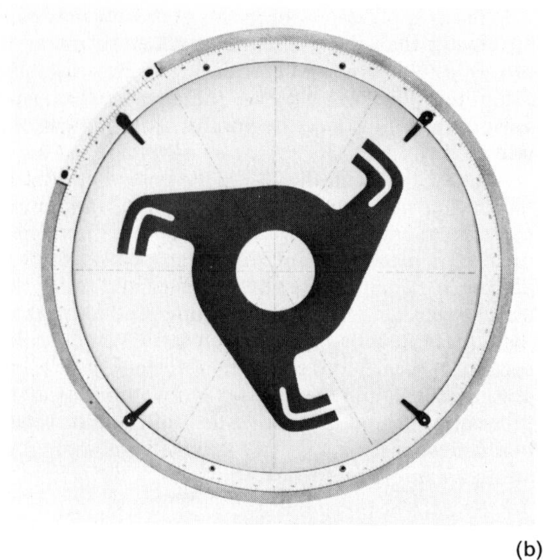

(b)

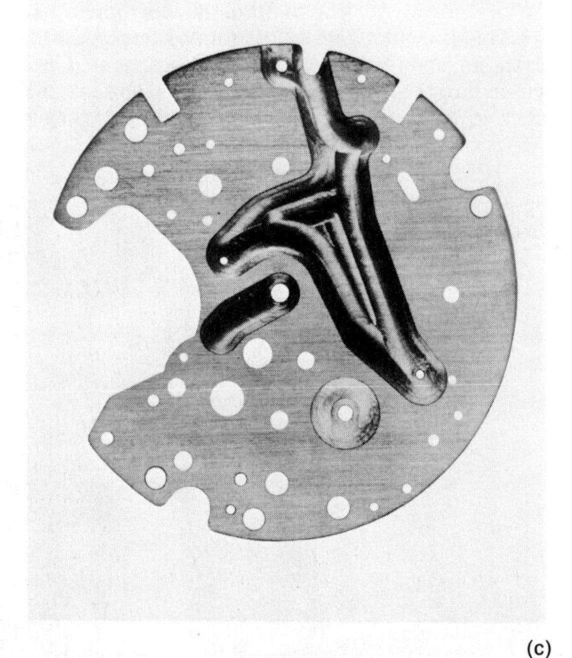

(c)

Figure 3.8 Measurement of geometry and lengths using the optical projector. (a) Optical system schematic. (b) Projected and enlarged image of profile of a component. (c) Oblique episcopic lighting to show surface detail.
Courtesy, Henri Hauser Ltd.

In these (see Figure 3.8(a)), the outline, Figure 3.8(b), of the article to be measured is projected on to a large screen. This can then be compared with a profile template placed around the image. It is also possible to project an image of the surface of an article, Figure 3.8(c), on to the viewing screen. The two forms of lighting can also be used in combination.

3.5.3 Electronic length measurement

Any physical principle that relates a length to a physical variable has the potential to be used for converting length to another equivalent signal. The most used output signal is the electronic form. Thus, most length sensors use a transduction relationship that converts length into an electrical entity either by a direct path or via one or more indirect conversion stages.

Most methods for smaller ranges make use of electromechanical structures, in which electrical resistance, inductance or capacitance vary, or make use of time and spatial properties of radiation. Basic cells of such units are often combined to form larger range devices having similar discrimination and dynamic range to those given by the best mechanical measuring machines.

For best results differential methods are utilized where practicable for this reduces the inherent errors (no transducers are perfect!) of the various systems by providing an in-built mechanism that compensates for some deficiencies of the transducer principle adopted. For example, to measure displacement it is possible to use two electrical plates forming a capacitor. As their separation varies, the capacitance alters to give a corresponding change in electrical signal. To use only one plate-pair makes the system directly susceptible to variations in the dielectric constant of the material between the plates; small changes in the moisture content in an air-gap can give rise to considerable error. By placing two plate-pairs in a differential connection, the effect of the air moisture can largely be cancelled out.

3.5.3.1 *Electrical resistance*

In essence some mechanical arrangement is made in which the electrical resistance between two ends of an interval is made to vary as the interval changes length.

Methods divide into two groups—those in which the resistance of the whole sensor structure remains constant, length being taken off as the changing position of a contact point, and those in which the bulk properties of the structure are made to change as the whole structure changes length.

In the first category is the slide-wire in which a single wire is used. A coiled system can provide a larger resistance gradient which is generally more suited to signal levels and impedance of practical electronic circuitry.

Figure 3.9(a) is a general schematic of sliding-contact length sensors. A standard voltage V_s is applied across the whole length of the resistance unit. The output voltage V_{out} will be related to the length l being measured as follows.

$$V_{out} = \frac{V_s}{L} \cdot l$$

Given that V_s and L are constant, V_{out} gives a direct measure of length l. The resistance unit can be supplied, V_s, with either d.c. or a.c. voltage. Errors can arise in the transduction process due to non-uniform heating effects causing resistance and length L change to the unit but probably the most important point is that the readout circuit must not load the resistance, for in that case the output-to-length relationship does not hold in a linear manner as shown above.

Sliding-contact sensors are generally inexpensive but can suffer from granularity as the contact moves from wire to wire, in wound forms, and from noise caused by the mechanical contact of the wiper moving on the surface of the wire. Wear can also be a problem as can the finite force imposed by the need to maintain the wiper in adequate contact. These practical reasons often rule them out as serious contenders for an application. Their use is, however, very simple to understand and apply. The gradient of the resistance with position along the unit can be made to vary according to logarithmic, sine, cosine and other progressions. The concept can be formed in either a linear or a rotary form. Discrimination clearly depends upon the granularity of the wire diameter in the wound types; one manufacturer has reduced this by sliding a contact along (rather than across) the wound wire as a continuous motion.

Resistance units can cover the range from around a millimetre to a metre with discrimination of the order of up to 1/1000 of the length. Non-linearity errors are of the same order.

The frequency response of such units depends more upon the mechanical mass to be moved during dynamic changes because the electrical part can be made to have low inductance and capacitance, these being the two electrical elements that decide the storage of electrical energy and hence slowness of electrical response.

Signal-to-noise performance can be quite reasonable but not as good as can be obtained with alternative inductive and capacitive methods; the impedance of a resistance unit set to give fine discrimination generally is required to be high with subsequent inherent resistance noise generation. These units are variously described in most general instrumentation texts.

The alternative method, Figure 3.9(b), makes use of strain of the bulk properties of the resistance, the most used method being the resistance strain gauge. As

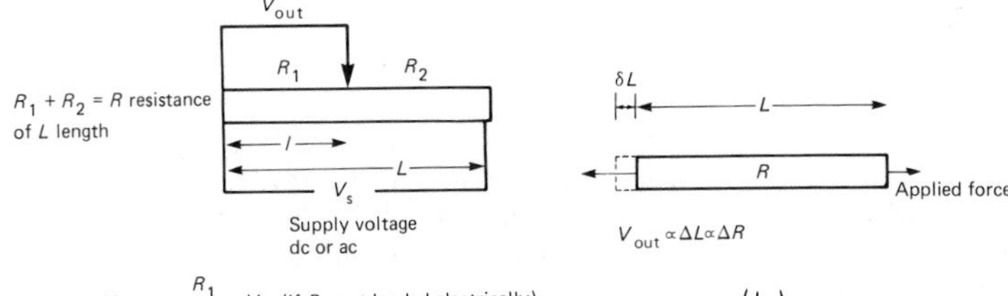

$$V_{out} = \frac{R_1}{R_1 + R_2} \cdot V_s \quad \text{(if } R_1 \text{ not loaded electrically)}$$

$$= \frac{l}{L} \cdot V_s$$

(a) (b)

Figure 3.9 Electrical-resistance length sensors. (a) Sliding contact along fixed resistance unit. (b) Resistance change due to change of bulk properties of a resistance element induced by strain of the element.

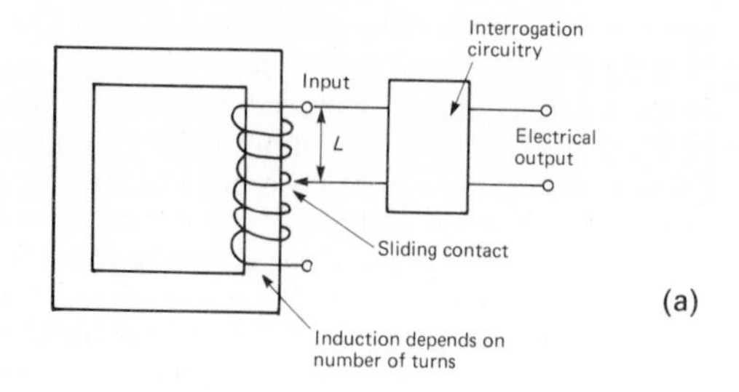

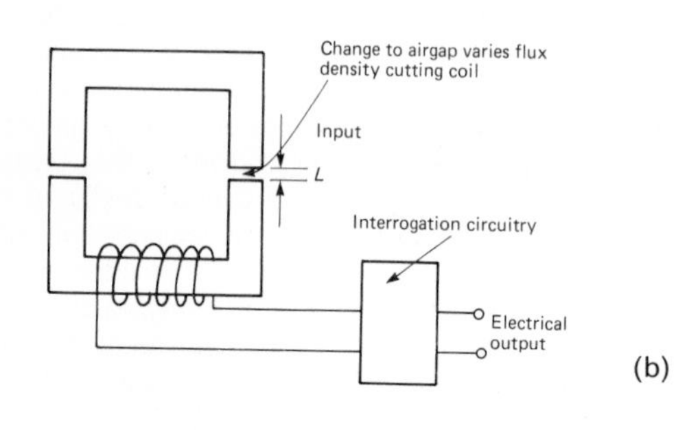

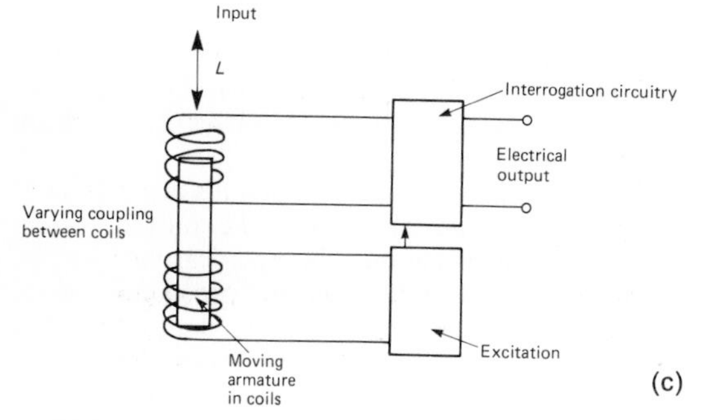

Figure 3.10 Electrical-inductance forms of sensor. (a) Turns variation with length change. (b) Reluctance variation with length change. (c) Mutual inductance change with length change.

strain gauges are the subject of Chapter 4 they will not be discussed further at this stage.

Al alternative bulk resistance method that sometimes has application is to use a material, such as carbon in disc form, using the input length change to alter the force of surface contact between the discs. This alters the pile resistance. The method requires considerable force from the input and, therefore, has restricted application. It does, however, have high electric current-carrying capability and can often be used to drive directly quite powerful control circuits without the need for electronic amplification. The bulk properties method can only transduce small relative length changes of an interval. Practical reasons generally restrict its use to gauge intervals of a few millimetres and to strains of that interval of around 1 per cent.

3.5.3.2 Electrical magnetic inductive processes

In general, the two main groups that use electrical inductive processes are those that vary the inductance value by geometry change, and those that generate a signal by the law of electromagnetic induction.

An electrical inductance circuit component is formed by current-carrying wire(s) producing a magnetic field which tends to impede current change in dynamic current situations. The use of a magnetic circuit enhances the effect; it is not absolutely essential, but is generally found in inductive sensors. Change of the magnetic field distribution of an inductor changes its inductance. Length sensors make use of this principle by using a length change of the mechanical structure of an inductance to vary the inductance. This can be achieved by varying the turns, changing the magnetic circuit reluctance or by inducing effects by mutual inductance. Various forms of electric circuit are then applied to convert the inductance change to an electronic output signal.

Figure 3.10 shows these three options in their primitive form. In some applications such simple arrangements may suffice but the addition of balanced, differential, arrangements and use of phase-sensitive detection, where applicable, is often very cost-effective for the performance and stability are greatly improved. Now described, in more detail, are examples of the mainly used forms of Figures 3.10(b) and 3.10(c).

Figure 3.11 shows a single-coil proximity detector that is placed close to a suitable, high magnetic permeability plate attached to or part of the subject. The sensor would be mounted around 2 mm from the plate. As the plate moves relative to the unit the reluctance of the iron circuit, formed by the unit, the plate and the air-gap, varies as the air-gap changes. When the unit has a permanent magnet included in the magnetic circuit then movement will generate a voltage without need for separate electronic excitation. It will not, however, produce a distance measurement when the system is stationary unless excited by a continuous a.c. carrier signal.

Where possible two similar variable-reluctance units are preferred, mounted one each side of the moving object, and connected into a bridge configuration giving common-mode rejection of

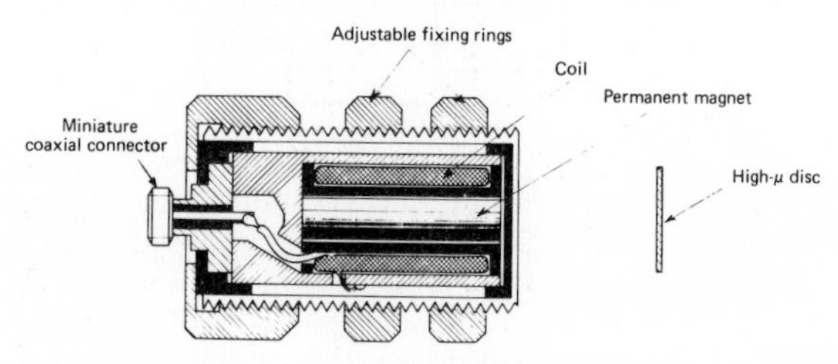

Figure 3.11 Magnetic-reluctance proximity sensor. Courtesy, Bruel & Kjaer Ltd.

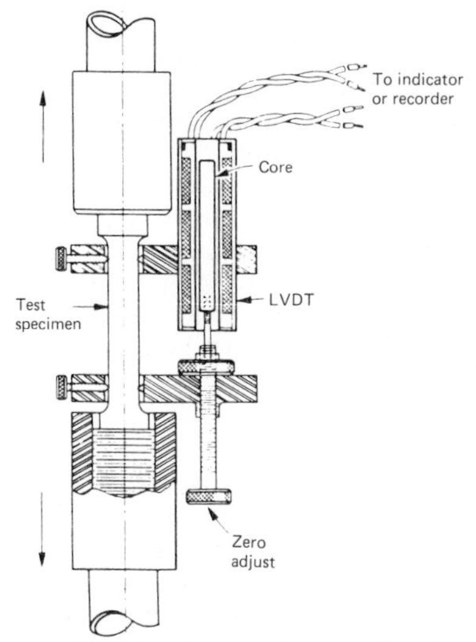

Figure 3.12 Cross-section of an LVDT inductive length sensor used to measure length change of a tensile test specimen. Courtesy, Schaevitz Engineering.

unwanted induced noise pick-up. These arrangements are but two of many possible forms that have been applied. Variable-reluctance methods are characterized by their relatively short range, poor linearity over longer ranges and the possible need to move a considerable mass in making the measurement with consequent restricted dynamic performance.

Mutual-inductance methods also exist in very many forms including the equivalent of Figure 3.11. Probably the most used is the linear variable-differential transformer LVDT. Figure 3.12 shows a cross-section through a typical unit mounted for monitoring length change of a tensile test specimen. A magnetic material core, normally a ferrite rod, moves inside three coils placed end to end. The centre coil is fed from an a.c. excitation supply thus inducing voltages into the outer two coils. (It can also be wound over the other two outer coils.) The two generated voltages will be equal when the core is positioned symmetrically. The voltage rises in one coil relative to the other when the core is off-centre. Difference between the two voltages is, therefore, related to the position of the core, and the relation can be made linear. Without circuitry to detect in which direction the core has moved from the null position, the output will be an a.c. signal of the excitation frequency which changes in amplitude with position and having direction in the signal as its phase.

Practical use generally requires a d.c. output signal (actually a signal having frequency components in it that are present in the measurand's movement) with direction information as signal polarity. This is easily achieved, at marginal additional expense, by the use of phase-sensitive detection (also known as lock-in detection or carrier demodulation). Figure 3.13(a) shows a block diagram of the subsystem elements that form a complete LVDT length-measuring system. Figure 3.13(b) shows the output relationship with position of the core. Modern units now often supply the phase-sensitive detection circuits inside the case of the sensor; these are known as d.c. LVDT units. Considerable detail of the operation of these and variations on the theme are available in Herceg (1976). Detail of phase-sensitive detection is in Volume 4 and Sydenham (1982b) where further references will be found in a chapter on signal detection by D. Munroe.

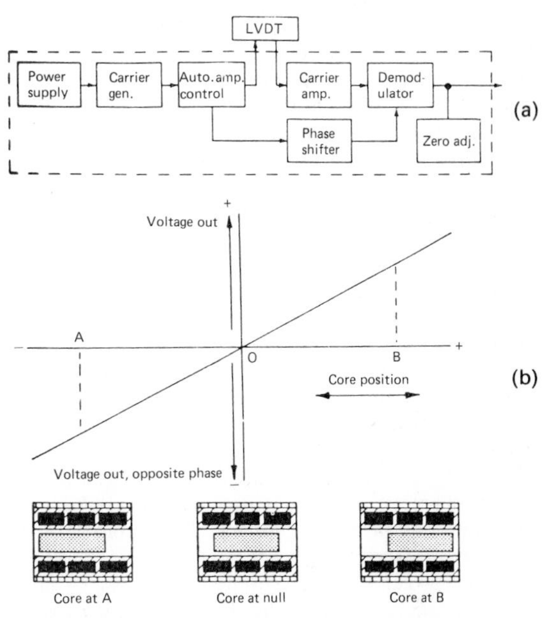

Figure 3.13 Phase-sensitive detection system used with practical LVDTs. (a) Block diagram of electronic system. (b) Input–output characteristics after phase-sensitive detection. Courtesy, Schaevitz Engineering.

A simpler non-transformer form of the LVDT arrangement can be used in which the need for a separate central excitation coil is avoided. With reference to the LVDT unit shown in Figure 3.12 the two outer coils only would be used, their inner ends being joined to form a centre-tapped linearly-wound inductor. This split inductor is then placed in an a.c. bridge to which phase-sensitive detection is applied in a similar manner to recover a polarized d.c. output signal.

Inductive sensors of the mutual-inductance form are manufactured in a vast range of sizes providing for length detection from as small as atomic diameters (sub-nanometre) out to a maximum range of around ± 250 mm. They are extremely robust, quite linear, very reliable and extremely sensitive if well designed. By mounting the core on the measurand object and the body on the reference frame it is also possible to arrange for non-interacting, non-contact measurement. Frequency response depends upon the carrier frequency used to modulate the coils; general practice sets that at around 50 kHz as the upper limit but this is not a strong constraint on design. Attention may also need to be paid to mechanical resonances of the transducer.

The second class of magnetically inductive length sensors, the magneto-electric kind, are those in which part of the electromagnetic circuit moves to generate a voltage caused by flux-cutting. For these the relevant basic expression is $e = -(N\,d\phi/dt)$ where e is the voltage generated as N turns are cut by flux ϕ in time t. These are strictly velocity, not displacement sensors, for the output is proportional to velocity. Integration of the signal (provided it has sufficient magnitude to be detected, for at low speeds the signal induced may be very small) will yield displacement. This form of sensor is covered in more detail in Chapter 6.

Magneto-electric sensors are prone to stray magnetic field pick-up for that can introduce flux-cutting that appears to be signal. Good shielding is essential to reduce effects of directly detected fields and also for the more subtle induced eddy current fields that are produced in adjacent non-magnetic materials if they are electrically conducting. Magnetic shielding is a highly developed engineering process that requires special materials and heat treatments to obtain good shielding. Manufacturers are able to provide units incorporating shielding and to advise users in this aspect. It is not simply a matter of placing the unit in a thick, magnetic material case! Herceg (1976) is a starting point on effective use of LVDT units and other inductive sensors.

When larger range is required than can be conveniently accommodated by the single unit (desired discrimination will restrict range to a given length of basic cell) it is possible to add inductive sensor cells, end-to-end, using digital logic to count the cells along the interval with analogue interrogation of the cell at the end of the measurand interval. This hybrid approach was extensively developed to provide for the metre distances required in numerically controlled machine tools. A form of long inductive sensor that has stood the test of time is the flat, 'printed', winding that is traversed by a sensing short, flat coil. Each cell of this continuous grid comprises a coil pair overlapped by the sense coil that forms a flat profile LVDT form of sensor.

Angles can be measured electro-magnetically using devices called Synchros. These inherently include means for transmitting the information to a distance and are therefore described under Telemetry in Volume 4.

3.5.3.3 Electrical-capacitance sensors

Electrical capacitance stores electrical energy in the electric field form; electrical inductors store energy in the magnetic field form. Electromagnetic theory relates the two forms of field and thus most concepts applied to magnetic-inductance sensing are applicable to electrical-capacitance structures.

It is, therefore, also possible to sense length change by using the input length to alter the structure of a capacitance assembly or to cause shape change to a solid material thereby directly generating charge. The electrical capacitance of a structure formed by two electrically conducting plates is given by

$$C = \frac{\varepsilon A}{l}$$

where C is the capacitance, ε the dielectric constant of the material between the plates in the area A where they overlap at a distance of separation l.

Thus a length sensor can be formed by varying the value of l which gives an inverse relationship between length input and capacitance change or by varying one length of the two plates that combine to provide the overlap area A; this latter alternative can give a direct relationship. It is also sometimes practical to vary ε by inserting a moving piece of different dielectric into the capacitance structure.

Simpler forms make use of a single capacitance structure, but for these, variation in ε can introduce error due to humidity and pressure changes of air, the most commonly used dielectric. Differential systems are more satisfactory. Figure 3.14 shows the basic

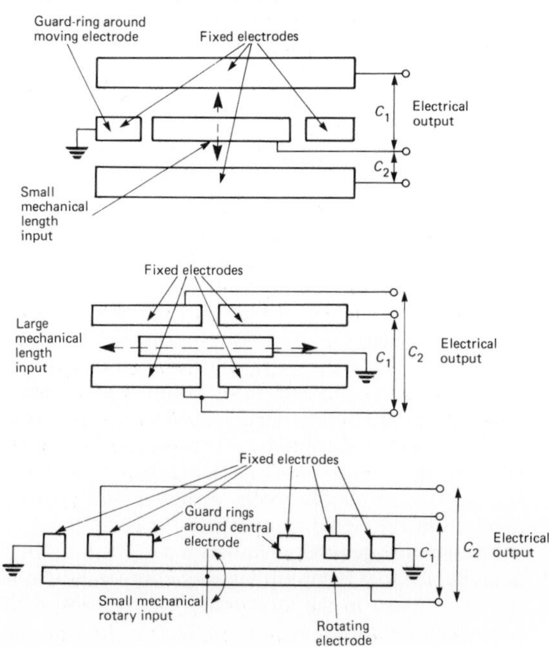

Figure 3.14 Some differential capacitance length-sensing structures.

configuration of differential capacitance sensors. They can be formed from flat plates or from cylindrical sections, whichever is convenient. The cylindrical form of the second design has been used in a highly accurate alternative to the LVDT. The guard rings shown are not needed if some non-linearity can be accepted.

Capacitance systems are characterized by high output impedance, need for relatively high excitation voltages, accuracy of plate manufacture and small plate clearance dimensions.

Potential sensitivity of the alternatives (inductive and capacitive) is virtually the same in practice: each having its own particular signal-to-noise problems. For low-sensitivity use, capacitance devices are more easily manufactured than the inductive alternatives.

Noise occurs in capacitance systems from charge pick-up produced by stray voltage potentials in the high impedance of the capacitance assembly. It is reduced by appropriate shielding and use of earthed guard plates that surround the active plates to collect and dump the unwanted charge. Capacitance structures lend themselves more for original equipment design rather than as ready-made sensor units applied after the basic plant is designed. This is because the layout of the working plant to be sensed can often provide directly one or more plates of the sensor as a non-contacting arrangement. For example, to monitor position of a pendulum in a tilt sensor it is straightforward to use the pendulum bob as the central plate that moves inside two plates added one to each side.

In general, therefore, it will be found that commercial sensor makers offer more inductive systems than capacitive alternatives, whereas in scientific and research work the tendency is to use capacitance systems as they are easier to implement at the prototype stage. Commercial suppliers also wish to offer a product that is self-contained and ready to apply and, therefore, a unit that can be verified before delivery.

At extreme limits of discrimination (subnanometres) capacitance sensing can be shown to be superior to inductive arrangements if properly designed. As with inductive systems they also need a.c. excitation to obtain a length change response for slowly moving events.

Forces exerted by the magnetic and electric fields of the two alternatives can be designed to be virtually non-existent. Use in sensitive force balance systems allows the same plates to be used to apply a d.c. voltage to the central plate of a differential system. The plate can thus be forced back to the central null position at the same time as a higher frequency excitation signal is applied for position detection.

Although the plate-separation capacitance method fundamentally provides an inverse relationship to length change the signal can be made directly proportional by placing the sensing capacitance in the feedback path of an operational amplifier.

3.5.4 Use of electromagnetic and acoustic radiation

Radiation ranging from the relatively long radio wavelengths to the short-wavelength X-rays in the electromagnetic (EM) radiation spectrum, and from audio to megahertz frequencies in the acoustic spectrum, has been used in various ways to measure length.

In the industrial range the main methods adopted have been those based upon optical and near-optical radiation, microwave EM and acoustic radiation. These are now discussed in turn.

3.5.4.1 Position-sensitive photocells

An optical beam, here to be interpreted as ranging in wavelength from infrared ($\approx 10\ \mu m$) to the short visible ($\approx 0.4\ \mu m$), can be used in two basically different ways to measure length. The beam can be used to sense movements occurring transverse to it or longitudinally with it.

Various position-sensitive optical detectors have been devised to sense transverse motion. Their range is relatively small, being of the order of only millimetres. They are simple to devise and apply and can yield discrimination and stability of the order of a micrometre.

Figure 3.15 outlines the features of the structure of the three basic kinds that have been designed. Consider that of Figure 3.15(a). A beam having uniform radiation intensity across its cross-section falls upon two equal characteristic photocells. When the beam straddles the two cells, thereby providing equal illumination of each, the differentially connected output will be zero. At that point any common-mode noise signals will be largely cancelled out by the system. Such systems have good null stability. As the beam moves to one side of the null the differential output rises proportionally until all of the beam's illumination falls on one cell alone. Direction of movement is established by the polarity of the output signal. Once the beam has become fully placed on one cell the output is saturated and remains at its maximum. These cells can be manufactured from one silicon slice by sawing or diffusing a non-conducting barrier in the top junction layer or can be made from separate cells placed side by side. Four cells, placed in two perpendicular directions in a plane, can be used to sense two axes of motion.

Linearity of the output of these cells depends upon their terminating conditions. Working range can be seen to be equal to twice the beam width which should not exceed the width of the half detector size. Sensitivity depends upon the level of beam illumination so it is important to have constant beam intensity to obtain good results.

In some applications the light-beam cross-section

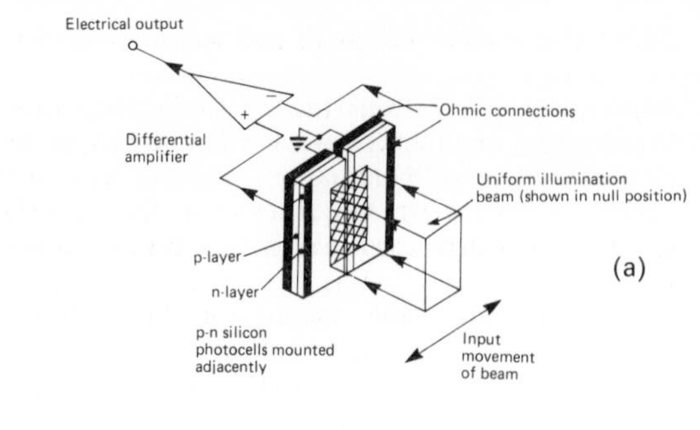

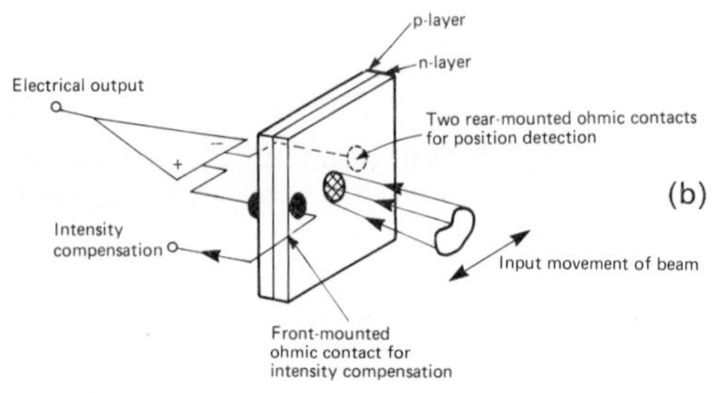

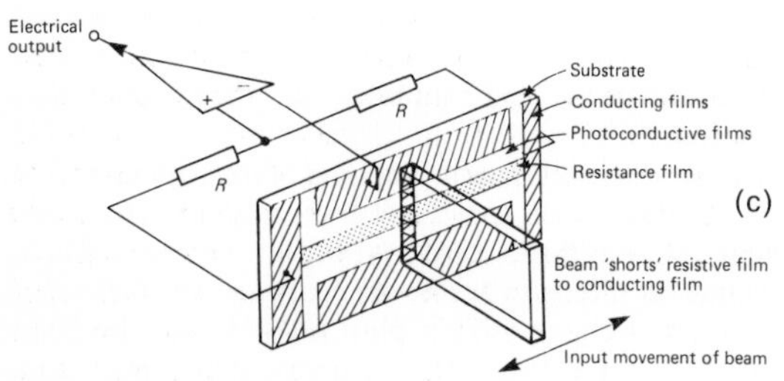

Figure 3.15 Optical position-sensitive detectors. (a) Split cell. (b) Lateral effect cell. (c) Photopotentiometer.

may vary with distance to the cell. In such cases the so-called Wallmark or lateral effect cell, Figure 3.15(b), may be more appropriate. In this case the two contacts are not rectifying as in the Figure 3.15(a) case but are, instead, ohmic.

It has been shown that the voltage produced between the two ohmic contacts is related to the position of the centroid of the beam's energy and to the intensity of the whole beam. Addition of the rectifying contact on the other side of the cell enables correction to be made for intensity changes making this form of cell able to track the movements of a spot of radiation that changes both in intensity and in size. Here also the beam must be smaller than the full working region of the cell surface. Detection limits are similar to those of the split cell form.

This cell has enjoyed a resurgence of interest in its design for the original logarithmic voltage-to-position characteristic can quite easily be arranged to be effectively linear by driving the cell into the appropriate impedance amplifier. It, too, is able to sense the motion of a beam in two axes simultaneously by the use of two additional contacts placed at right angles to those shown.

Optical position-sensitive photocells, such as these, have found extensive use in conjunction with laser sources of radiation in order to align floors, ceilings and pipes and to make precise mechanical measurement of geometry deviations in mechanical structures.

The third form of optical position detector is the photopotentiometer shown in Figure 3.15(c). This form, although invented several years before micro-electronic methods (it uses thick-film methods of manufacture) has also found new interest due to its printable form. The input beam of light falls across the junction of the conducting and resistive films causing, in effect, a wiper contact action in a Wheatstone bridge circuit. The contact is frictionless and virtually stepless. The range of these units is larger than for the position-sensitive photocells but they are rather specialized; few are offered on the market. Their response is somewhat slow (10 ms) compared with the cells detailed above (which have microsecond full scale times) due to the time response of the photoconductive materials used. The light beam can be arranged to move by the use of a moving linear shutter, a moving light source or a rotating mirror.

Moiré fringe position sensing methods make use of mechanical shuttering produced by ruled lines on a scale. These produce varying intensity signals, at a reference position location, that are in a fixed phase relationship, see Figure 3.16. These signals are interrogated to give coarse, whole line cycle counts with cycle division ranging from simple four-times digital division up to around 1 part in 100 of a cycle by the use of analogue subdivision methods. Moiré fringe scales are able to provide large range (by butting sections)

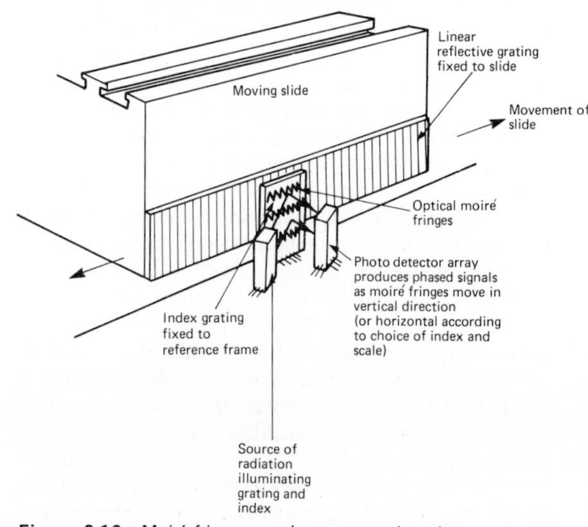

Figure 3.16 Moiré fringes used to measure length.

and a discrimination level at the subdivision chosen which can be as small as 1 μm. Accuracy is limited by the placement of the lines on the scale, by the mounting of the scale and by the temperature effects that alter its length. The method is suitable for both linear and rotary forms of sensing.

Although there was much developmental activity in moiré methods in the 1950 to 1965 period their design has stabilized now that the practicalities have been realized.

Moiré methods have also found use for strain investigation, a subject discussed in Chapter 4.

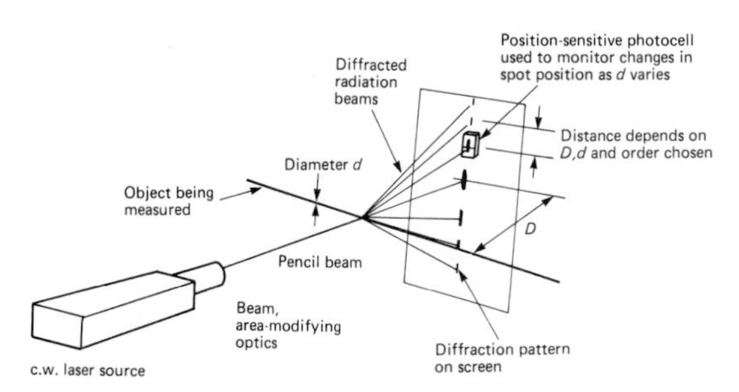

Figure 3.17 Use of diffraction to gauge fine diameters.

The easily procured coherent properties of continuous wave laser radiation has provided a simple, yet highly effective method for monitoring the diameter of small objects such as wire as it is being drawn. The radiation, being coherent, diffracts at the intersection with the wire producing a number of diffraction beams at points past the wire. Figure 3.17 shows the method. As the wire size reduces the spots diverge giving this method improved precision as the object size becomes smaller.

The position of the spots can be sensed with a position-sensitive photocell as described above. Where digital output of beam movement is needed it is also possible to use a linear array of photodetectors each operating its own level detector or being scanned, sequentially, into a single output channel. Linear arrays with over 200 elements are now commonplace.

Optical lenses and mirrors can be used to alter the beam movement geometry in order to scale the subject's movement amplitude to suit that of an optical position detector.

3.5.4.2 Interferometry and transit-time methods

Where long length (metres and above) measurements are needed it is possible to use a suitable beam of radiation sensed in its longitudinal direction. Several different methods are available.

If the beam has time-coherent properties (either superimposed or inherently in the carrier) it will then be possible to use interference methods to detect phase differences between a reference part of the beam and that sent to the subject to be reflected back. Laser, microwave sources and coherently generated acoustic radiation each can be used in this interference mode. The shorter the wavelength of the radiation the smaller the potential discrimination that can be obtained. Thus with optical interferometers it is practical to detect length differences as small as a nanometre but only around a few millimetres when microwave radiation is used.

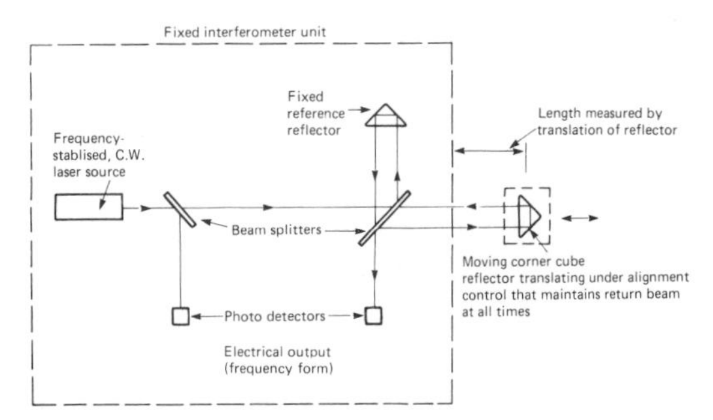

Figure 3.18 Basic layout of the frequency output form of laser length-measuring interferometer.

Figure 3.18 shows the basic layout of the optical elements needed to form a laser-based interferometer. That shown incorporates frequency stabilization and Zeeman splitting of the radiation features that give the system a highly stable and accurate measurement capability and a frequency, rather than amplitude form, of output representing length. A commercial unit is shown in Figure 3.5. Corner cubes are used instead of the flat mirrors originally used in the classical Michelson interferometer. They make adjustment very straightforward for the angle of the cube to the incoming radiation is not critical. Usually one corner cube is held fixed to provide a reference arm. The other corner cube must be translated from a datum position to give length readings for the method is inherently incremental. Allowing both corner cubes to move enables the system to be configured to also measure small angles to extreme precision.

The laser interferometer is, without doubt, the superior length-measuring instrument for general-purpose industrial work but its cost, line-of-sight beam movement restriction, incremental nature and need for path condition control (for the best work) does eliminate it from universal use. Its dynamic measuring range covers from micrometres to tens of metres, a range not provided by any other electronic length sensor.

Interferometry requires a reflector that gives adequate energy return without wavefront distortion. At optical wavelengths the reflecting surface must be of optical quality. Where very fine, micrometre, discrimination is not required the use of microwave radiation allows interferometry systems that can operate directly on to the normal machined surface of components being machined. Acoustic methods can yield satisfactory results when the accuracy needed is only of the order of 1 part in 1000.

Radiation methods can also make use of the time of flight of the radiation. For light this is around 300 mm in a nanosecond and for acoustic vibration from 300 mm to 6 m in a millisecond, depending upon the medium. In 'time-of-flight' methods the radiation, which can here be incoherent, is modulated at a convenient frequency or simply pulsed. The radiation returning from the surface of interest is detected and the lapsed time to go and return is used to calculate the distance between the source and the target. These methods do not have the same discrimination potential that is offered by interferometry but can provide in certain applications (for EDM systems used over kilometre ranges) uncertainty of the order of a few parts in 10^6. By the use of more than one modulation frequency it is possible to provide absolute ranging by this method, a feature that is clearly required for long distance measurements. The need for a controlled movement path over which the reflector must traverse the whole distance, as is required in incremental interferometers, is unworkable in surveying operations.

The interference concept shown in Figure 3.18 for one-dimensional movement can be extended to three-dimensional measurement application in the holograph method. Holography provides a photographic image, in a plate known as a hologram, that captures the three-dimensional geometric detail of an object. The object of interest is flooded with coherent radiation of which some reflects from the surfaces to be optically combined with reference radiation taken directly from the source. As the two are coherent radiations their wavefronts combine to form a flat two-dimensional interference pattern. The hologram bears little pictorial resemblance to the original object and has a most unexpected property. When the hologram is illuminated by coherent light the object can be seen, by looking through the illuminated hologram, as an apparent three-dimensional object.

This basic procedure can be used in several forms to provide highly discriminating measurements of the shape of objects.

A first method places a similar object to that for which a hologram has been made in the image space of that of the hologram. This, in effect, superimposes the standard object over the real object. Differences between the two can then be decided by eye. This is not a very precise method but does suit some inspection needs.

In another method for using holography a second hologram is formed on the same plate as the first was exposed on. The combined pair is developed as a single plate. When viewed, as explained above, this will reproduce an apparent object on which are superimposed fringes that represent shape differences between the two units. Each fringe width, as a guide, represents detailed differences of the order of the wavelength of the radiation. This form of holography is, therefore, a very powerful method for detecting small differences. It has been used, for example, to detect imperfections in car tyres (by slightly altering the internal pressure) and to investigate shape changes in gas cylinders. It is very suitable for non-destructive testing but is expensive and somewhat slow in its use.

Fast moving objects can also be gauged using optical holography in the so-called time-lapse pulse holography method. Two holograms are exposed on top of each other on an undeveloped plate as mentioned above but in this situation they are formed by the same object which presents itself periodically at known times, for example a turbine blade rotating inside an aircraft engine. The laser source is pulsed as the object passes using synchronized electronic circuitry.

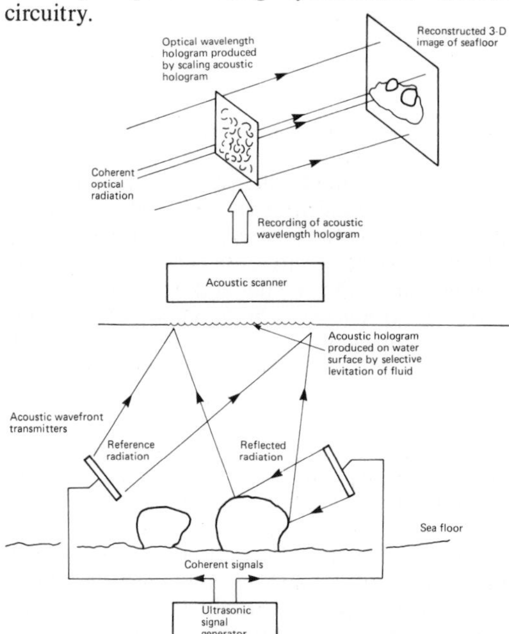

Figure 3.19 Holography applied to sea-floor mapping. Two radiations are used to convert the image size for reasons of convenience.

Holography is suitable for use with any form of coherent radiation; optical, microwave and acoustic systems have been reported. It is also possible to mix the radiations used at various stages in order to produce, and view, the hologram with different absolute size scales. For example, a sea-floor sand-profile mapping system, Figure 3.19, uses acoustic radiation inside the sea space to obtain an acoustic interference hologram which is then viewed by optical radiation for reasons of convenience.

The most serious disadvantages of holography are the cost of the apparatus, slowness to produce an output and difficulties in obtaining numerical measurements from the recorded information.

3.5.5 Miscellaneous methods

The above descriptions have shown that even for a few restricted classes of sensor there are many principles that can be used to produce transduced length signals. A comprehensive coverage would require several volumes on this parameter alone. This short subsection is included to emphasize the availability of many more methods that may be appropriate in given circumstances. Many of the unusual methods are less likely to be marketed for potential sales would not justify quantity manufacture. In applications of the aerospace industry, in original equipment needs of science and in industrial testing, in development and in isolated applications they may be the most viable methods to adopt. It should not be construed that lack of commercial interest implies that a method is necessarily unworkable. Here are a few of these less commonly used methods.

Magneto-resistive sensing elements are those in which their electrical resistance varies with the level of ambient magnetic field. These can be used as linear, or as proximity, sensors by moving the sensor relative to a field which is usually provided by a permanent magnet.

Thickness of a layer being deposited in a deposition chamber can be measured by several means. One way is to monitor the mass build-up on a test sample placed in the chamber alongside that being coated. Another method is to directly monitor the change in optical transmission during deposition.

Statistical calculation on the signal strength of an ionizing radiation source can be used to determine distance from the source.

Pressure formed, or liquid displaced, can be used to drive a pressure- or volume-sensitive device in order to measure movement of the driving element. This method has been used in the measurement of volumetric earth strain as it can provide very sensitive detection due to the cube-law relationship existing between volume change input and length output.

The following chapter deals specifically with strain measurements. Chapter 6 on vibration, and Chapter 5, on level measurement, each include descriptions of length sensors.

3.6 Automatic gauging systems

Tool-room and factory gauging has its roots in the use of manually-read measuring machines and tools such as those shown in Figures 3.7 and 3.8. These required, in their non-electronic forms, high levels of skill in their use and are very time-consuming. In general, however, they can yield the best results given that the best machines are used.

The advent of electronic sensing of length and angle has gradually introduced a transformation in the measurement practices in the tool-room and on the factory floor. The cost of providing, using manual procedures, the very many inspection measurements needed in many modern production processes has often proven to be uneconomic and far too slow to suit automatic production plants. As an example piston manufacture for a car engine can require over twenty length parameters to be measured for each piston produced on the final grinding machine. The time available to make the measurements is of the order of fractions of minutes. It has, in such instances become cost-effective to design and install automatic measuring machines that generate the extensive data needed.

Automatic measuring systems are characterized by their ability to deliver electronic signals representing one or many length dimensions. In simple applications the operator places the component in a preset, multi-probe system. In totally automated plant use is often made of pick-and-place robots to load the inspection machines.

Automatic inspection systems began their development in the 1950s when they were required to complement the then emerging numerically controlled metal-working machine tools. They made use of similar measuring sensors as did the tools but differed from the metal working machine in several ways.

Where inspection machines are hand-operated the operator can work best when the system effectively presents no significant inertial forces to the input probe as it is moved. This can be achieved by a design that minimizes the moving masses or by the use of closed-loop sensor control that effectively reduces the sluggish feel due to the inertia of the moving mass present. For small-size systems (those around a metre in capacity) multi-point inspection needs can be met economically by the use of short-range length sensors. These come into contact with the surfaces to be measured as the component is placed in the test set-up. Values are recorded, stored and analysed. The component may need to be rotated to give total coverage of the surfaces of interest. Figure 3.20 shows such an apparatus being used to automatically inspect several length dimensions of a gearbox shaft.

When the size of the object to be inspected is large the use of multiple probes can be too expensive and a single probe may be used to check given locations as a serial operation. Manual methods of point-to-point movement have, in some applications, given way to automatic, surface contour-following, probes and to the use of robot arms that are preprogrammed to move as required; see Figure 3.21.

The reliability of electronics, its cost-effectiveness and its capability to be rapidly structured into circuits that can suit new data-processing, recording and display situations has made transducer measurement of length parameters a strong competitor for the traditional manually-operated measuring machines. In most cases, however, the quality of length measurements made with automatic transducer methods still rests largely upon the mechanical structures of the sensing systems and upon the user's appreciation of the effects of temperature, operation of transducer and presentation to the subject, all of which can generate sources of error.

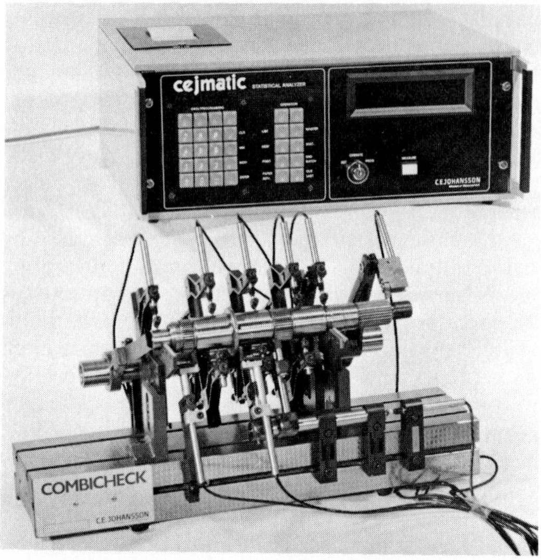

Figure 3.20 Electronic gauge heads being used in a versatile test apparatus set up to inspect several length parameters of a gearbox shaft. Courtesy, C.E. Johansson.

3.7 References

Batson, R. G. and Hyde, J. H. *Mechanical Testing; Vol. 1. Testing of Materials of Construction*, Chapman and Hall, London, (1931)

Garratt, J. D. 'Survey of displacement transducers below 50 mm', *J. Phys. E: Sci. Instrum.*, **12**, 563–574, (1979)

Herceg, E. E. *Handbook of Measurement and Control*, Schaevitz Engineering, Pennsauken, (1976)

Hume, K. J. *Engineering Metrology*, Macdonald, London, (1970)

Kissam, P. *Optical Tooling for Precise Manufacture and Alignment*, McGraw-Hill, New York, (1962)

Mansfield, P. H. *Electrical Transducers for Industrial Measurement*, Butterworths, London, (1973)

Neubert, K. K. P. *Instrument Transducers*, Clarendon, Oxford, 2nd ed. (1975)

Norton, H. N. *Handbook of Transducers for Electronic Measuring Systems*, Prentice-Hall, Englewood Cliffs, New Jersey, (1969)

Oliver, F. J. *Practical Instrumentation Transducers*, Pitman, London, (1971)

Rolt, R. H. *Gauges and Fine Measurements*, 2 vols, Macmillan, London, (1929)

Sharp, K. W. B. *Practical Engineering Metrology*, Pitman, London, (1970)

Sydenham, P. H. 'Linear and angular transducers for positional control in the decametre range', *Proc. IEE*, **115**, 7, 1056–1066, (1968)

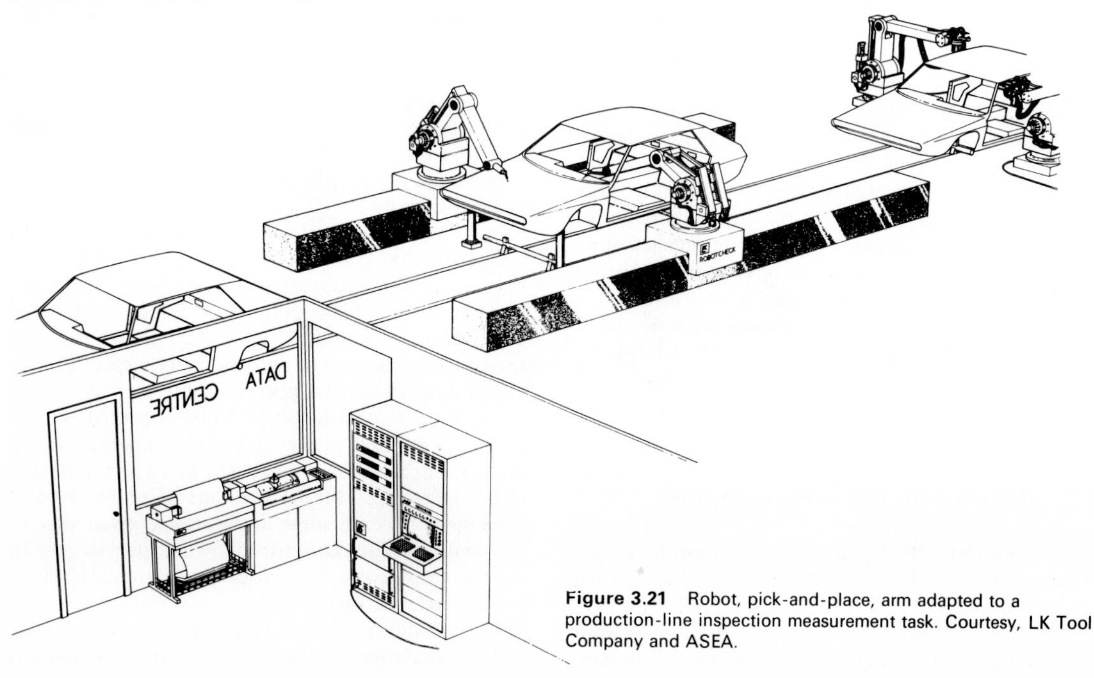

Figure 3.21 Robot, pick-and-place, arm adapted to a production-line inspection measurement task. Courtesy, LK Tool Company and ASEA.

Sydenham, P. H. 'Position sensitive photo cells and their application to static and dynamic dimensional metrology', *Optica Acta*, **16**, 3, 377–389, (1969)

Sydenham, P. H. 'Review of geophysical strain measurement', *Bull., N.Z., Soc. Earthquake Engng.*, **4**, 1, 2–14, (1971)

Sydenham, P. H. 'Microdisplacement transducers', *J. Phys., E. Sci., Instrum.*, **5**, 721–733, (1972)

Sydenham, P. H. *Transducers in Measurement and Control*, Adam Hilger, Bristol; or ISA, Research Triangle, (1984).

Sydenham, P. H. 'The literature of instrument science and technology', *J. Phys. E.: Sci. Instrum.*, **15**, 487–491, (1982a)

Sydenham, P. H. *Handbook of Fundamentals of Measurement Systems Vol. 1 Theoretical Fundamentals*, Wiley, Chichester, (1982b)

Sydenham, P. H. *Handbook of Measurement Science Vol. 2 Fundamentals of Practice*, Wiley, Chichester, (1983)

Woltring, H. J. 'Single and dual-axis lateral photodetectors of rectangular shape', *IEEE TRANS ED*, 581–590, (1975)

4 Measurement of strain

B. E. NOLTINGK

4.1 Strain

A particular case of length measurement is the determination of strains, i.e. the small changes in the dimensions of solid bodies as they are subjected to forces. The emphasis on such measurements comes from the importance of knowing whether a structure is strong enough for its purpose or whether it may fail in use.

The interrelation between stress (the force per unit area) and strain (the fractional change in dimension) is a complex one, involving in general three dimensions, particularly if the material concerned is not isotropic, i.e. does not have the same properties in all directions. A simple stress/strain concept is of a uniform bar stretched length-wise, for which Young's modulus of elasticity is defined as the ratio stress:strain, i.e. the force per unit of cross-sectional area divided by the fractional change in length

$$E=\frac{F}{A}\div\frac{\Delta l}{l}$$

The longitudinal extension is accompanied by a transverse contraction. The ratio of the two fractions (transverse contraction)/(longitudinal extension) is called Poisson's ratio, denoted by μ, and is commonly about 0.3. While we have talked of increases in length, called positive strain, similar behaviour occurs in compression, which is accompanied by a transverse expansion.

Another concept is that of shear. Consider the block PQRS largely constrained in a holder, Figure 4.1. If this is subjected to a force F as shown, it will distort, PQ moving to P′Q′. The 'shear strain' is the ratio PP′/PT, i.e. the angle PTP′ or $\Delta\theta$ (which equals angle QUQ′) and the *modulus of rigidity* is defined as (shear stress)/(shear strain) or

$$C=\frac{F}{A}\div\Delta\theta$$

when A is the area PQ × depth of block. In practical situations, shear strain is often accompanied by bending, the magnitude of which is governed by Young's modulus.

There is some general concern with stress and strain at all points in a solid body, but there is a particular interest in measuring strains on surfaces. It is only there that conventional strain gauges can readily be used and wide experience has been built up in interpreting results gained with them. At a surface, the strain normal to it can be calculated because the stress is zero (apart from the exceptional case of a high fluid pressure being applied), but we still do not usually know the direction or magnitude of strains in the plane of the surface so that for a complete analysis three strains must be measured in different directions.

4.2 Bonded resistance strain gauges

In the early 1940s, the bonded resistance strain gauge was introduced and it has dominated the field of strain measurement ever since. Its principle can be seen from Figure 4.2. A resistor R is bonded to an insulator I, which in turn is fixed to the substrate S whose strain is to be measured. (The word 'substrate' is not used universally with this meaning; it is adopted here for its convenience and brevity.) When S is strained, the change in length is communicated to R if the bonding is adequate; it can be shown that the strain will be transmitted accurately even through a mechanically compliant insulator provided there is sufficient overlap, i.e. if I is larger than R by several times the thickness of either of them. Strains of interest are commonly very small; for elastic behaviour, where concern is usually concentrated, strains do not exceed about 10^{-3}. Many metals break if they are stretched by a few per cent and changes in length of a few parts in a million are sometimes of interest but when these are used to produce even small changes in the resistance of R we can take advantage of the precision with which

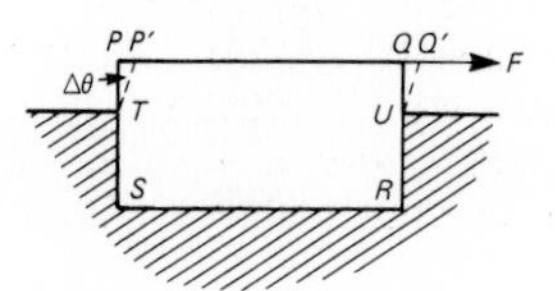

Figure 4.1 Shear strain.

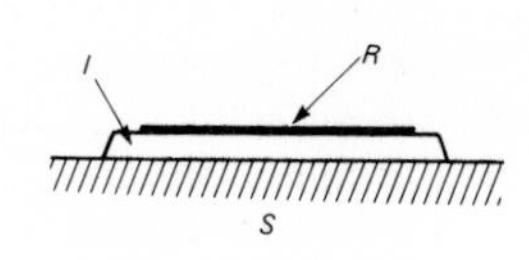

Figure 4.2 Principle of resistance strain gauge.

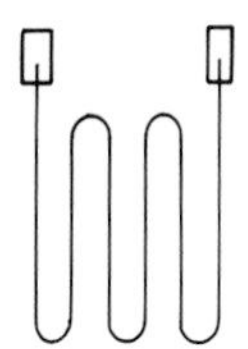

Figure 4.3 Layout of wire gauge.

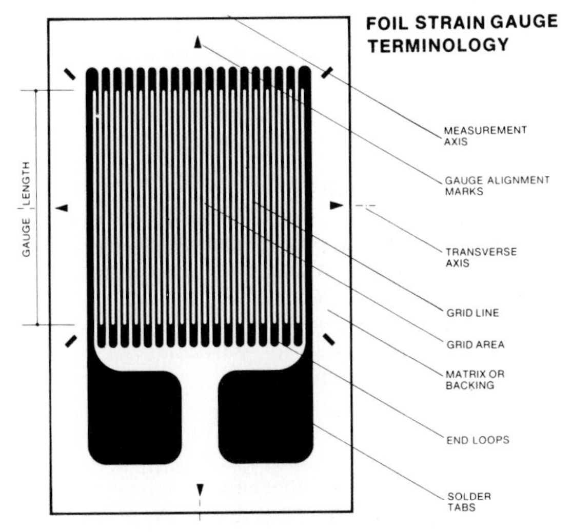

Figure 4.4 Shape of foil gauge. Courtesy, Micro-Measurements Division, Measurements Group Inc.

resistance can be measured in order to get a precise figure for strain.

The resistance of a conductor of length l, cross-sectional area A and resistivity ρ is

$$R=\frac{\rho l}{A}$$

When a strain $\Delta l/l$ is imparted, it causes a fractional change of resistance.

$$\frac{\Delta R}{R}=\left(1+2\mu+\frac{l}{\rho}\frac{\Delta\rho}{\Delta l}\right)\frac{\Delta l}{l}$$

since there will be a Poisson contraction in A and there may also be a change in resistivity. The ratio $(\Delta R/R)/(\Delta l/l)$ is called the gauge factor of a strain gauge. If there were no change in resistivity, it would be $1+2\mu$ or about 1.6 for most metals, whereas it is found to be 2 or more, demonstrating that the sensitivity of strain gauges is increased by a change in ρ.

Nickel alloys are commonly used as the strain-sensitive conductor, notably Nichrome (nickel–chromium) and Constantan (copper–nickel). As well as paper, epoxy resins and polyimide films are used for the backing insulator.

Strain gauges are available commercially as precision tools; units supplied in one batch have closely similar characteristics, notably a quoted gauge factor.

4.2.1 Wire gauges

It is easier to measure resistances accurately when their values are not too low and this will also help to avoid complications in allowing for the effect of lead resistance in series with the active gauge element. On the other hand gauges should not be too big, in order to measure strain effectively 'at a point'; this calls for dimensions of the order of a centimetre, or perhaps only a few millimetres where very localized strains are to be studied. Both considerations point to the need for very fine wire and diameters of 15–30 micrometres are used. The effective length is increased by having several elements side by side as shown in Figure 4.3. Larger tags are attached at the ends of the strain-sensitive wire for connecting leads to.

4.2.2 Foil gauges

An alternative to using wire is to produce the conductor from a foil—typically 4 micrometres thick—by etching. Figure 4.4 illustrates a typical shape. Foil gauges have the advantage that their flatness makes adhesion easier and improves heat dissipation (see p. 71) as well as allowing a wider choice of shape and having the tags for the leads integral with the strain-sensitive conductor, and are in fact more widely used now than wire gauges.

4.2.3 Semiconductor gauges

Another version of strain gauge employs semiconductor material, commonly silicon. Because the resistivity is higher, the sensitive element can be shorter, wider and simpler: Figure 4.5. The great advantage of semiconductor strain gauges is that their resistivity can be very sensitive to strain, allowing them to have gauge factors many times (typically 50) greater than those of simple metals, but they tend to have higher temperature sensitivity and are less linear. They can be made integral with structural components and are used in this way for pressure measurement (see Chapter 9).

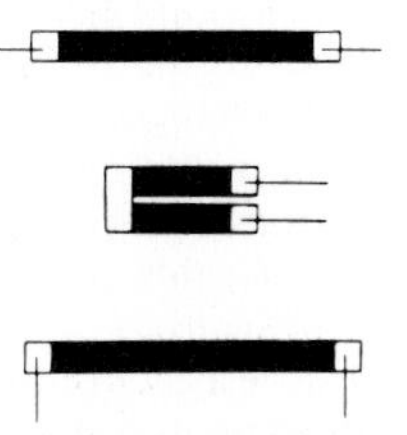

Figure 4.5 Examples of semi-conductor gauges. Courtesy, Kulite Semiconductor Products Inc.

4.2.4 Rosettes

We pointed out earlier that a full analysis of strain involves measurements in more than one direction. In fact, three measurements are required on a surface because strain can be represented as an ellipse, for which the magnitudes and directions of the axes must be established. The directions chosen for strain measurements are commonly either at 120° or at 45° and 90° to each other.

If we are dealing with large structures, it may be expected that strain will only vary gradually across a surface and three closely spaced individual gauges can be thought of as referring to the same point. When there is little room to spare, it is desirable to have the three gauges constructed integrally, which anyhow simplifies installation. Such a unit is called a *rosette*. The three units may be either close together in one plane or actually stacked on top of each other (Figure 4.6).

Figure 4.6 Rosette of gauges. Courtesy, Micro-Measurements Division, Measurements Group Inc.

4.2.5 Residual stress measurement

The state of the surface at the time when a strain gauge is bonded to it has of course to be taken as the strain zero relative to which subsequent changes are measured. The gauge essentially measures increments of strain with increments of load. For many purposes of calculating stresses and predicting life, this is the most important thing to do.

However, during fabrication, and before a gauge can be attached, some stresses can be locked up in certain parts and it may be desirable to know these. This cannot be done with any accuracy non-destructively but if we deliberately remove some material the observed strain changes in neighbouring material can tell us what forces were previously applied through the now absent material. One technique is to strain-gauge a small area of interest, noting the changes in the gauge readings as that area is freed by trepanning. An alternative procedure is to drill a simple hole inside an array of strain gauges that remain attached to the main surface; changes in the strain they show can again indicate what the residual stress was. An array for this purpose is shown in Figure 4.7.

4.3 Gauge characteristics

We have discussed the *gauge factor* at some length; that is what enables resistance to be used at all to measure strain. Other features of strain gauges are important for successful instrumentation. Information about the characteristics of particular gauges is available from manufacturers.

4.3.1 Range

The materials that strain gauges are made from cannot be expected to stretch by more than a few per cent at most and still retain their properties in linear relationships; generally non-linearity is introduced before permanent damage occurs. Metals vary in the strain range over which they can be used; semi-conductors have an appreciably shorter range. Although their limited range is an obvious theoretical restriction on the use of strain gauges, they can in fact cover most of the common field of interest for metals and other hard structural materials. Strain gauges are not generally suitable for use on rubber.

Figure 4.7 Array of gauges for measuring residual stress. Courtesy, Micro-Measurements Division, Measurements Group Inc.

4.3.2 Cross-sensitivity

We have so far described the action of a strain gauge in terms of strain in the direction of the length of its conductor: this is the strain it is intended to measure. But, as explained on p. 66, some strain is generally present in the substrate also in a direction at right angles to this, and gauges are liable to respond in some degree to this. For one thing, part of the conducting path may be in that direction; for another the variation of resistivity with strain is a complex phenomenon. The cross-sensitivity of a gauge is seldom more than a few per cent of its direct sensitivity and for foil gauges can be very small, but it should be taken into account for the most accurate work.

4.3.3 Temperature sensitivity

The resistance of a strain gauge, as of most things, varies with temperature. The magnitude of the effect may be comparable with the variations from the strain to be measured, and a lot of strain gauge technology has been devoted to ensuring that results are not falsified in this way.

Several effects must be taken account of. Not only does the resistance of an unstrained conductor vary with temperature but the expansion coefficients of the gauge material and of the substrate it is bonded to mean that temperature changes cause dimensional changes apart from those, resulting from stress, that it is desired to measure.

It is possible to eliminate these errors by compensation. Gauge resistance is commonly measured in a bridge circuit (see p. 71) and if one of the adjacent bridge arms consists of a similar strain gauge (called a dummy) mounted on similar but unstressed material whose temperature follows that of the surface being strained, then thermal, but not strain effects will cancel and be eliminated from the output.

Self-temperature compensated gauges are made in which the conductor material is heat treated to make its resistivity change with temperature in such a way as to balance out the resistance change from thermal expansion. Because the expansion coefficient of the substrate has an important effect, these gauges are specified for use on a particular material. The commonly matched materials are ferritic steel (coefficient 11×10^{-6} K^{-1}), austenitic steel (16×10^{-6} K^{-1}) and aluminium (23×10^{-6} K^{-1}).

4.3.4 Response times

In practice, there are few fields of study where strain gauges do not respond quickly enough to follow the strain that has been imposed. An ultimate limit to usefulness is set by the finite time taken for stress waves to travel through the substrate, which means that different parts of a strain gauge could be measuring different phases of a high-frequency stress cycle. But with stress-wave velocities (in metals) of the order 5000 m/s, a 10 mm gauge can be thought of as giving a point measurement at frequencies up to 10–20 kHz. Of course it is necessary that the measuring circuits used should be able to handle high-frequency signals.

It must be noted that strain gauges essentially measure the change in strain from the moment when they are fixed on. They do not give absolute readings.

Very slowly varying strains present particular measurement problems. If a strain gauge is to be used over periods of months or years without an opportunity to check back to its zero reading, then errors will be introduced if the zero has drifted. Several factors can contribute to this: creep in the cement or the conductor, corrosion or other structural changes. Drift performance depends on the quality of the installation; provided that it has been carried out to high standards, gauges used at room temperature should have their zero constant to a strain of about 10^{-6} over months. At high temperatures it is a different matter; gauges using ceramic bonding can be used with difficulty up to 500/600 °C but high-temperature operation is a specialized matter.

4.4 Installation

Sometimes strain gauges are incorporated in some measuring device from the design stage. More often they are used for a stress survey of a pre-existing structure. In either case it is most important to pay very close attention to correct mounting of the gauges and other details of installation. The whole operation depends on a small unit adhering securely to a surface, generally of metal. Very small changes in electrical resistance have then to be measured, necessitating close control of any possible resistances that may be either in series or parallel to that of interest—i.e. from leads or leakage.

Of course it is important to ensure that a gauge is mounted at the correct site—often best identified by tape. It may be noted that gauges can be mounted on cylindrical surfaces with quite small radii, but any double curvature makes fixing very difficult. We have already referred to the use of another gauge for temperature compensation. The introduction of any such 'dummies' must be thought out; it is possible that an active gauge can be used for compensation, so doubling the signal, if a place can be identified where the strain will be equal but opposite to that at the primary site, e.g. the opposite side of a bending beam.

The surface where the gauge is to be fixed must be thoroughly cleaned—probably best by abrasion followed by chemical degreasing. Cements commonly used are cellulose nitrate up to 100 °C, epoxy up to

200 °C and ceramic above that where special techniques must be used. Gauge manufacturers may specify a particular cement for use with their product.

After the gauge is fixed down, its leads should be fastened in position and connected (by soldering or spot-welding) to the gauge. It is most important for leads to be mounted securely to withstand the vibration they may be subject to; in practice there are more failures of leads than in strain gauges themselves.

Unless the installation is in a friendly environment, it must then be protected by covering with wax, rubber, or some such material. The chief purpose of this is to exclude moisture. Moisture could cause corrosion and, also serious, an electrical leakage conductance. It must be remembered that 10^8 ohms introduced in parallel with a 350-ohm gauge appears as a 3 in a million reduction in the latter; such a paralleling can be caused between leads or by an earth leakage depending on the circuit configuration and gives a false indication of strain of 2×10^{-6}.

The various stages of installation are illustrated in Figure 4.8.

Figure 4.8 Stages of installing gauges. Courtesy, HBM.

1. Roughening of the application area

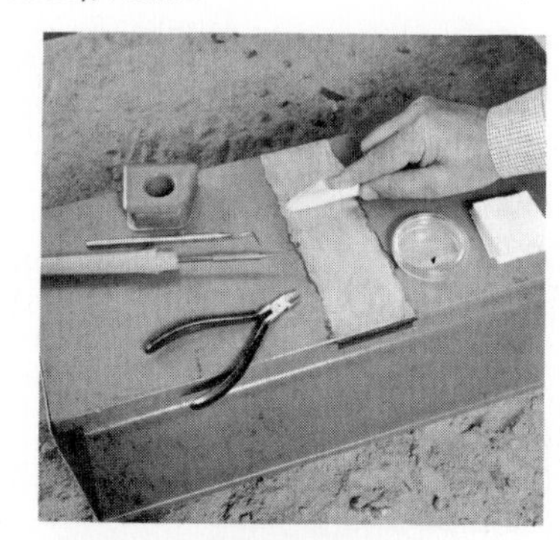
2. Cleaning of the application area

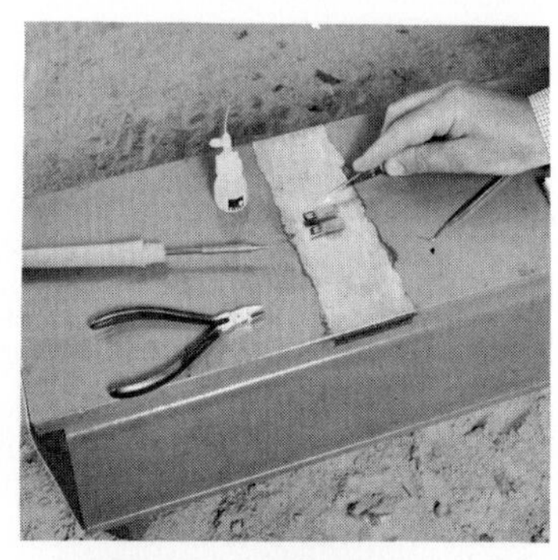
3. Positioning of the strain guage with tape

4. Applying the adhesive

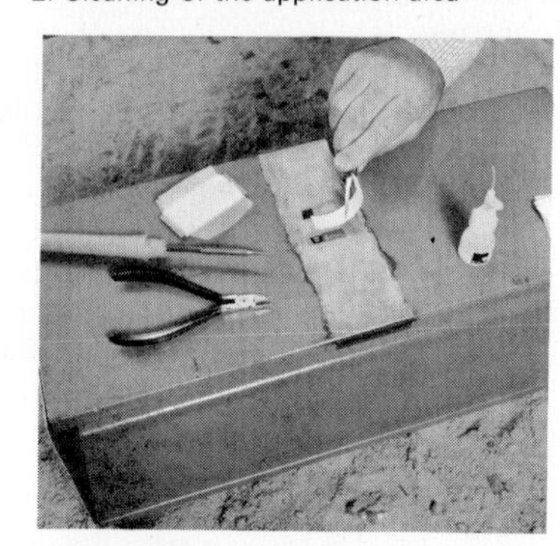
5. Spreading the adhesive

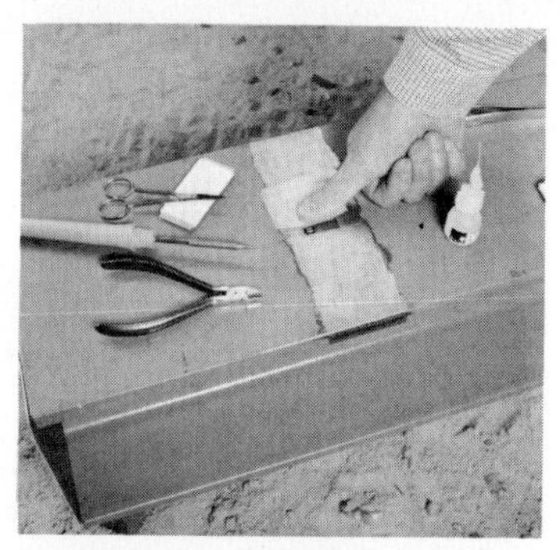
6. Pressing the strain guage

7. Soldering the strain gauge ribbons

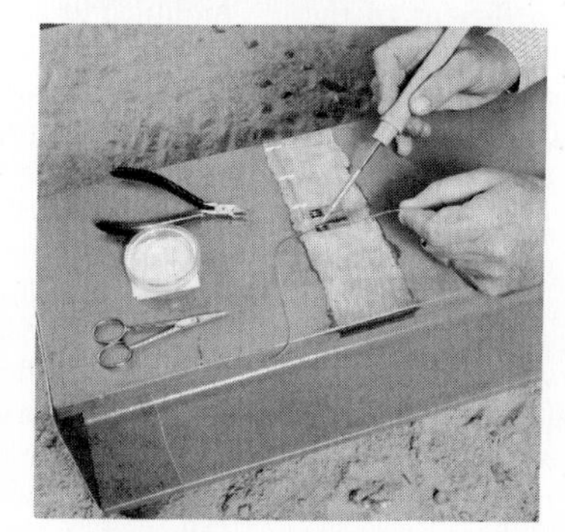
8. Soldering and fixing the cables

9. Covering the measurement point

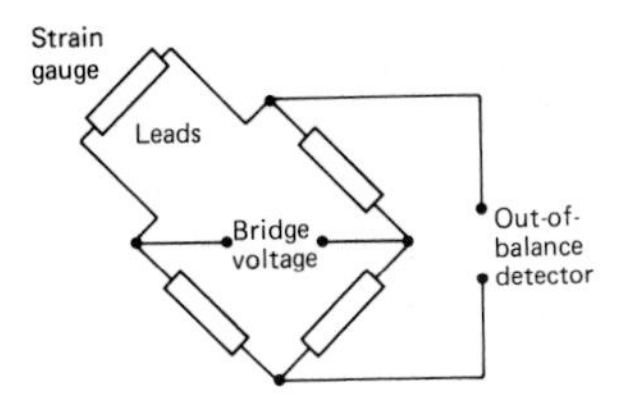

Figure 4.9 Simple bridge circuit (quarter-bridge).

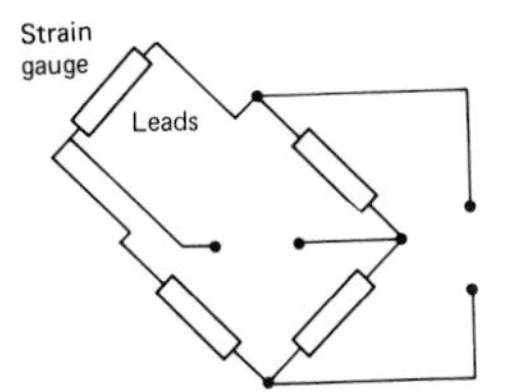

Figure 4.10 Quarter-bridge circuit with three long leads.

4.5 Circuits for strain gauges

For measurement of its small resistance changes, a strain gauge is generally connected in a Wheatstone bridge. This may be energized with d.c., but a.c.—at frequencies of the order of kilohertz—is commoner; a.c. has the advantage of avoiding errors from the thermocouple potentials that can arise in the leads when the junctions of dissimilar metals are at different temperatures.

Gauges are often mounted some distance from their associated measuring equipment and care must be taken that the long leads involved do not introduce errors. In a simple gauge configuration (Figure 4.9), the two leads will be directly in series with the live gauge, and any changes in their resistance, for instance from temperature, will be indistinguishable from strain. This can be overcome by having three leads to the gauge (Figure 4.10); one lead is now in series with each of two adjacent arms, so giving compensation (for equal-ratio arms) provided changes in one lead are reproduced in the other. The third lead, going to the power source, is not critical. These are called 'quarter-bridge' arrangements.

A 'half-bridge' set-up is sometimes used (Figure 4.11). This is when two strain gauges are both used in the measurement as explained on p. 69.

The third possibility is a 'full-bridge' (Figure 4.12) when all four arms consist of gauges at the measurement site, the four long leads being those connecting the power source and out-of-balance detector. Their resistances are not critical so it is not necessary even to ensure that changes are equal. As with most bridge circuits, the power source and the detector can be interchanged. We have called the power source 'bridge voltage', implying that the supply is at constant potential; it can alternatively come as a constant current and this has some advantages for linearity.

Bridges can be balanced, to take up component tolerance, by fine adjustment of series or parallel elements in the arms. Instead, the zero can be set within the amplifier that commonly forms part of the detector. Changing a high resistance across a strain gauge can be used to simulate a known strain and so calibrate all the circuit side of the measuring system. It is possible to have measurements made in terms of the adjustment needed to re-balance a bridge after a strain has occurred but more often the magnitude of the out-of-balance signal is used as an indication.

The larger the voltage or current applied to a strain gauge bridge, the higher will its sensitivity be. The practical limit is set by self-heating in the gauge. If a gauge is appreciably hotter than its substrate, temperature errors are introduced. Compensation from a similar effect in another gauge cannot be relied on because the cooling is unlikely to be identical in the two cases. Self-heating varies a lot with the details of an installation but, with metal substrates, can generally be ignored below 1 milliwatt per square millimetre of gauge area.

We have described the basic circuitry as it concerns a single strain gauge. Tests are often made involving large numbers of gauges. For these, there is available elaborate equipment that allows a multiplicity of gauges to be scanned in quick succession, or simultaneous recordings made of a number of high-speed dynamic strain measurements.

4.6 Vibrating wire strain gauge

Although bonded-resistance strain gauges are the type that has much the widest application, one or two other principles are made use of in certain situations. One of these is that of the vibrating-wire strain gauge.

If a wire is put under tension, then its natural

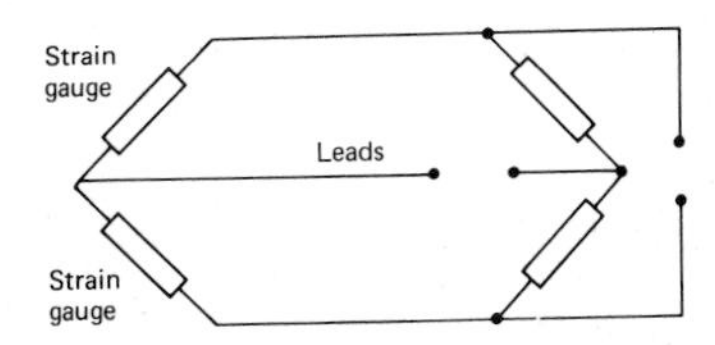

Figure 4.11 Half-bridge circuit.

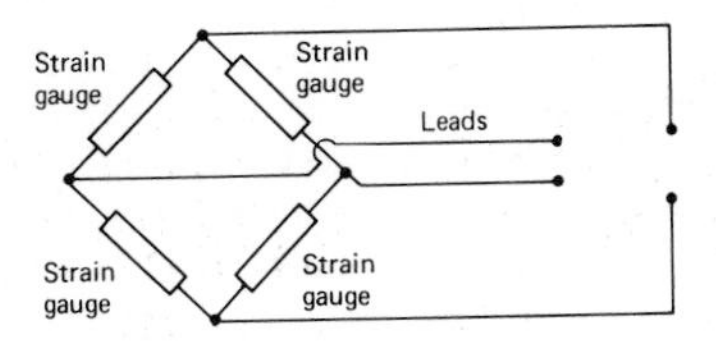

Figure 4.12 Full-bridge circuit.

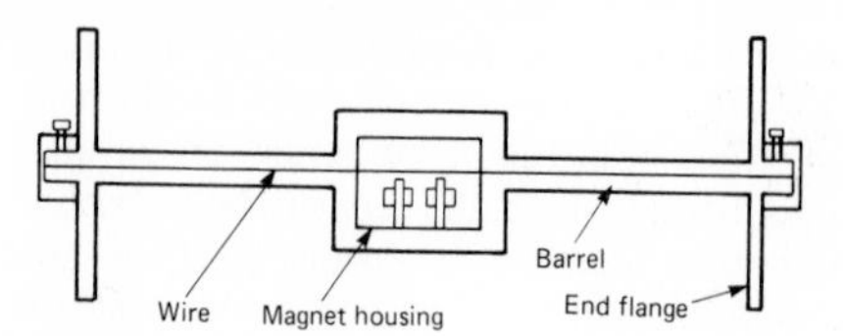

Figure 4.13 Vibrating-wire strain gauge. Courtesy, Strainstall Ltd.

frequency of vibration (in its first mode) is

$$f=\frac{1}{2l}\sqrt{\frac{T}{m}}$$

where l is its length, T its tension and m its mass per unit length.

The fixing points of the wire can be bonded to material whose strain changes are to be measured. As the latter stretches, l changes and, more significantly, T changes following Hooke's law. Strain can then be determined by monitoring natural frequency, easily done if the wire is magnetic and a solenoid is placed nearby to attract it. Wire diameter is typically 0.25 mm, operating frequency 1 kHz. The commonest circuit arrangement is to excite the wire with a single current pulse, measuring the frequency of the damped vibrations that ensue. A sketch of a typical device is given in Figure 4.13.

With the number of items that go to make up a vibrating-wire gauge, it is considerably larger (typically 100 mm long) than a bonded-resistance gauge. Because of the large force needed to stretch it, thought must be given to the gauge's mounting.

In fact, the largest application of such gauges has been to the measurement of *internal* strains in concrete, where both these factors are attended to. By embedding the gauge in the concrete when the concrete is cast, with electrical leads coming out to some accessible point, good bonding to the end-points is ensured. A large gauge-length is desirable in order to average the properties of the material, which is very inhomogeneous on a scale up to a few centimetres. By choosing appropriate dimensions for the components of a vibrating-wire strain gauge, it is possible to make its effective elastic modulus the same as that of the concrete it is embedded in; the stress distribution in the bulk material will not then be changed by the presence of the gauge. A strain range up to 0.5 per cent can be covered.

It has been found that vibrating-wire strain gauges can be very stable; the yielding that might be expected in the vibrating wire can be eliminated by pre-straining before assembly. With careful installation and use at room temperature, the drift over months can correspond to strains of less than 10^{-6}.

4.7 Capacitive strain gauges

It is possible to design a device to be fixed to a substrate so that when the latter is strained the electrical *capacitance* (rather than the *resistance*) of the former is changed. Figure 4.14 is a diagram showing the principles of such a gauge. When the feet are moved nearer together, the arched strips change curvature and the gap between the capacitor plates P changes. The greater complexity makes these devices several times more expensive than simple bonded-resistance strain gauges, and they are seldom used except when their unique characteristic of low drift at high temperature (up to 600 °C) is important. They are most commonly fixed to metal structures by spot-welding. Although the capacitance is only about a picofarad, it can be measured accurately using appropriate bridge circuits; because both plates are live to earth, the effects of cable capacitance can be largely eliminated.

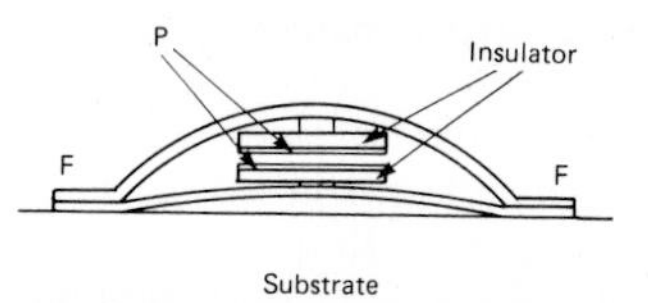

Figure 4.14 Capacitive strain gauge. Courtesy, G. V. Planar Ltd.

4.8 Surveys of whole surfaces

A strain gauge only gives information about what is happening in a small region. Sometimes it is desirable to take an overview of a large area.

4.8.1 Brittle lacquer

One way of surveying a large area is to use brittle lacquer, though the technique is much less accurate than using strain gauges and does not work at all unless the strains are large. It has particular value for deciding where to put strain gauges for more accurate measurements.

A layer of special lacquer is carefully and consistently applied to the surface to be studied. The lacquer is dried under controlled conditions, whereupon it becomes brittle and therefore cracks if and when the part is strained above a certain threshold. Moreover, the higher the surface strain, the closer together are the cracks. It is best to coat a calibration bar in the same way and at the same time as the test part. Bending the bar then gives a range of known strains along it and the crack pattern observed at different points on the live surface can be compared with that seen on the calibration bar.

In this way, the critical points where there are the highest stresses on the surface of a structure can be

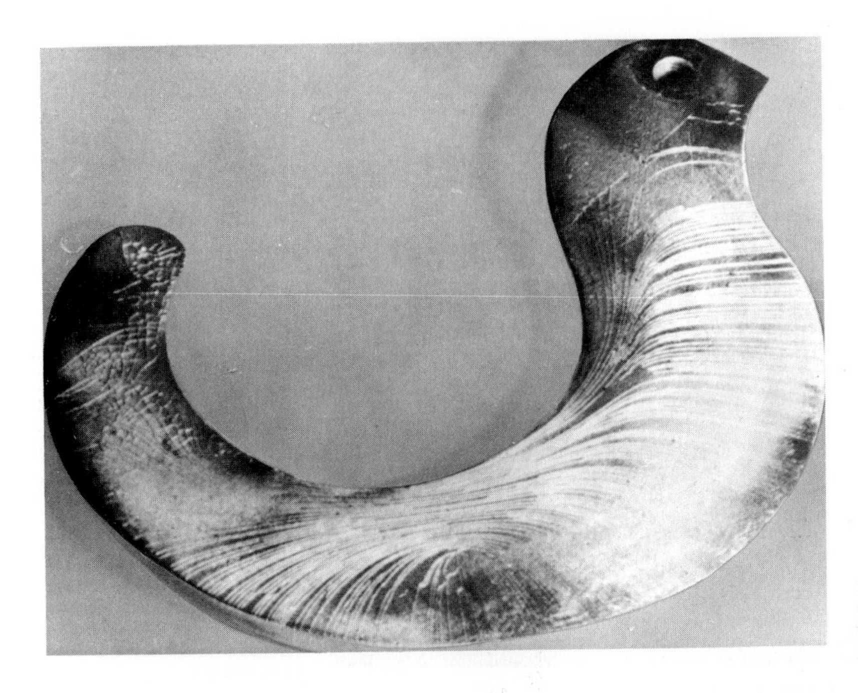

Figure 4.15 Brittle lacquer used on a specimen. Courtesy, Photolastic Division, Measurements Group Inc.

quickly recognized and the strain levels identified within about ±25 per cent (of those levels) over a range of strains from 0.05 per cent to 0.2 per cent. Because the cracks form perpendicularly to the maximum principal stress, the technique has the considerable additional advantage of showing the directions of principal stresses all over a structure. Figure 4.15 shows the sort of crack pattern that can be observed.

4.8.2 Patterns on surfaces

Large strains can be determined simply by inscribing a pattern on a surface and noting how it changes. Figure 4.16 shows the changes of shape observed in one such investigation.

The sensitivity to smaller strains can be increased by using moiré fringes. When a fine grating is seen through another grating that is comparable but not identical, dark and brighter regions—called 'fringes'—will alternate. The dark regions correspond to where spaces in one grating block light that has come through gaps in the other grating; bright regions arise when the gaps are superposed. The small difference between the gratings can be one of orientation, or of separation of their elements. For instance, if one grating has 1000 lines per centimetre and its neighbour 1001 lines, there will be a dark fringe every centimetre, with bright ones in between them. Now suppose a 1000-line grating is etched on a surface and another placed just above it; a strain of 10^{-3} in the surface will change the former into a 1001-line grating and mean that fringes (seen in this case in light reflected off the

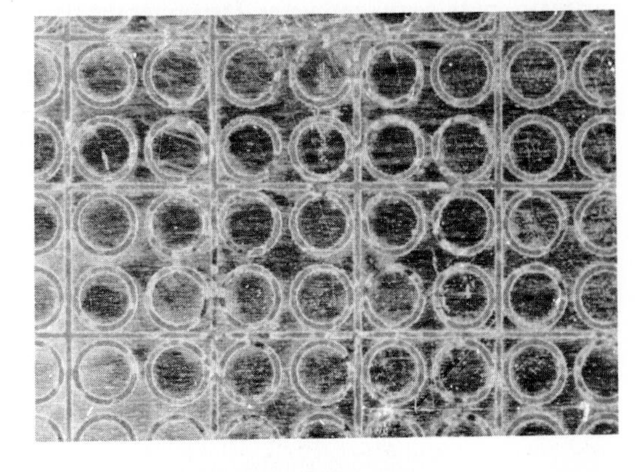

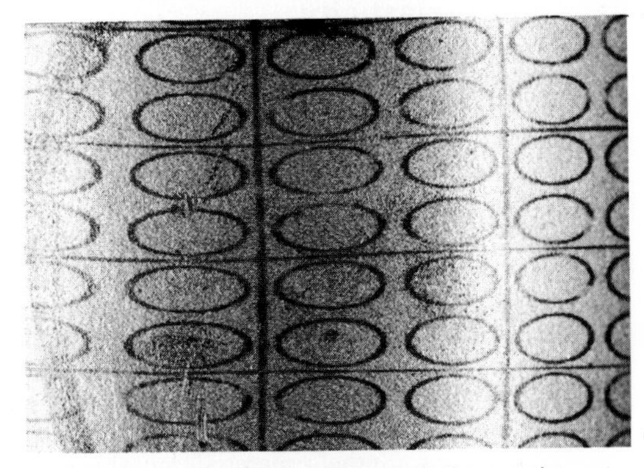

Figure 4.16 Distortion of a pattern under large strain. Courtesy, South Australian Institute of Technology.

Figure 4.17 Polariscope in use. Courtesy, Sharples Stress Engineers Ltd.

surface) appear every centimetre. The larger the strain, the more closely spaced the fringes.

Fringes appearing parallel to the original grating lines will be a measure of the direct strain of one grating relative to the other. Fringes appearing perpendicular to the original grating lines will indicate rotation of one grating relative to the other. In general the fringes will be at an angle to the grating lines, therefore one pair of gratings will give a direct strain and a shear strain component. Two pairs, i.e. a grid or mesh, will give two direct strains and the associated shear strain and will thus permit a complete surface strain determination to be made, i.e. principal strains and principal strain directions.

4.9 Photo-elasticity

For many years, the phenomenon of photo-elasticity has been employed in experimental studies of stress distribution in bodies of various shapes. The effect made use of is the birefringence that occurs in some materials and its dependence on stress.

Light is in general made up of components polarized in different directions; if, in a material the velocities of these components are different, the material is said to be birefringent. The birefringence is increased (often from zero in stress-free material) by stress, commonly being proportional to the difference in stress in the two directions of polarization. The effect was originally discovered in glass; synthetic materials, notably epoxy resins, are much more commonly used now.

In practice, a model of the structure to be examined is made out of photo-elastic material. This is placed in a rig or *polariscope* such as the one shown in Figure 4.17, and loaded in a way that corresponds to the load imposed on the original. By re-combining components of the light ray with polarizations parallel to the two principal stresses, fringes are produced and their position and number give information about strain in the model. The first-order fringe occurs when there is a phase difference of 360° between the components; the nth order when there is a $360n°$ difference.

As discussed for strain gauges, both the direction and the magnitude of the principal stresses come into stress analysis, and this complicates the situation. To find directions, a polariscope system as indicated in Figure 4.18 can be used; if the axes of polarizer and analyser are at right angles and parallel to the principal stresses, there will be no interference, just a black spot

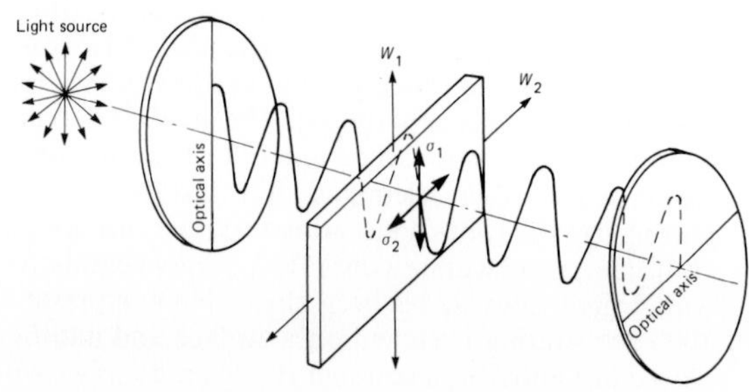

Figure 4.18 Use of a polariscope to determine principal stress directions. Courtesy, Sharples Stress Engineers Ltd.

whatever the load may be. So the 'isoclinics'—loci of points having the same direction of principal stresses—can be established.

For example, if a two-dimensional model of a loaded notched beam were examined in such a crossed polariscope two types of fringes would be observed: a black fringe, the isoclinic, joining all points where the principal stress directions were parallel to the axes of polarization, and coloured fringes, the 'isochromatics', contours of equal principal stress difference. The first-order isochromatic would pass through all points of the model where the stress had a particular value of $P-Q$, where P and Q are the two principal stresses. Similarly the nth-order isochromatic would pass through all points where the stress had n times that value.

By using simple tensile calibration strips it is possible to determine the value which corresponds to each fringe order. Since the stress normal to the unloaded boundaries of the model is zero, i.e. $Q=0$, it is a relatively simple matter to determine the stress all along the unloaded boundaries. Determination of the stresses in the interior of the model is also possible but requires complex stress separation.

Normally a monochromatic light source is used, but white light has the advantage that the first-order fringe can be distinguished from higher orders.

Birefringence all along the ray path through the model will contribute to the phase difference between the two optical components. The effect measured is therefore an integral of stress along that path. This means that fringe patterns in photo-elasticity are most easily interpreted with thin—or effectively two-dimensional—models. There is a technique for studies in three dimensions. This is to load the model in an oven at a temperature high enough to 'anneal' out the birefringence. Subsequent slow cooling means that when the load is removed at room temperature birefringence is locked into the unloaded model, which can then be carefully sliced; examination of each slice in a polariscope will show the original stresses in that particular region.

4.10 References

Holister, G. S. *Experimental Stress Analysis, Principles and Methods*, Cambridge University Press (1967)

Kuske, A. and Robertson, G. *Photoelastic Stress Analysis*, John Wiley and Sons (1974)

Theocaris, P. S. *Moiré Fringes in Strain Analysis*, Pergamon Press (1969)

Window, A. L. and Holister, G. S. (eds) *Strain Gauge Technology*, Allied Science Publishers (1982)

5 Measurement of level and volume

P. H. SYDENHAM

5.1 Introduction

Many industrial and scientific processes require knowledge of the quantity of content of tanks and other containers. In many instances it is not possible, or practical, to directly view the interior. Parameters of interest are generally level of the contents, volume, or simply the presence of substances. Sensors may be needed, Figure 5.1, to detect high or low level states for alarm or control use, to provide proportional readout of the level with respect to a chosen datum, for automatic control purposes or for manually read records.

Simple installations may be able to adopt inexpensive manual methods such as a dip-stick. Automatic control applications, however, will require control signals for operation of a process actuator or alarm. For these cases there are available several options of output signal which include indirect electric contacts and electronic proportional outputs, and direct flow and pneumatic valving.

As well as the obvious liquid substances, such as water, oil, petroleum and milk, level sensors have been successfully applied to measurement of solids such as flour, mineral ores, food grain and even potatoes and coal. Two-phase systems are also often measured, examples being determination of liquid and froth levels in beer making and for mineral slurries.

Due to the extensive need for this basic process parameter there are available very many commercial equipments; their installation details are important. A useful tutorial introduction to level measurement is

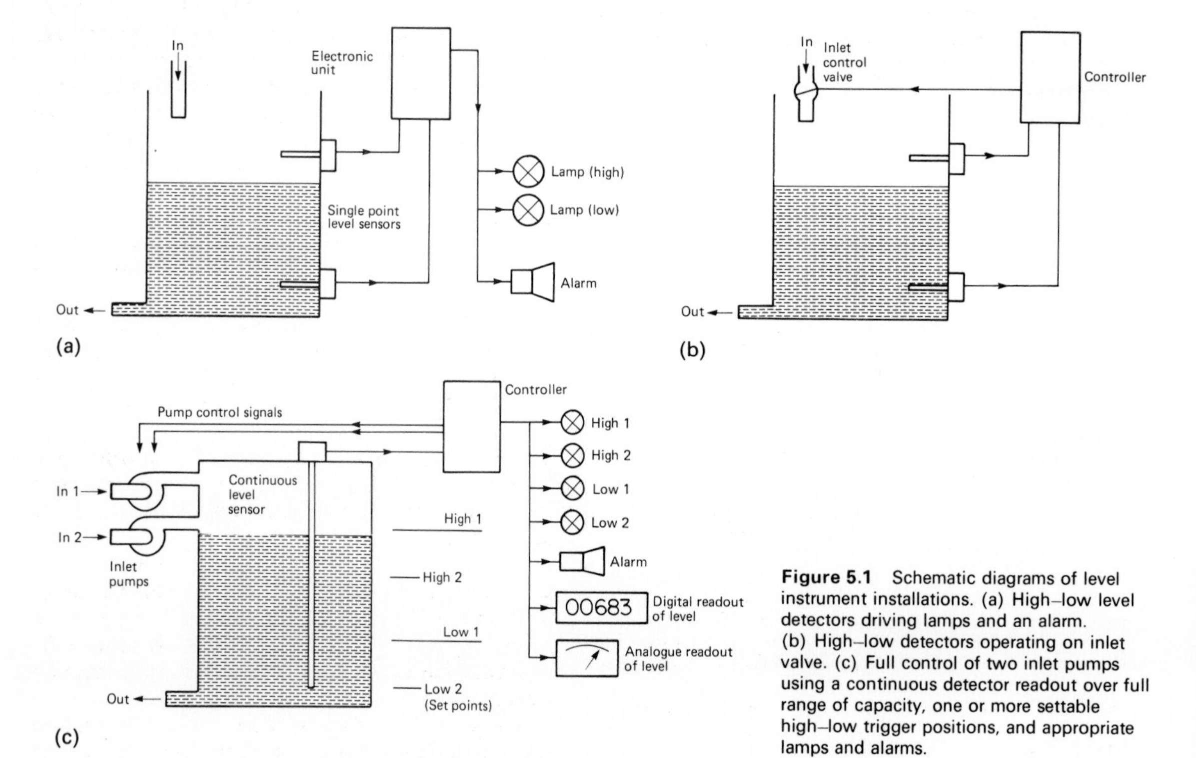

Figure 5.1 Schematic diagrams of level instrument installations. (a) High–low level detectors driving lamps and an alarm. (b) High–low detectors operating on inlet valve. (c) Full control of two inlet pumps using a continuous detector readout over full range of capacity, one or more settable high–low trigger positions, and appropriate lamps and alarms.

available in Lazenby (1980). Norton (1969), O'Higgins (1966) and Miller (1975) also make valuable contributions.

5.2 Practice of level measurement

5.2.1 Installation

Suppliers of level-sensing systems generally provide good design support for installation, enabling the prospective user to appreciate the practical problems that arise and offering wide variation in the sensor-packaging and systems arrangements.

Positioning of the sensor head, or heads, should be chosen with due regard for the problems of turbulence caused by contents flowing in and out. Positioning in order to control errors is also important. For example, when a stilling tube is placed external to the container, its contents may be at a different temperature to those in the container. The complete sensor may need to be fully removable without imposing the need to empty the container.

It is often necessary to incorporate followers, such as shown in Figure 5.2, in the sensing system to constrain the unwanted degrees of freedom of such components as floats.

Corrosion effects, caused by the contents, on the components of the sensing arrangements must also be carefully considered. High temperatures, corrosive materials and abrasion in granular-material measurement can progressively alter the characteristics of the system by producing undue friction, changing the mass of floats and simply reducing the system to an unworkable state.

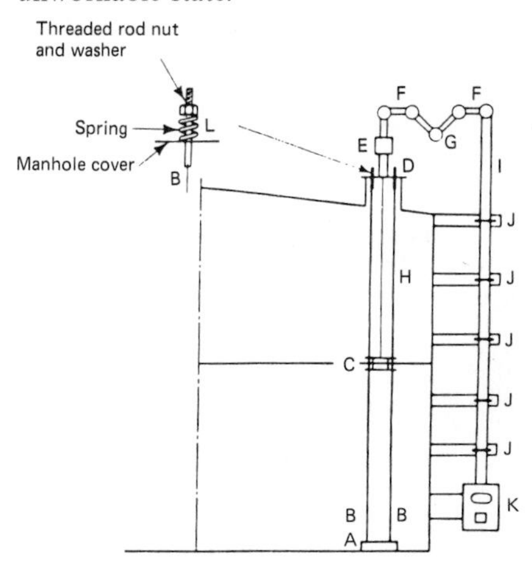

Figure 5.2 Installation of float-type level indicator with guide wires on a fixed-roof tank. A, guide wire anchor. Wires may be anchored to a heavy weight or the bottom of the tank. B, float guide wires. C, float having sliding guides which move freely on the guide wires. D, manhole sufficiently large for float and anchor weight to pass through. E, flexible joint, F, pulley housings, G, vapour seal (if required). H, float tape. I, tape conduit. J, sliding guides. K, gauge head. L, guide wire tension adjustment.

Where the requirement is to operate simple high, or low, level alarms or switch controls the level sensor should preferably have in-built back-lash which provides a toggle action (hysteresis) so that the sensing contacts do not dither at the control point. Some systems incorporate this in their mechanical design (an example being given later in Figure 5.5), others in the electronic circuits.

Gauges based on the use of a radioactive source will need installation and operation within nucleonic device standards. These gauges use very small strength sources and pose an absolutely minimal hazard in themselves. They are described in Volume 3.

If installed without due consideration, the installation itself may introduce a hazard due to the nature of the mechanical components of the system causing blockages in the system.

5.2.2 Sources of error

A first group of errors are those associated with problems of defining the distributed contents by use of a single measurement parameter made at one point in the extended surface of the whole. As a general guide, definition of the surface, which is used to decide the contents, can be made to around 0.5 mm in industrial circumstances. Methods that sense the surface can be in error due to surface tension effects that introduce hysteresis. Where the quantity of a particular substance is of concern, any build-up of sediment and other unwanted residues introduces error.

Granular materials will not generally flow to form a flat surface as do liquids. The angle of repose of the material and the form of input and output porting will give rise to error in volume calculations if the actual geometry is not allowed for in use of a single point sensor.

Turbulence occurring at the sensor, caused by material flow in the container or by vibrations acting on the container, may also be a source of error. It is common practice to mount the sensor in some form of integrating chamber that smooths out transient dynamic variations. A common method is the use of a stilling pipe or well that is allowed to fill to the same level as the contents via small holes—see Figures 5.3 and 5.4. The time rate responses of such still tubes, however, become important in fast moving systems as they can introduce phase-shift and amplitude attenuation.

Changes of the mass of floats, due to sediment build-up or corrosion, will alter the depth of immersion of float sensors. A systematic error also exists due to the actual depth to which the float sinks to provide its necessary buoyancy force. This varies with material density which often varies with temperature.

A second class of errors arise due to temperature and, to a lesser extent, pressure changes to the

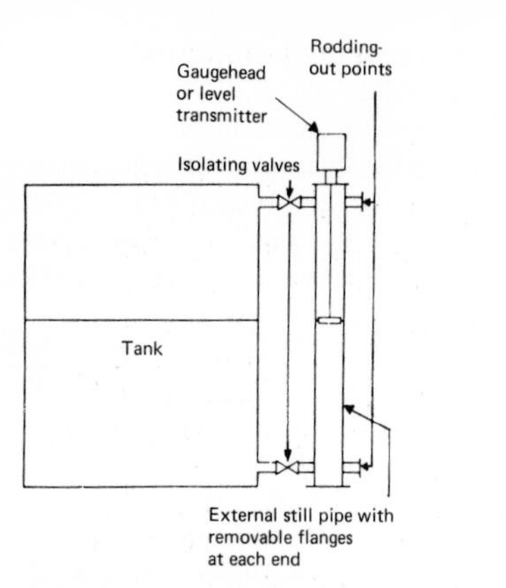

Figure 5.3 Integrating chamber used to average transient variation. Internal still-pipe.

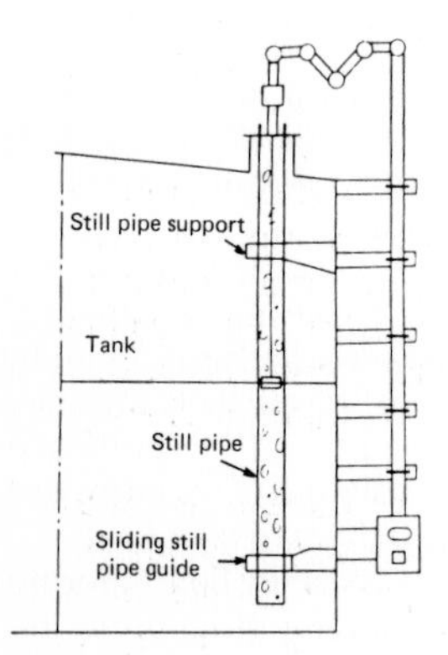

Figure 5.4 Integrating chamber used to average transient motion. External still-pipe.

contents. Where the required measurement is a determination of the volume or mass of the contents, use is made of level as an indirect step toward that need. All materials change volume wich changing temperature. It may therefore, be necessary to provide temperature measurements so that level outputs can be corrected.

For some forms of level sensor external still tubes should be situated to retain the same temperature as that of the tank because localized heating, or cooling, can cause the contents of the still tube to have a different density from that existing in the tank. Methods that are based upon use of buoyancy chambers, that produce a measurement force rather than following the surface, will produce force outputs that vary with temperature due to altered buoyancy upthrust as the density of the fluid changes.

Floats are generally made from waterproofed cork, stainless steel, copper and plastic materials. The material used may need to be corrosion-resistant. Where the contents are particularly corrosive, or otherwise inhospitable to the components of the sensing systems, it is preferable to reduce, to the absolute miñimum, the number of subsystem parts that are actually immersed in the contents.

Considerable use is made of magnetic coupling between the guided float and the follower. Figure 5.5 shows one such arrangement.

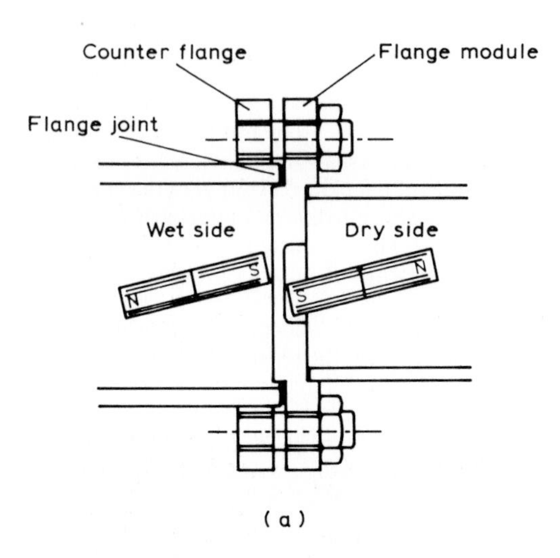

Figure 5.5 Repulsion of like magnetic poles providing non-immersed sensing and toggle action to a float sensor. One commercial form. Courtesy, BESTA Ltd.

Nucleonic gauging offers the distinct advantage, see Figure 5.6, that no part of the level-detecting system need be inside the container. It is discussed further in Volume 3.

Finally, on general choice of level-sensing system, Table 5.1 from Lazenby (1980) provides guidelines for selecting appropriate methods.

Table 5.1 Some guidelines for selecting a suitable level sensor. Adapted from Lazenby (1980).

Is remote control or indication desirable?	A YES excludes mechanical float gauges, sight glasses, dipsticks and other devices designed specifically for local control.
With level indicators, is time spent in taking a reading important?	A YES excludes dipsticks, sight glasses, mechanical float-gauges and certain balance systems.
Can the sensor contact the material being measured?	A NO eliminates all but ultrasonics, radiation, radar, and optical and load cells.
Must weight be measured, rather than height?	A YES means the choice is limited to load cells; but in uniform-sided tanks, other devices such as capacitance meters can be calibrated for weight, particularly if a liquid is being measured.
Are there objections to mechanical moving parts?	A YES gives one a choice of sight glasses—and capacitance, ultrasonic, radiation, conductivity, radar, load-cell, optical, thermistor, and bubbler devices.
Is the application in a liquid?	A YES eliminates vibrators and certain paddle types.
Is the application for a powdered or granular material?	A YES eliminates dipsticks, sight glasses, floats, thermistors, conductivity devices, pressure (except pressure switches) instruments, bubblers, displacers, sight glasses.
Do level indicators have to be accurate to about 2%?	A YES eliminates thermistors, vibrators, paddles, optical devices, suspended tilting switches, and conductivity instruments, as those types only provide control. All other types can be considered, but the poorest accuracies probably come from float gauges and radiation instruments.
Do level indicators need to have an accuracy that is a lot better than 1%?	A YES reduces the list to dipsticks, some of the displacers, and balance devices.

5.3 Calibration of level-measuring systems

Contents that are traded for money, such as petrol and alcohol, must be measured to standards set by the relevant Weights and Measures authority. Official approval of the measuring system and its procedures of use and calibration is required. In such cases the intrinsic value of the materials will decide the accuracy of such measurements and this often means that the system and calibrations must comply to very strict codes and be of the highest accuracy possible.

The use of the indirect process of determining volumetric or mass contents, based upon a level measurement, means that a conversion coefficient, or chart of coefficients, must be prepared so that the level measurements can be converted into the required measurement form.

Calibration tables for a large fabricated tank are most easily prepared using the original engineering construction drawings. This, however, is not an accurate or reliable method.

A more accurate, and traceable, method (known as 'strapping') is to actually survey the container's dimensions after it is built. This can be a time-consuming task. The values can be used to calculate the volume corresponding to different levels. From this is compiled a conversion chart for manual use or a 'look-up table' for computer use.

By far the most accurate method, however, is a direct volumetric calibration of the container by which a suitable fluid (usually water) is pumped in and out, to provide two readings, the tank passing it through an accurate flow-metering station. Whilst this is in process level data are recorded, enabling the conversion factors to be provided for each level measurement value. These results will often require correction for temperature as has been already discussed.

Highly accurate level measurement requires continuous monitoring of the various error sources described earlier so that on-going corrections can be made. A continuous maintenance programme is needed to clean floats and electrodes and to remove unwanted sediment.

In many instances the use of hand dipping is seen as the on-going calibration check of the level measurement level. For this, rods or tapes are used to observe the point where the contents wet the surface along the mechanical member. Obviously this cannot be used for dry substances; for those the rod or tape is lowered until the end rests on the surface.

In each case it is essential to initially establish a permanent measurement datum, either as the bottom of the tank where the rod strikes or as a fiducial mark at the top. This mark needs to be related to the transducer system's readout and to the original calibration.

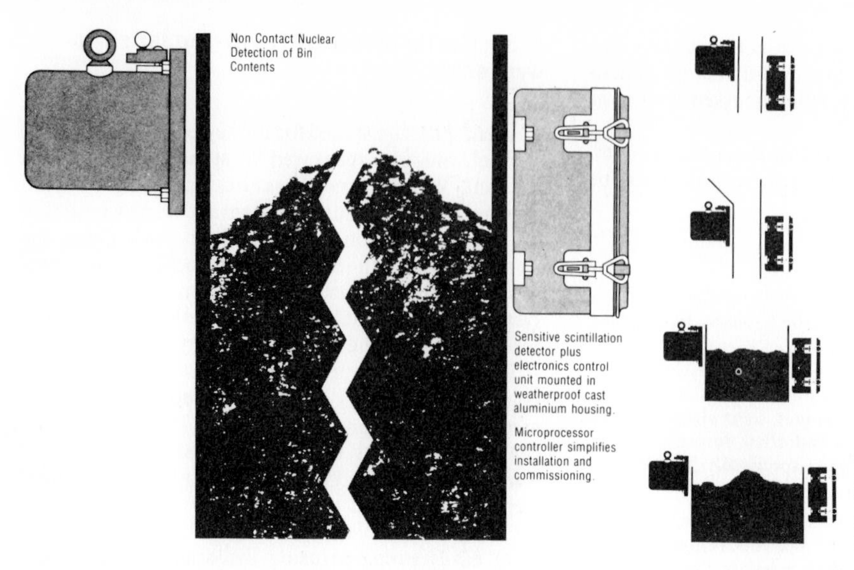

Figure 5.6 Nucleonic gauging system needs mounting only on the outside of existing pipes or containers. Courtesy, Mineral Control Instrumentation.

5.4 Methods providing full-range level measurement

Methods used to measure or control level in a container group into those that can provide continuous readout over the whole range of level experienced and those that sense a small level change using this to operate alarms and switches, or to control the motion of a full-range follower mechanism that, in turn, drives a secondary output transducer or displacement.

Attention is first given to the full range methods that have found wide acceptance.

5.4.1 Sight gauges

A device for reading the level of contents within a closed container, such as a steam boiler, is the simple externally mounted sight-glass. This generally consists of a tube of toughened glass connected through unions and valves into the tank wall. The diameter of the tube must be large enough not to cause 'climb' of the contents due to capillary action; clearly then the level will follow that of the contents. Figure 5.7(a) gives the basic structure of such a device. Where the contents are under pressure it will be necessary to use safety devices to control pressure release in case of tube breakage. Valves are usually incorporated to allow the whole fitting to be removed without having to depressurize the container. Figure 5.7(b) shows a configuration incorporating these features.

A modern development of the above sight gauge concept is the magnetic level indicator shown in Figure 5.8. As the float, containing a bar magnet, follows the liquid surface in the still tube the individual, magnetically actuated, flaps rotate to expose a differently coloured surface that is coated with luminous paint. The float is chosen to suit the specific gravity of the fluid.

The magnetic action also operates individual switches for control and alarm purposes. Discrimination is to around 5 mm. Magnets must not be operated beyond their Curie point at which temperature they lose their desired properties. As a guide these systems can measure liquids under pressures up to 300 bars at temperatures up to 400 °C.

In some circumstances it may be possible to view the surface of the liquid from above but not from the side. In this case a hook gauge, Figure 5.9, can be used to enable the observer to detect when the end of the dipstick rod just breaks the surface.

5.4.2 Float-driven instruments

The magnetic indicator described above is one of a class of level indicators that use a float to follow the liquid surface. Where a float is used to drive a mechanical linkage that operates a remotely located readout device of the linkage motion, there is need to ensure that the linkage geometry does not alter the force loading imposed on the float, for this will alter its immersion depth and introduce error. Frictional forces exerted by the linkage can also introduce error.

Compensation for changes in linkage weight, as a float moves, is achieved by using such mechanisms as counterbalance masses and springs. Figure 5.10 shows the construction of a sophisticated form that uses a pre-wound 'Neg'ator' (also called 'Tensator') spring torque motor that has its torque characteristic tailored to vary as more tape is to be supported during windout.

The production costs of precision mechanical

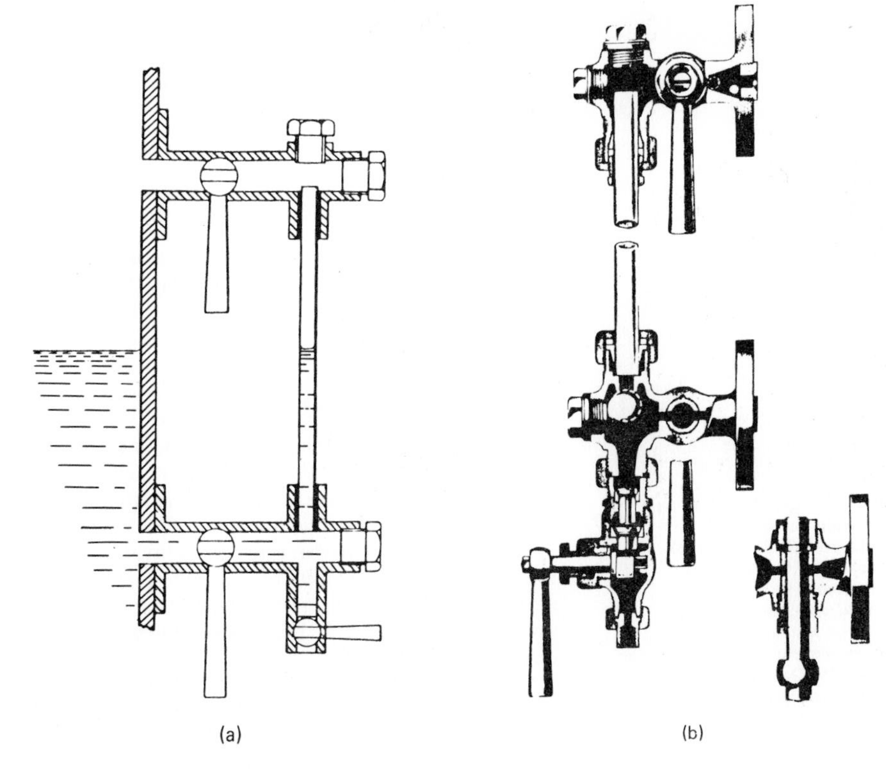

Figure 5.7 Sight-glass level indicator. (a) Basic schematic. (b) Sight-glass with automatic cut-off. Courtesy, Hopkinsons Ltd.

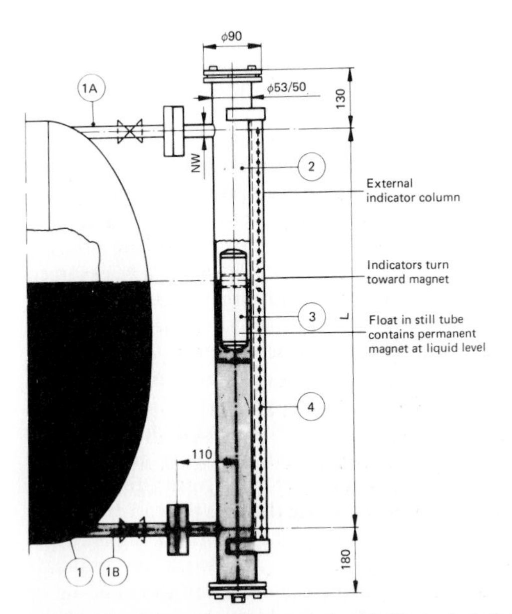

Figure 5.8 Schematic of magnetic level indicator installation. Courtesy, Weka-Besta Ltd.

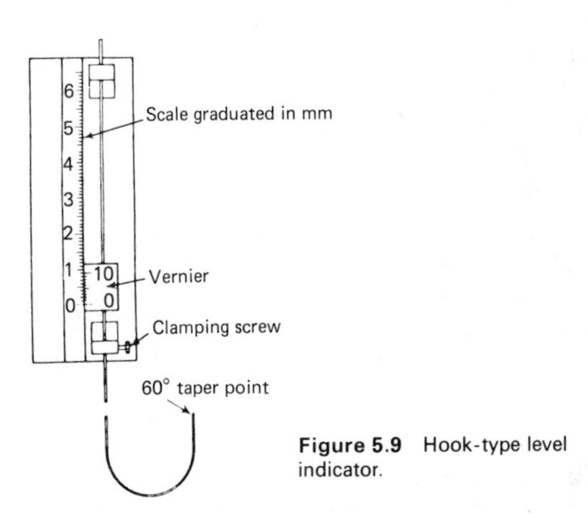

Figure 5.9 Hook-type level indicator.

systems can make them less attractive than electronic equivalents but such systems do have the advantages that no electrical power supply is needed and that the system is easily understood by a wider range of plant operators.

5.4.3 Capacitance probes

The electrical capacitance C between two adjacent electrically conducting surfaces of area A, separated by

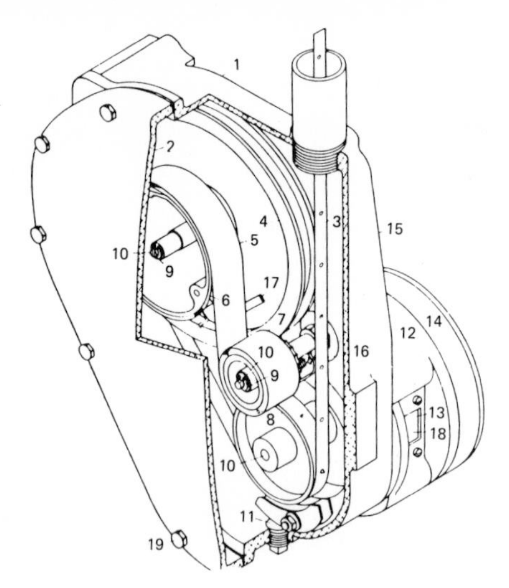

Figure 5.10 Spring torque motor compensated float-type transfer system. 1, Precision cast main housing. 2. Side cover. 3, Perforated steel tape type 316 stainless. 4, Moulded thermosetting phenolic tape drum. 5, Broad Neg'ator Motor, stainless steel. 6, Power drum. 7, Storage drum. 8, Precision made sprocket. 9, P.T.F.E. bearings, 10, Type 316 stainless steel shafts. 11, Drain plug, 12, Digital counter housing. 13, Reading window. 14, Stainless steel band covers adjustment slots. 15, Operation checker handle (out of view). 16, Operation checker internal assembly. 17, Neg'ator motor guide, stainless steel. 18, Counter assembly in the chamber beyond tank pressure and vapours. 19, Cap screws drilled for sealing. Courtesy, Whessoe Ltd.

distance d, is given by

$$C = \varepsilon \frac{A}{d}$$

The constant of proportionality ε is the dielectric constant of the material between the plates. An electrode is suspended in the container, electrically insulated from it. Presence of liquid or granular material around the electrode alters the capacitance between the electrode and the walls. The capacitance is sensed by electronic circuitry. Figure 5.11 is a cut-away view of one form.

The electrode is tailored to the situation; forms include rigid metal rods, flexible cables, and shielded tubes. Capacitance sensors rely on uniform contact being maintained between the contents and a long thin electrode. Where they are used for level sensing of granular materials, such as wheat, the material has a tendency to pile non-uniformly around the electrode, producing what is known as 'rat-holing'. Placing the electrode at an angle to the vertical helps reduce this as it alters the angle of repose of the material helping it to follow the stem more consistently. As the method provides continuous readout of level over its full electrode length, circuitry can also be used to provide multiple on-off setpoints for alarms and control functions. The same principle is used for single point sensing, in which case a simpler electrode and circuitry can be used. Electrical potential and power are usually low enough to eliminate hazards.

Weighing of the contents

The volume of a container's contents can of course be inferred from weight measurements; these are discussed in Chapter 8.

5.4.4 Upthrust buoyancy

A long vertical tubular float will exert an upward force proportional to the depth of immersion in the fluid. These are also sometimes referred to as 'displacers'. The float does not rise to follow the surface but is used instead to exert a force that is usually converted into a torque by a radius arm with a counteracting torque shaft. Force-balance can also be used to determine the upthrust force. Figure 5.12 is an assembly view of one design.

Upthrust depends upon the specific gravity of the fluid so instruments employing it must be calibrated for a stated density. Density varies with temperature. For the best accuracy correction is needed; some reduction in the actual error magnitude, however, occurs due to the float becoming a little larger in volume as its temperature increases.

5.4.5 Pressure sensing

Providing the contents behave as a liquid that flows to equalize pressures at a given depth (some granular materials may not fulfil this requirement) then pressure acting upon a given area at the bottom of a tank is proportional only to the density of the fluid and the head of pressure. In most cases density can be assumed to be uniform, thereby allowing a pressure sensor, placed on the bottom, to be used as a measure of tank level. Pressure gauges are described in Chapter 9.

Lying in the same class are purge methods. The pressure needed to discharge gas or liquid from a nozzle placed at the bottom of the tank depends upon the head of liquid above and its density. Bubblers, as these are called, are simple to arrange and give readout as a pressure-gauge reading that can be read directly or transduced into a more suitable form of signal.

Obviously bubblers do not work in granular materials. The addition of small quantities of liquid or gas must not significantly affect the contents of the tank.

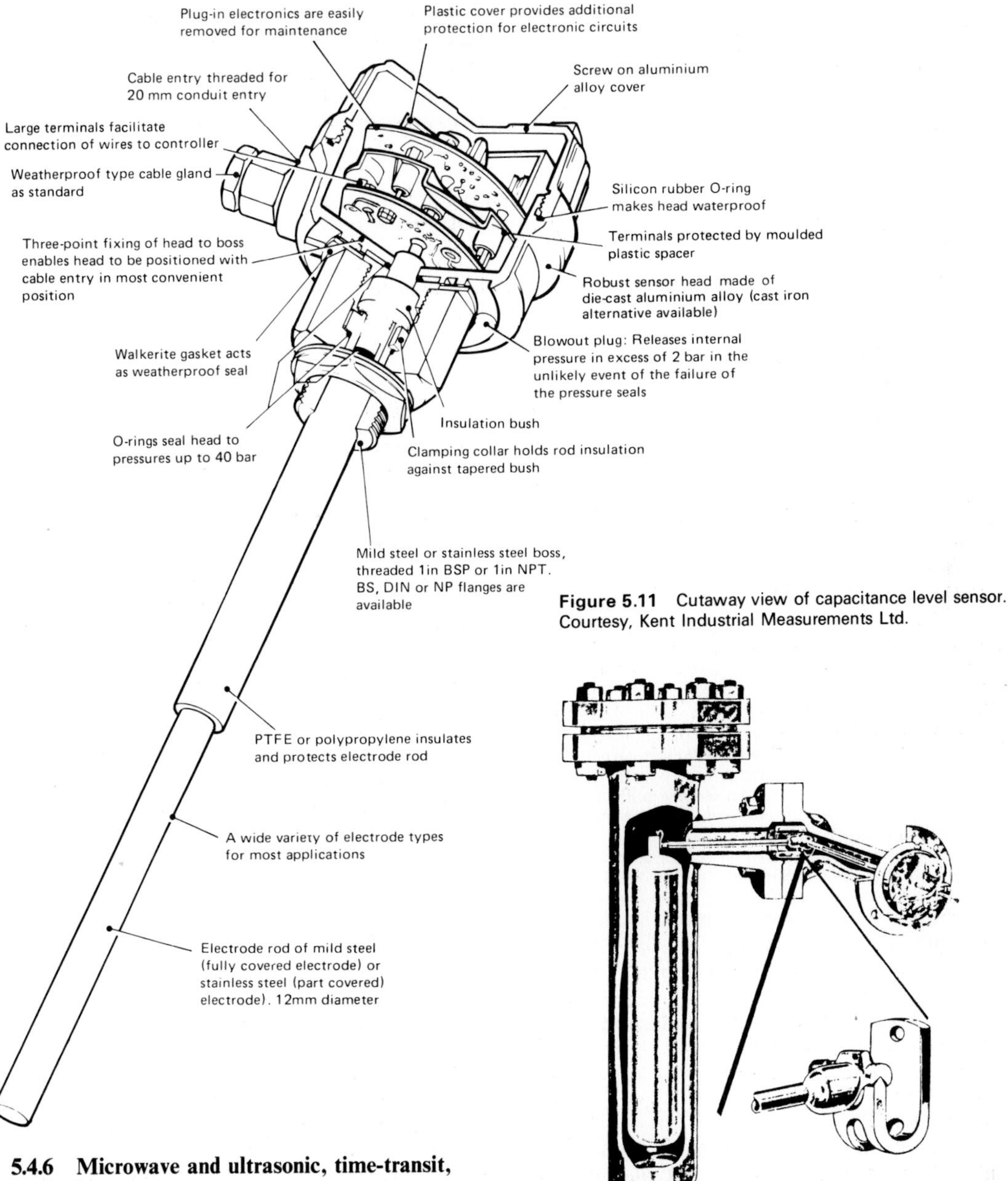

Figure 5.11 Cutaway view of capacitance level sensor. Courtesy, Kent Industrial Measurements Ltd.

Figure 5.12 Assembly view of Fisher torque tube unit. Courtesy, GEC Elliot Control Valves Ltd.

5.4.6 Microwave and ultrasonic, time-transit, methods

A source of coherent radiation, such as ultra-sound or microwaves, can be used to measure the distance from the surface to the top of the tank or the depth of the contents. In essence a pulse of radiation is transmitted down to the surface where some proportion is bounced back by the reflecting interface formed at the surface. The same concept can be used with the waves being sent upward through the material to be reflected downward from the surface. With relatively sophisticated electronic circuitry it is possible to measure the flight time and, given that the velocity of the waves is known, the distance may then be calculated.

Many variations exist upon this basic theme. The choice of radiation, use from above or from below and of frequency depend much upon the material and the accuracy sought.

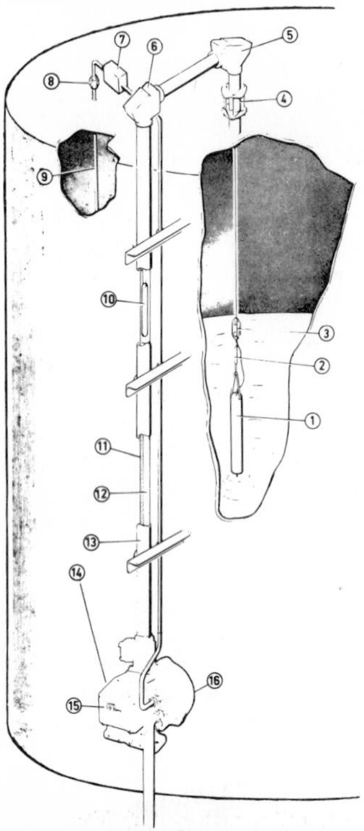

Figure 5.13 Schematic of self-balancing level gauge using RF surface sensing. Courtesy, GEC-Elliot Process Instruments Ltd. 1. Sensing element. 2. Tape insulator. 3. Tape counter-weight. 4. Flexible coupling used on fixed roof only. 5. Pulley box over tank. 6. Pulley box over tankside unit. 7. Temperature cable junction box. 8. Temperature bulb mounting kit. 9. Averaging resistance thermometer bulb. 10. Cable counter-weight. 11. Stainless steel perforated measuring tape. 12. Radio frequency cable. 13. 65 mm dia. standpipe. 14. Servo-electronic box. 15. Level indication. 16. Tape retrieval housing.

Although pulses are sent the repetition rate is fast enough for the output to appear continuous. The method can be made suitable for use in hazardous regions.

5.4.7 Force or position balance

In these methods a short-range sensor, such as a float resting in the surface or a surface sensor of electronic nature, is used to provide automatic control signals that take in, or let out, cable or wire so that the sensor is held at the same position relative to the surface. Figure 5.13 gives the arrangement of one such system that makes use of a radio-frequency surface sensor to detect the surface.

Self-balancing level sensors offer extreme ranges and variable forces exerted by changing mechanical linkage geometry are made negligible. Very high accuracies can be provided, the method being virtually an automated tape measure.

5.5 Methods providing short-range detection

In many applications there is only a need to sense the presence or absence of contents in order to operate on–off switches or alarms. In some continuous-reading systems a short proportional range is needed to control the driven measuring member. This section addresses short-range detectors of level.

5.5.1 Magnetic

Movement of a permanent magnet floating in the surface of the liquid can be sensed by using the magnet to operate a switch contact set. Figure 5.5 shows a system actuated by a rising radius arm and incorporating a toggle snap action. An alternative arrangement uses the rising magnet to close a magnetic reed switch contact, as shown in Figure 5.14, either as a coaxial arrangement, or as a proximity sensor.

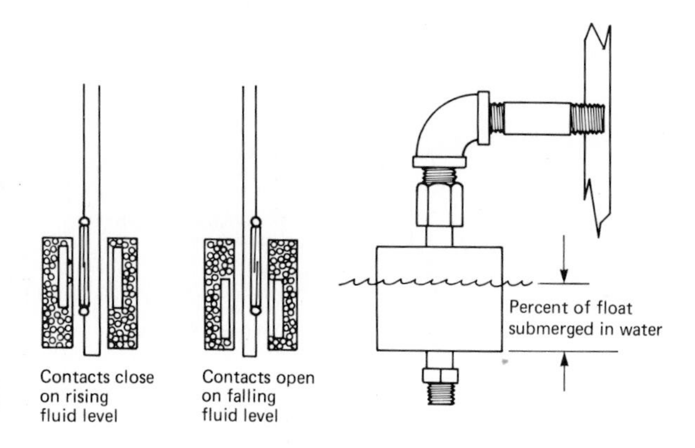

(a)

Float
Fluid
Magnet
Close
Open

(b)

Figure 5.14 Magnetic level switch using magnetic reed contact set. (a) Coaxial. (b) Proximity.

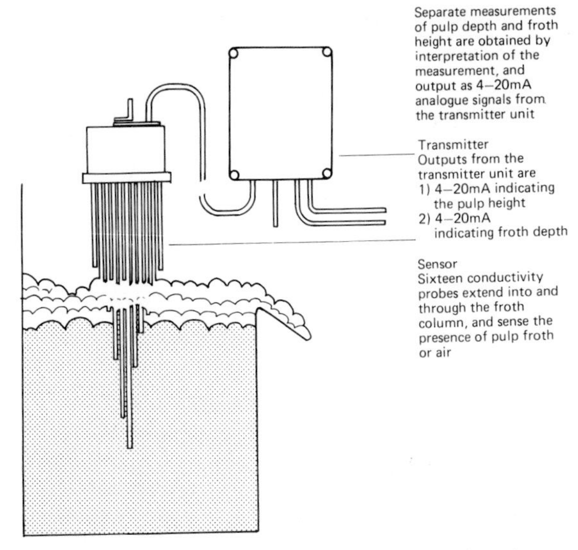

Figure 5.15 Multiple-conductivity probe sensing pulp and froth layers over set increments. Courtesy, Mineral Control Instrumentation.

5.5.2 Electrical conductivity

Liquids such as sewage, sea water and town supply water, which contain dissolved salts, have conductivities higher than pure water. The conductivity of most liquids is much higher than that of air so an electrical circuit, depending on current flow, can discriminate between air and liquid and so detect the interface. Figure 5.15 is a multiple-probe system used to distinguish the various layers in a pulp–froth–air system, as is found in mineral processing.

Conductivity probes are used for digital monitoring of the level of boiler water. Conductivity can also be used to provide continuous range measurement, for as the liquid rises up an electrode the resistivity between the electrode and a reference surface changes in a proportional manner.

5.5.3 Infrared

When fluid wets an optical surface the reflectance of that surface changes considerably enabling detection of liquid when it rises to cover the optical component.

The optical arrangement that is commonly used is a prism, arranged as shown in Figure 5.16. Infrared

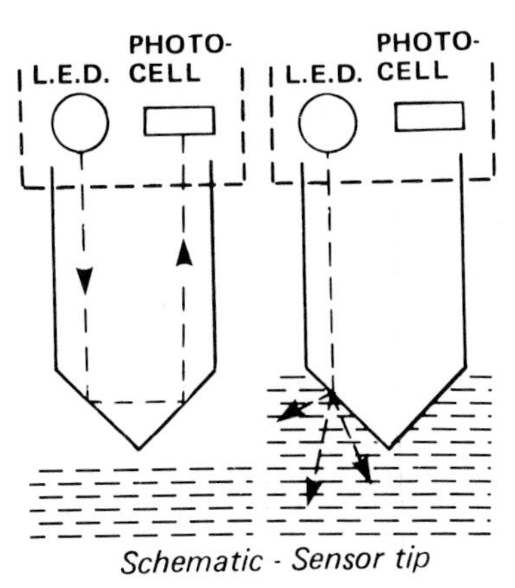

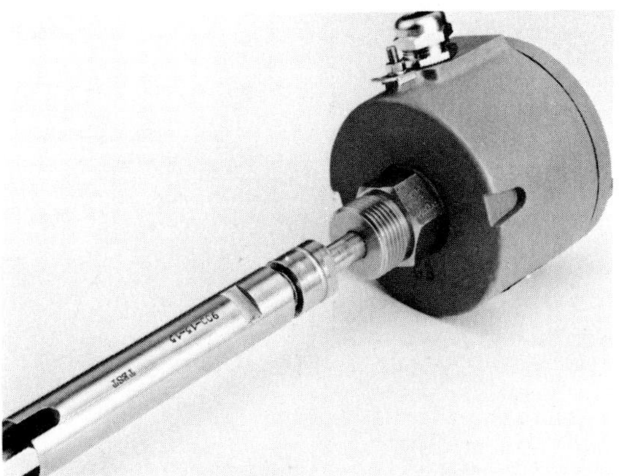

Figure 5.16 Infrared discrete-position level sensor. Principle and physical equipment. Courtesy, Kent Industrial Measurements Ltd.

radiation is used, this being easily produced with light-emitting diodes and readily detected. When the prism outer surface is wetted the majority of the radiation passes through the quartz-glass prism into the liquid, dropping the signal level given out by the photocell.

This method does not require the installation of electrical connections into the tank and, therefore, lends itself to use where intrinsically safe working is needed. Typical discrimination is around 1 mm.

5.5.4 Radio frequency

This form of surface sensor is used in the system shown in Figure 5.13. The tank gauge unit contains an RF (radio-frequency) oscillator tuned to around 160 MHz. Its signal, modulated at 50 Hz, is transmitted to the sensing probe located on the end of the cable line. The probe is a tuned antenna set to be resonant at the carrier frequency. When the tip is brought close to the liquid its resonant frequency is altered. Demodulation at the probe produces a 50 Hz signal that is fed back along the cable as a voltage level depending upon the relationship between oscillation frequency and the resonance of the antenna. This is compared with a reference voltage to produce an error signal that is used to drive the cable to place the probe at the present null position with respect to the surface.

5.5.5 Miscellaneous methods

The following are some of the other principles that have been used to sense the presence of a liquid. The turning moment exerted to rotate a turning paddle will vary when material begins to cover the paddle. The resonant frequency of a vibrating tuning fork will change as it becomes immersed. The electrical resistance of a heated thermistor will vary depending upon its surroundings.

5.6 References

Lazenby, B. 'Level monitoring and control', *Chemical Engineering*, **87**, 1, 88–96, (1980)

Miller, J. T. (ed.) *The Instrument Manual*, United Trade Press, (5th edn, 1975)

Norton, H. N. *Handbook of Transducers for Electronic Measuring Systems*, Prentice-Hall, Englewood Cliffs, New Jersey, (1969)

O'Higgins, P. J. *Basic Instrumentation—Industrial Measurement*, McGraw-Hill, New York, (1966)

6 Vibration

P. H. SYDENHAM

6.1 Introduction

6.1.1 Physical considerations

Vibration is the name given to measurands describing oscillatory motion. Several different measurable parameters may be of interest—relative position, velocity, acceleration, jerk (the derivative of acceleration) and dynamic force being those most generally desired.

For each parameter it may be the instantaneous value, the average value or some other descriptor that is needed. Accuracy of the order of 1 part in 100 is generally all that is called for.

Vibration, in the general sense, occurs as periodic oscillation, as random motion or as transient motion, the latter more normally being referred to as shock when the transient is large in amplitude and brief in duration.

Vibration can occur in linear or rotational forms of motion, the two being termed respectively translational or torsional vibrations. In many ways the basic understanding of each is similar because a rotational system also concerns displacements. Translational forms are outlined in the following description; there will usually exist an equivalent rotational system for all arrangements described.

In vibration measurement it is important to decide whether or not a physically attached mechanical sensor can be used, corresponding to a contacting or non-contacting technique.

Adequate measurement of vibration measurands can be a most complex problem. The requirement is to determine features of motion of a point, or an extended object, in space relative to a reference framework, see Figure 6.1.

A point in space has three degrees of freedom. It can translate in one or more of three directions when referred to the cartesian coordinate system. Rotation of a point has no meaning in this case. Thus to monitor free motion of a point object requires three measurement sensing channels.

If the object of interest has significant physical size it must be treated as an extended object in which the rotations about each of the three axes, described above, provide a further three degrees of freedom. Thus to monitor the free motion of a realistic object may need up to six sensors, one for each degree of freedom.

In practice some degrees of freedom may be nominally constrained (but are they really?) possibly eliminating the need for some of the six sensors. Practical installation should always contain a test that evaluates the degree of actual constraint because sensors will often produce some level of output for the directions of vibration they are not primarily measuring. This is called their cross-axis coupling factor, transverse response or some such terminology.

In many installations the resultant of the motion vector may lie in a constant fixed direction with time. In such cases, in principle, only one sensor will be required provided it can be mounted to sense in that direction. If not, as is often the case, more than one unit will be required, the collective signals then being combined to produce the single resultant.

The potential frequency spectrum of vibration parameters extends, as shown in Figure 6.2, from very slow motions through frequencies experienced in machine tools and similar mechanical structures to the supersonic megahertz frequencies of ultra-sound. It is not possible to cover this range with general-purpose sensors. Each application will need careful

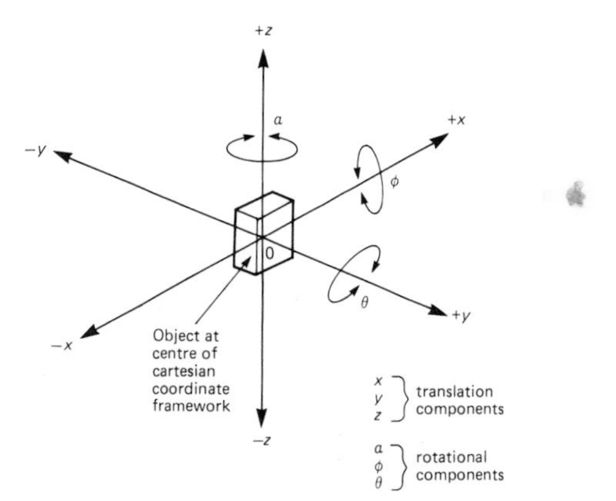

Figure 6.1 Possible motions of an extended object in space relative to a cartesian framework.

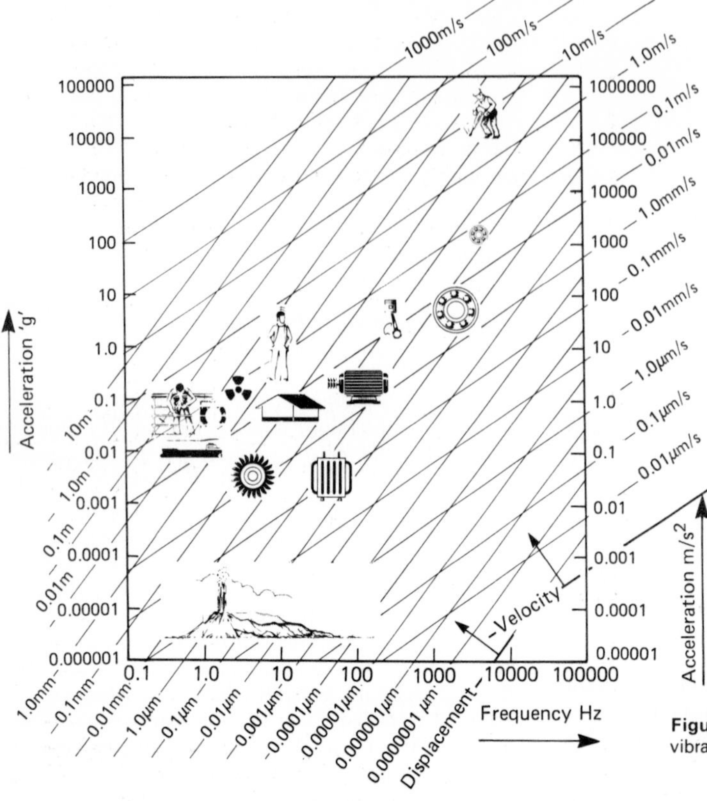

Figure 6.2 Frequency spectrum and magnitude of vibration parameters. Courtesy, Brüel & Kjaer.

consideration of its many parameters to decide which kind of sensor should be applied in order to make the best measurement.

A complicating factor in vibration measurement can be the distributed nature of mechanical systems. This leads to complex patterns of vibration, demanding care in the positioning of sensors.

Mechanical systems, including human forms, given as an example in Figure 6.3, comprise mass, spring compliance (or stiffness) and damping components. In the simplest case, where only one degree of freedom exists, linear behaviour of this combination can be well described using linear mathematical theory to model the time behaviour as the result of force excitation or some initial position displacement.

Vibration can be measured by direct comparison of instantaneous dimensional parameters relative to some adequately fixed datum point in space. The fixed point can be on an 'independent' measurement framework (fixed reference method) or can be a part that remains stationary because of its high inertia (seismic system).

In general a second-order linear system output response q_o is related to an input function q_i by the

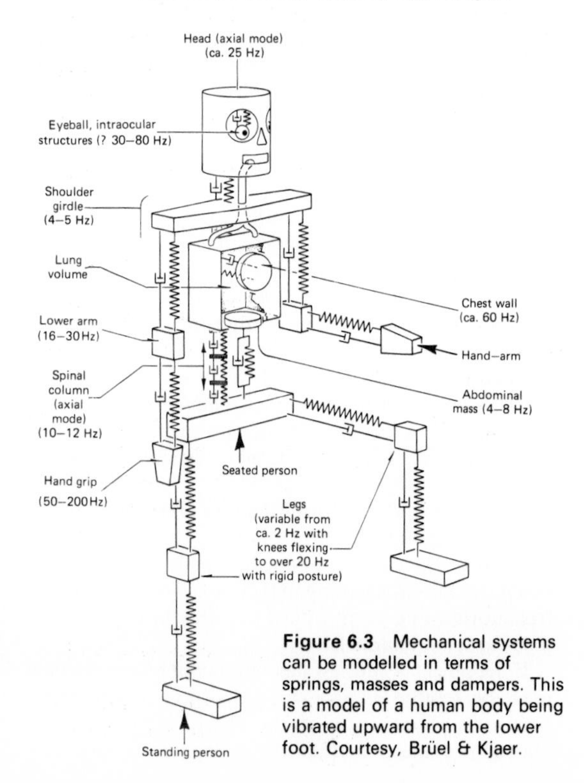

Figure 6.3 Mechanical systems can be modelled in terms of springs, masses and dampers. This is a model of a human body being vibrated upward from the lower foot. Courtesy, Brüel & Kjaer.

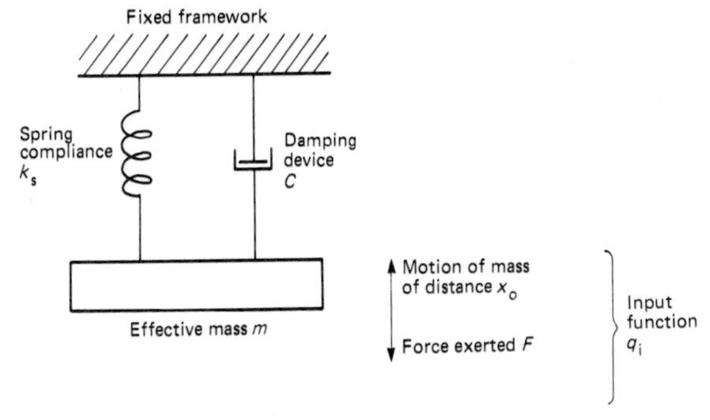

Figure 6.4 One-degree-of-freedom spring, mass and damper system model.

differential equation

$$\frac{a_2\,d^2q_o}{dt^2}+\frac{a_1\,dq_o}{dt}+a_0q_o=q_i$$

(spring–mass–damper system) (input driving function)

For the specific mechanical system of interest here, given in Figure 6.4, this becomes

$$\frac{m\,d^2x_0}{dt^2}+\frac{c\,dx_0}{dt}-k_sx_0=q_i$$

where m is the effective mass (which may need to include part of the mass of the spring element or be composed entirely of it), c is the viscous damping factor and k_s the spring compliance (expressed here as length change per unit of force applied).

Where the damping effect is negligible, the system will have a frequency at which it will naturally vibrate if excited by a pulse input. This natural frequency ω_n is given by

$$\omega_n=\sqrt{\frac{k_s}{m}}$$

Presence of damping will alter this value, but as the damping rises the system is less able to provide continuous oscillation.

The static sensitivity is given by the spring constant, either as k_s the spring compliance or as its reciprocal, that is, expressed as force per unit extension.

The influence of damping is easily described by a dimensionless number, called the damping ratio, which is given by

$$\xi=\frac{c}{2\sqrt{k_s\cdot m}}$$

It is usually quoted in a form that relates its magnitude with respect to that at $\xi=1$.

These three important parameters are features of the spring–mass–damper system and are independent of the input driving function.

Such systems have been extensively analysed when excited by the commonly met input forcing functions (step, impulse, ramp, sinusoid). A more general theory for handling any input function other than these is also available. In practice the step, impulse, and continuous sinusoidal responses are used in analyses, as they are reasonably easy to apply in theory and in practical use.

As the damping factor ξ increases the response to a transient step force input (applied to the mass) can vary from sinusoidal oscillation at one extreme (underdamped) to a very sluggish climb to the final value (overdamped). These responses are plotted in Figure 6.5. In the case of continuous sinusoidal force input the system frequency response varies as shown in Figure 6.6. Note the resonance build-up at ω_n which is limited by the degree of damping existing. Thus the damping of the system to be measured or of the sensor, if it is of the seismic kind, can be of importance as a modifier of likely system responses. As damping increases the system response takes on the form of the lower first-

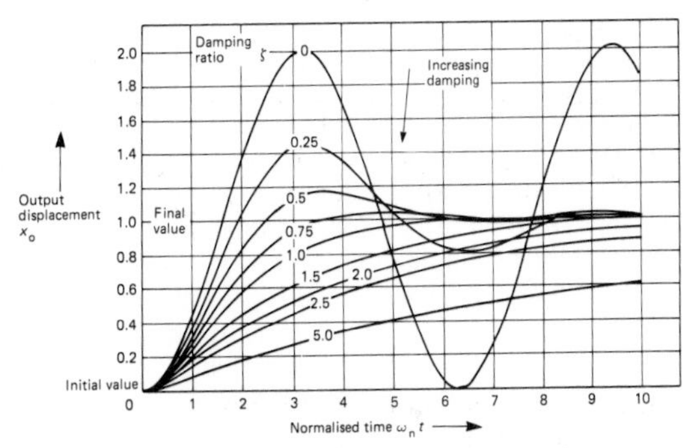

Figure 6.5 Displacement responses of second-order system to input step of force.

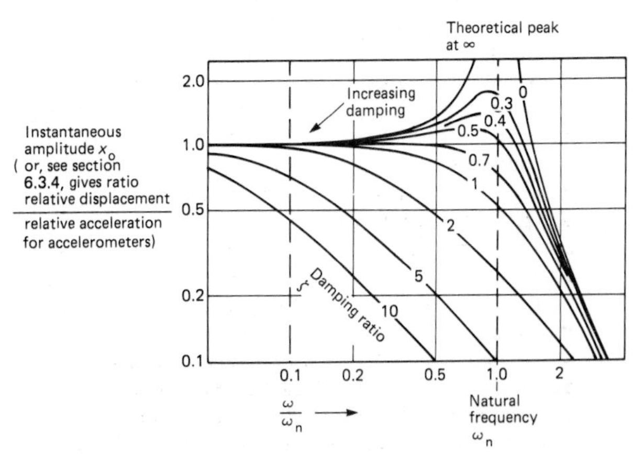

Figure 6.6 Displacement responses of second-order system to continuous sinusoidal force input. The same curves relative displacements of a seismic mass to the acceleration of the mass. See section 6.3.4.

order, exponential response, system and it cannot oscillate.

Useful introductions to this aspect of vibrations are to be found in Oliver (1971), the dynamic behaviour of systems being expounded in more depth in Crandall (1959), Harris and Crede (1961), Sydenham (1983), Trampe-Broch (1980), and Wallace (1970).

The above discussion, given with respect to vibration of the measurand, is also the basis of understanding the operation of seismic vibration sensors, as will be seen later.

It is a property of second-order systems, therefore, to have a natural frequency of vibration. This is the frequency at which they vibrate when given impulse energy that is not overridden by continuous forced vibrations. Thus a sensing system that is second-order and not damped will (due to noise energy inputs) produce outputs at its natural frequency that are not correlated with frequencies occurring in the system of interest. Use of seismic vibration sensors must, therefore, recognize these limitations.

In practice it is also often more convenient to sense a measurand by an indirect means and obtain the desired unit by mathematical processing. For example, accelerometers are conveniently used to obtain forces (from force = mass × acceleration) and hence stresses and strains. Acceleration signals can be twice integrated with respect to time to yield displacement. Sensors that operate as velocity transducers can yield displacement by single integration.

Integration is generally preferred to differentiation as the former averages random noise to a smaller value compared to the signal whereas the latter, in reverse, can deteriorate the signal-to-noise ratio. Mathematical signal manipulation is common practice in vibration measurement as a means to derive other related variables.

6.1.2 Practical problems of installation

With vibration measurement it is all too easy to produce incorrect data. This section addresses several important installation conditions that should be carefully studied for each new application.

6.1.2.1 Cross-coupling

Transducers may exhibit cross-axis coupling. Wise practice, where possible, includes a test that vibrates the sensor in a direction perpendicular to the direction of normal use. Rotational sensitivity may also be important. These tests can be avoided each time they are used if the sensors are precalibrated for this source of error and, of course, are still within calibration. Sensors that have no such parameter quoted should be regarded as potential sources of error until proven otherwise.

6.1.2.2 Coupling compliance

The compliance of the bond made between the sensor and the surface it is mounted on must be adequately stiff. If not, the surface and the sensor form a system that can vibrate in unpredictable ways. As an example an insufficiently stiff mounting can give results that produce much lower frequency components than truly exist. In extreme cases the sensor can be shaken free as it builds up the unexpectedly low resonance frequency of the joint to dangerous amplitude levels. As a guide the joint should be at least ten times stiffer than the sensor so that the resonant frequency of the joint is well above that of the sensor.

6.1.2.3 Cables and pre-amplifiers

Certain types of sensor, notably the piezo-electric kind, are sensitive to spurious variation in capacitance and charge. Sources of such charges are the tribo-electric effect of vibrating cables (special kinds are used, the design of which allows for movement of the cable), varying relative humidity that alters electric field leakage (this becomes important when designing long-term installations) and pre-amplifier input condition variations.

6.1.2.4 Influence errors

Ideally the sensor should operate in a perfect environment wherein sources of external error, called influence parameters, do not occur. In vibration sensing possible influence error sources include temperature variation of the sensor, possible magnetic field fluctuations (especially at radio frequency) and existing background acoustic noise vibrations. Each of these might induce erroneous signal.

A good test for influence parameters is to fully connect the system, observing the output when the measurand of interest is known to be at zero level. Where practical the important error inputs can be systematically varied to see the sensor response. Many a vibration measurement has finally been seen to be worthless because some form of influence error turned out to be larger than the true signal from the measurand. Vibrations apparently occurring at electric mains frequency (50 or 60 Hz) and harmonics thereof are most suspect. Measurement of mechanical vibration at these frequencies is particularly difficult because of the need to separate true signal from influence error noise.

6.1.2.5 Subject loading by the sensor

Vibration sensors contain mass. As this mass is made smaller the sensitivity usually falls. Addition of mass to a vibrating system can load the mass of that system, causing shifts in frequency. For this reason manu-

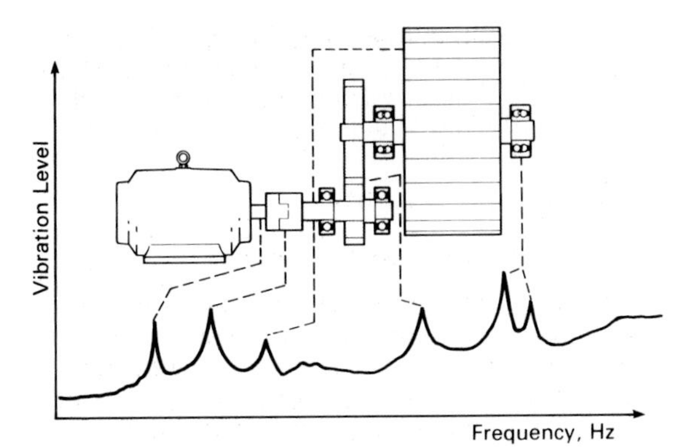

Figure 6.7 In machine health monitoring the normal vibration levels of parts of the installation are recorded to provide a normal signature. Variations of this indicate changes in mechanical conditioning. Courtesy, Brüel & Kjaer.

facturers offer a wide range of attached type sensors. Provided the mass added is, say, 5 per cent or less of the mass of interest, then the results will be reasonable. Cables can also reduce mechanical compliance, reducing the system amplitude. Where a system is particularly sensitive to loading, the use of non-contact, fixed-reference, methods may be the only way to make a satisfactory measurement.

6.1.2.6 Time to reach equilibrium

When damping of a structure is small, the time taken for a resonance to build up to its peak value is large. When using forced vibration to seek such a resonance, it is therefore important not to sweep the excitation input frequency too rapidly.

6.1.3 Areas of application

When searching for information about a measurement technique it is usually helpful to have an appreciation of the allied fields which use the same equipment. Vibration, of course, will be of interest in very many applications but a small number can be singled out as the main areas to which commercial marketing forces have been directed.

6.1.3.1 Machine health monitoring

A significant field of interest is that of machine health, or condition, monitoring; failures can often be avoided by 'listening' to the sounds and vibrations made by the system. An example is shown in Figure 6.7. Vibration and other forms of sensor are applied to the operating system, first whilst running in early life, and then at periodic intervals during life. If the frequency/amplitude data (the so-called signature) has changed then this can provide diagnostic information suggesting which component is beginning to fail. It can then be conveniently replaced before a major, untimely, breakdown occurs. Introduction to this aspect is to be found in Bently Nevada (1982) and Wells (1981).

6.2 Amplitude calibration

Static amplitude (displacement) is easily calibrated using a standardized micrometer, displacement sensor or optical interferometry. Dynamic calibrations may be made either by comparison, using a technique of known accuracy and frequency response or by using a calibrated vibration generator.

6.2.1 Accelerometer calibration

Figure 6.8 shows outlines of three methods for the calibration of accelerometers and other vibration-

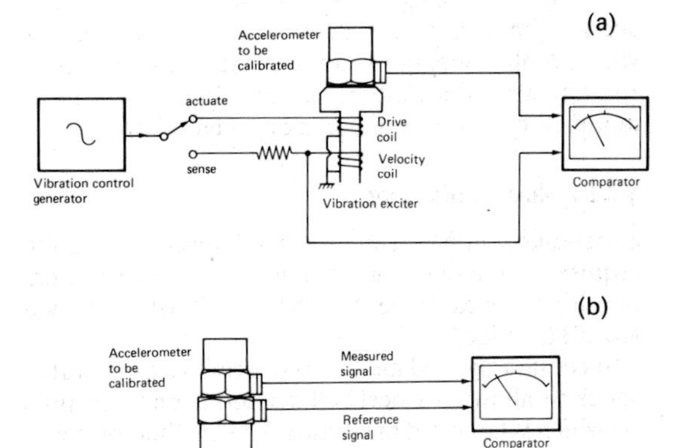

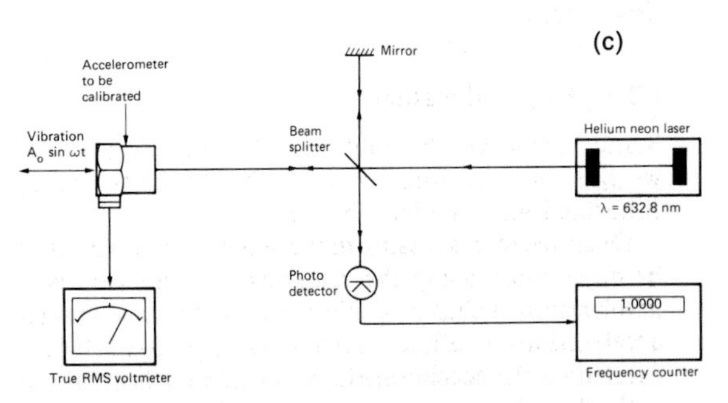

Figure 6.8 Two alternatives for calibrating accelerometers. (a) Calibrated vibration exciter shaking accelerometer at calibrated levels—the reciprocity method. (b) Back-to-back, calibration of a calibrated accelerometer against one to be calibrated—comparison method. (c) Absolute measurement using optical interferometry.

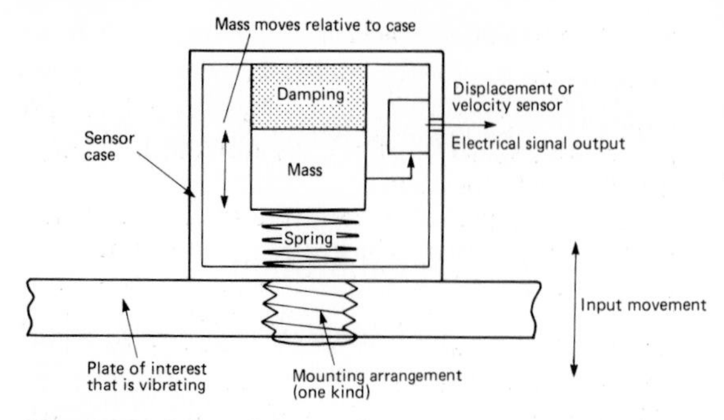

Figure 6.9 Schematic layout of open-loop, seismic-form, vibration sensor.

measuring sensors. Calibration is normally performed at 500 rad s^{-1}.

Other methods that can be used are to subject the accelerometer to accelerations produced by the earth's force. Simple pseudo-static rotation of an accelerometer in the vertical plane will produce accelerations in the 0 to ± 1 g range (g is used here for the earth's acceleration). Larger values can be obtained by whirling the accelerometer on the extremity of a rotating arm of a calibrating centrifuge, or it can be mounted on the end of a hanging pendulum.

6.2.2 Shock calibration

Short-duration acceleration, as produced by impact, requires different approaches to calibration. Accelerations can exceed 10 000 g and last for only a few milliseconds.

A commonly used method is to produce a calibrated shock by allowing a steel ball to free-fall on to an anvil on which is mounted the sensor. This method provides an absolute calibration but, as with all of the above described methods, has uncertainties associated with the practical method. In this case one source of error is caused by the difficulty of releasing a ball to begin its downward path without imparting some velocity at time zero.

6.2.3 Force calibration

Static forces can be calibrated by applying 'dead-weights' to the force sensor, the 'weights' being calibrated masses. (See Chapter 7.)

Dynamic forces arising in vibration can more easily be determined using the relationship force = mass × acceleration. A shaking table is used to produce known accelerations on a known mass. In this way the forces exerted on the accelerometer can be determined along with the corresponding output voltage or current needed to produce transducer sensitivity constants.

Space does not permit greater explanation but there are several detailed accounts of vibration sensor calibration available in the literature—Endevco (1980), Harris and Crede (1961), Herceg (1972), Norton (1969), Oliver (1971) and Trampe-Broch (1980). National and international standards are extensively listed in Brüel and Kjaer (1981).

6.3 Sensor practice

6.3.1 Mass–spring seismic sensors

Whereas the fixed reference methods do have some relevance in the practical measurement of vibration the need for a convenient datum is very often not able to be met. In the majority of vibration measurements use is made of the mass–spring, seismic, sensor system.

Given the correct spring–mass–damping combination a seismic system attached to a vibrating surface can yield displacement, velocity or acceleration data. Unfortunately the conflicting needs of the three do not enable one single design to be used for all three cases. However, it is often possible to derive one variable from another by mathematical operations on the data.

Two forms of seismic sensor exist. The first, called open-loop, makes use of the unmodified response of the mass moving relative to the case to operate either a displacement or a velocity sensing transducer. The second form closes the loop (and is, therefore, referred to as a closed-loop or servo seismic sensor) using the output signal to produce an internal force that retains the mass in the same relative position with respect to the case, the magnitude of the force being a measure of the vibration parameter.

6.3.1.1 Open-loop sensors

The fundamental arrangement of the open-loop seismic sensor form is as given in Figure 6.9. Actual construction can vary widely depending upon how the spring force and damping are provided and upon the form of the sensor used.

The spring element can be produced as a distinct mechanical element, Figure 6.10 is an example made

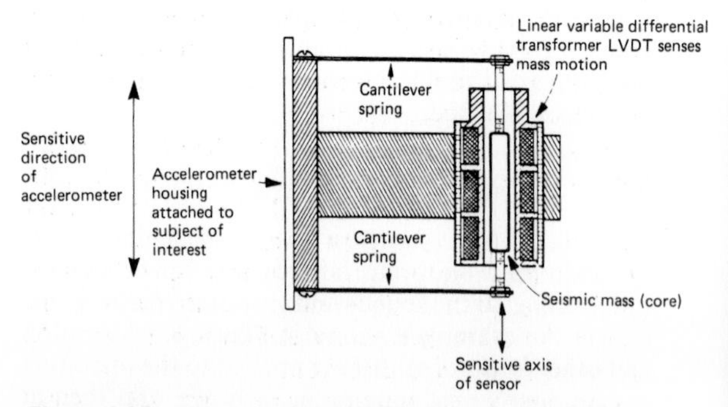

Figure 6.10 Diagrammatic view of a spring–mass seismic sensor that uses parallel flexure-strip spring suspension and inductive sensor of mass displacement. Courtesy, Schaevitz Engineering.

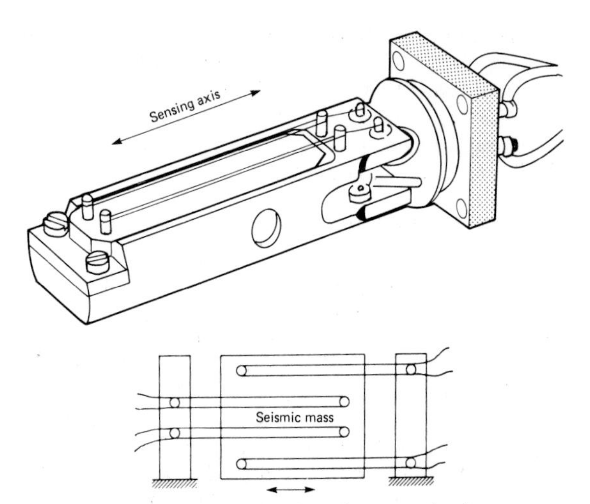

Figure 6.11 Displacement sensing of mass motion in accelerometers can be achieved by many methods. This unit uses unbonded strain gauges. Courtesy, Statham Instruments Inc.

with flexure strips; alternatively perforated membranes, helical coils, torsional strips and the like can be used. Otherwise, the compliance of the mass itself may be the spring, for example in the piezo-electric crystal which also acts as the sensing element.

Important design parameters of a spring are the compliance, amplitude range, fatigue life, constancy of rate with time, temperature and other influence effects and the suitability to be packaged to produce a suitable sensor unit. Except for the highest natural frequency sensors the masses used can be regarded as completely rigid compared with the spring element.

Rotary forms of the linear arrangement, shown in Figure 6.9, are also available.

Sensing methods that have been used include electrical-resistance sliding potentiometer, variable inductance (see for instance Figure 6.10), variable reluctance, variable capacitance, electrical metallic strain gauges (bonded and unbonded as in Figure 6.11) and semiconductor strain gauges, piezo-electric crystal and magnetostrictive elements, position-sensitive optical detectors and electromagneto principles (that provide direct velocity sensing).

Sensors are often encapsulated. The encapsulation takes many forms ranging from miniature units of total weight around 1 g through to 0.5 kg units where the sensing mass must be physically large. As simultaneous measurements in two or three directions are often required, seismic sensors are also made that consist of two or three units, as shown in Figure 6.12, mounted in different directions.

Compensation for temperature is needed in many designs. This is either performed in the electronic circuitry or by incorporating some form of thermo-mechanical device into the spring–mass–sensor layout.

6.3.1.2 Servo accelerometers

The performance of open-loop seismic sensors can be improved with respect to their sensitivity, accuracy and output signal amplitude by forming the design into a closed-loop form.

Figure 6.13 gives the schematic diagram of one kind of closed-loop system which is based upon a moving-coil actuator and capacitance displacement sensor. The mass upon which the acceleration is to be exerted is able to rotate on the end of a freely supported arm. This is attached to the electrical coil placed in the permanent magnetic field supplied by the magnet assembly. Acceleration applied to the mass attempts to rotate the arm causing displacement. This unbalances the capacitive displacement sensor monitoring the relative position of the mass. Displacement signals

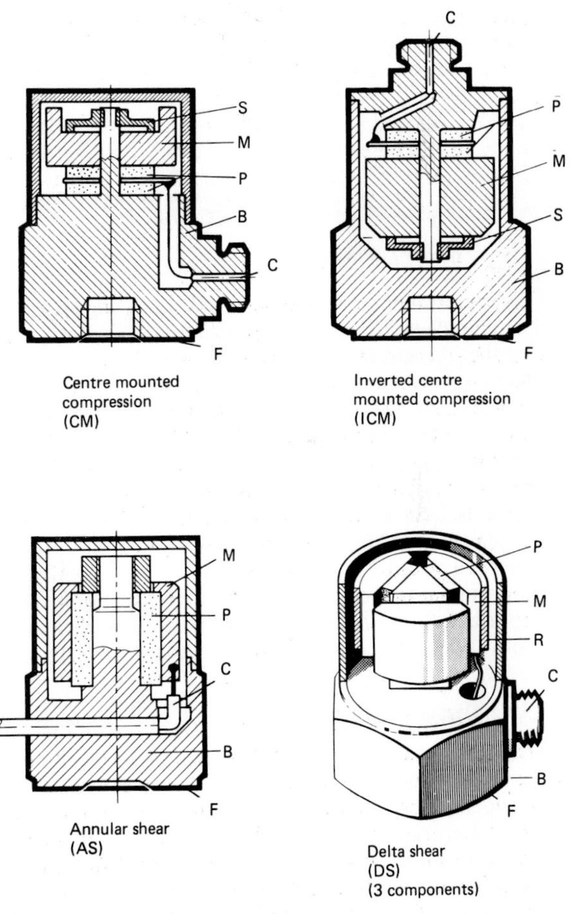

Figure 6.12 Examples of single- and three-axis accelerometers based on the piezo-electric sensor. Courtesy, Brüel & Kjaer.

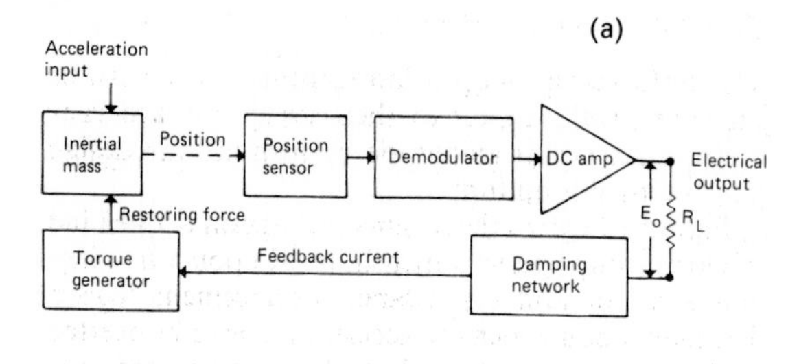

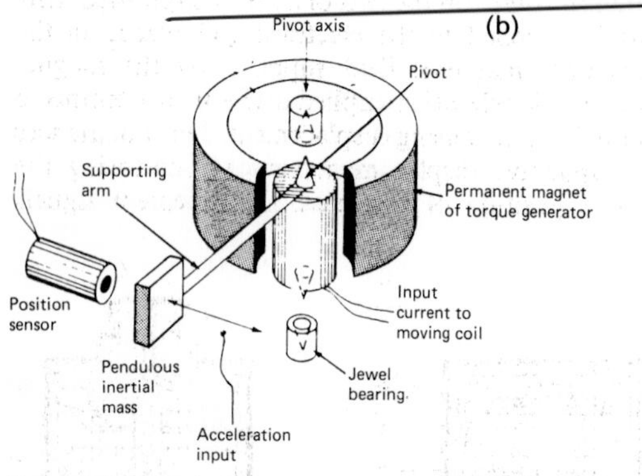

Figure 6.13 Basic component layout of one form of closed-loop accelerometer. Courtesy, Schaevitz Engineering.

produce an input to the difference-sensing amplifier. The amplifier drives a corresponding electric current into the coil causing the arm to rotate back to the null displacement position. Provided the loop response is rapid enough the mass will be retained in a nearly constant place relative to the displacement sensor. Acceleration variations are, thereby, converted to variations in coil current. In this way the displacement sensor is used in the, preferred, null-balance mode wherein error of linearity and temperature shift are largely avoided. Only the more easily achieved proportionality between coil current and force is important. Servo instruments are further described in Jones (1982), Herceg (1972) and Norton (1969).

6.3.2 Displacement measurement

Where a fixed reference method is applicable it is possible to employ any suitable displacement sensor. Spurious phase shift in the system may be a concern but in some applications phase is unimportant. The reader is directed to Chapter 3 for an introduction to displacement devices.

It is sometimes more convenient to integrate the signal from a velocity transducer mounted to make use of a fixed reference.

Where a fixed reference method is inconvenient one of several forms of seismic sensor system can be employed as follows.

The second-order equations of motion, given in Section 6.1.1 for a mass moving relative to a fixed reference frame (the mode for studying the movement of vibrating objects), can be reworked to provide response curves relating the displacement amplitude of the seismic mass to the amplitude of its case. This is the seismic sensor output. Figure 6.14 is the family of response curves showing the effects of operating frequency and degree of damping. Given that the case is moving in sympathy with the surface of interest it can be seen, from the curves, that for input vibration frequencies well above the natural frequency of the seismic sensor the measured output displacements will be a true indication (within a percent or so) of the movements of the surface. This form of seismic displacement sensor is also often called a vibrometer. It is possible to lower the frequency of operation by using a damping factor with a nominal value of 0.5. This, however, does introduce more rapidly changing phase shift error with frequency which may be important. The lowest frequency of use above which the response remains virtually flat is seen to be where the various damping factor curves approach the horizontal line equal to unity ratio, to within the allowable signal tolerance.

Given that the chosen damping remains constant and that a system does follow the second-order response it is also possible to provide electronic frequency compensation that can further lower the useful frequency of operation by a small amount.

Thus to directly measure displacement amplitudes with a seismic sensor it must have a natural frequency set to be below the lowest frequency of interest in the subject's vibration spectrum. In this mode the seismic

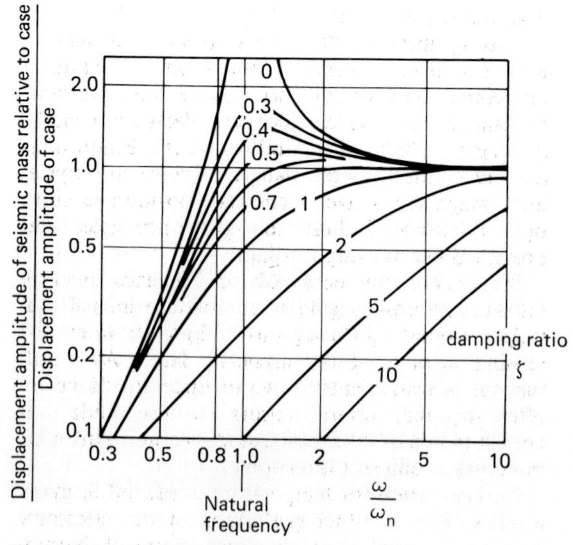

Figure 6.14 Responses relevant to displacement and velocity sensing with seismic sensors.

mass virtually remains stationary in space acting as a fixed reference point. It is also clear that the seismic sensor cannot measure very low frequencies for it is not possible to construct an economical system having a low enough resonant frequency.

The curves are theoretical perfections and would apparently indicate that the seismic sensor, in this case, will have flat response out to infinite frequency. This is not the case in practice for as the frequency of vibration rises the seismic sensor structure begins to resonate at other frequencies caused by such mechanisms as the spring vibrating in modes other than the fundamental of the system.

Given that the low frequency range of accelerometers can extend down to less than 1 Hz (see Section 6.3.4) it may often be more practical to twice integrate an accelerometer signal, in order to derive displacement amplitude, rather than to make use of a direct-reading displacement design of seismic sensor.

6.3.3 Velocity measurement

The prime method used to generate a direct velocity signal makes use of the law of electromagnetic induction. This gives the electrical voltage e generated as N turns of an electric coil cut magnetic flux ϕ over time t as

$$e = -N\frac{d\phi}{dt}$$

Velocity sensors are self-generating, producing a voltage output that is proportional to the velocity at which a set of turns moves through a constant and uniform magnetic field.

Many forms of this kind of sensor exist. The commonly used, moving-coil, arrangement comprises a cylindrical coil vibrating inside a magnetic field that is produced by a permanent electromagnet. A commonly seen arrangement, Figure 6.15(a), is that typified by the reversible-role moving-coil, loud-speaker movement. For this form the output voltage V_{out} is given by

$$V_{out} = -Blv \,.\, 10^{-9}$$

where B is the flux density in tesla, l the effective length of conductor contributing in total flux-cutting and v the instantaneous velocity, expressed in m s^{-1}, of the coil relative to the magnet. Given that the design ensures that the field is uniform in the path of the fixed conductor length the sensor can provide very linear output.

The sensors were adopted in early seismology studies because of their inherently high output at relatively low velocities. The coil impedance will generally be low, enabling signals with good signal-to-noise ratios to be generated along with reduction of error caused by variations in lead length and type. They are, however, large with resultant mass and rigidity problems. They tend to have relatively low resonant frequencies (tens of hertz), which restricts use to the lower frequencies. Output tends to be small at the higher frequencies. It will be apparent that these sensors cannot produce signals at zero velocity because no relative movement occurs to generate flux-cutting.

A second variation of the self-generating velocity

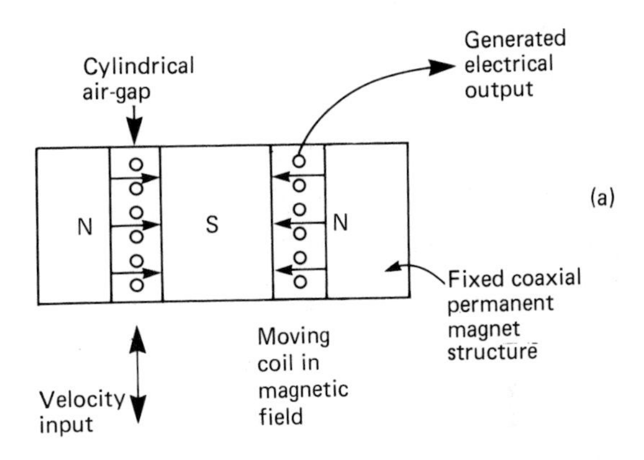

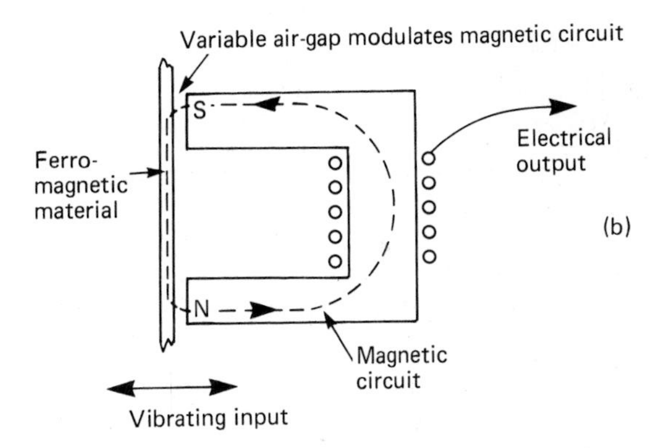

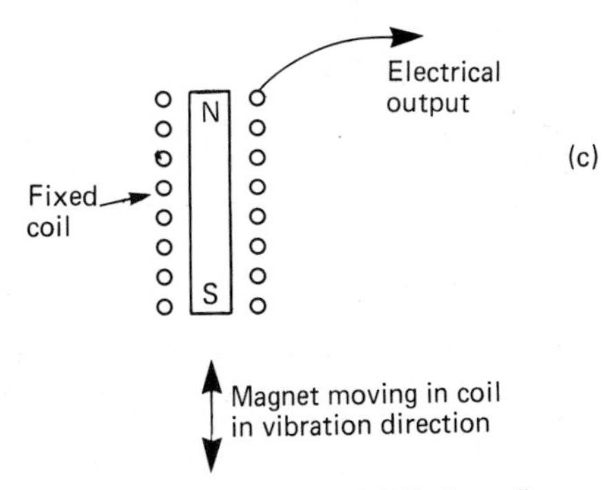

Figure 6.15 Forms of velocity sensor. (a) Moving coil. (b) Variable reluctance. (c) Moving permanent magnet.

sensor, the variable-reluctance method, uses a series magnetic circuit containing a permanent magnet to provide permanent magnetic bias. A part of this circuit, the armature, is made so that the effective air-gap is varied by the motion to be monitored. Around the magnetic circuit is placed a pick-up coil. As the armature moves the resulting flux variation cuts the coil generating a signal that can be tailored by appropriate design to be linear with vibration amplitude. This form of design has the advantage that the armature can readily be made as part of the structure to be monitored, as shown in Figure 6.15(b). This version is not particularly sensitive, for the air-gap must be at least as large as the vibration amplitude. As an example a unit of around 12 mm diameter, when used with a high magnetic permeability moving disc set at 2 mm distance, will produce an output of around 150 mV/m s^{-1}.

A third method uses a permanent magnet as the mass supported on springs. One example is shown in Figure 6.15(c). Vibration causes the magnet to move relatively to the fixed coil thereby generating a velocity signal. This form can produce high outputs, one make having a sensitivity of around 5 V/m s^{-1}.

Where a fixed reference cannot be used this form of sensor, instead of a displacement sensor, can be built into the seismic sensor arrangement. In such cases the vibrating seismic sensor will then directly produce velocity signals. These will follow the general responses given in Figure 6.14. From those curves it can be seen that there is a reasonably flat response above the natural frequency which is inherently quite low.

6.3.4 Acceleration measurement

The fixed-reference method of measuring acceleration is rarely used, most determinations being made with the seismic form of sensor. For the seismic sensor system the mass and the spring compliance are fixed. Consideration of the $F=m.a$ law and spring compliance shows that displacement of the mass relative to the sensor case is proportional to the acceleration of the case. This means that the curves, plotted in Figure 6.6 (for sinusoidal input of force to a second-order system), are also applicable as output response curves of accelerometers using displacement sensing. In this use the vertical axis is interpreted as the relative displacement of the mass from the case for a given acceleration of the case.

The curves show that a seismic sensor will provide a constant sensitivity output representing sensor acceleration from very low frequencies to near the natural frequency of the spring–mass arrangement used. Again the damping ratio can be optimized at around 0.5–0.6 and electronic compensation added (if needed) to raise the upper limit a little further than the resonance point.

At first sight it might, therefore, appear that a single, general-purpose design could be made having a very high resonant frequency. This, however, is not the case for the deflection of the spring (which is a major factor deciding the system output sensitivity) is proportional to $1/\omega_n^2$. In practice this means that as the upper useful frequency limit is extended the sensor sensitivity falls off. Electronic amplification allows low signal output to be used but with additional cost to the total measuring system.

At the low-frequency end of the accelerometer response the transducers become ineffective because the accelerations produce too small a displacement to be observed against the background noise level.

6.3.4.1 Typical sensors

As a guide to the ranges of capability available, one major manufacturer's catalogue offers accelerometers with sensitivities ranging from a small 30 $\mu V/ms^{-2}$ through to 1 V/ms^{-2} with corresponding sensor weights of 3 g and 500 g and useful frequency ranges of 1–60 000 Hz and 0.2–1000 Hz. Sensors have been constructed for even higher frequencies but these must be regarded as special designs. A selection are shown in Figure 6.16.

The many constraints placed upon the various performance parameters of a particular seismic sensor can be shown on a single chart such as Figure 6.17, Harris and Crede (1961).

As the accelerometer spring is often required to be stiff compared with that of the seismic displacement sensor it will not always need to make use of coiling, a device for decreasing the inherent spring constant of a material. Accelerometer springs may occur as stamped rigid plates, as flat cusped spring washers, or as a sufficiently compliant clamping bolt. In the case of piezo-sensitive material use is often made of the compliance of the material.

Figure 6.16 A range of accelerometers is required to cover the full needs of vibration measurement. Courtesy, Inspek Supplies, New South Wales.

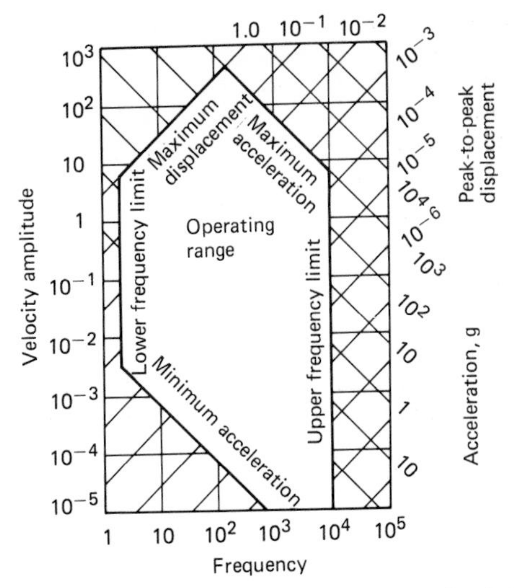

Figure 6.17 Useful linear operating range of an individual, seismic vibration sensor can be characterized with this form of chart. Courtesy, McGraw-Hill.

6.3.4.2 Response to complex waveforms

The response curves given relate to seismic sensors excited by sinusoidal signals. To predict the behaviour of a certain sensor, such as an accelerometer, when used to measure other continuous or discrete waveforms it is first necessary to break down the waveform into its Fourier components. The response, in terms of amplitude and phase, to each of these is then added to arrive at the resultant response. It has been stated above that damping can be added to extend the useful bandwidth of a seismic sensor. However, where this is done it generally increases the phase shift variation with frequency. A signal comprising many frequencies will, therefore, produce an output that depends largely on the damping and natural frequency values of the sensor. A number of responses are plotted, such as that in Figure 6.18, in Harris and Crede (1961) to which the reader is referred. Generally the damping value for best all-round results is that near the critical value.

6.3.4.3 The piezo-electric sensor

Numerous sensing methods have been devised to measure the motion of the mass in a seismic sensor. We discuss here the most commonly used method: others are described in Endevco (1980), Harris and Crede (1961), Herceg (1972), Norton (1969) and Oliver (1971).

Force applied to certain crystalline substances, such as quartz, produces between two surfaces of a suitably shaped crystal an electric charge that is proportional to the force. This charge is contained in the internal electrical capacitance formed by the high-dielectric material and two deposited conducting surfaces. The descriptive mathematical relation for this effect is

$$q = a \cdot F \cdot k_s$$

where q is the electrical charge generated by force F (in newtons) applied across the faces of a piezo-electric device having a mechanical compliance of spring rate k_s ($\mathrm{m\,N^{-1}}$) and a more complex material constant a (of dimensions $\mathrm{C\,m^{-1}}$).

The constant a depends on many factors including the geometry of the crystal, position of electrodes and material used. Typical materials now used (natural quartz is less sensitive and, therefore, less applicable) include barium titanate with controlled impurities, lead zirconate, lead niobate and many that are trade secrets. The material is made from loose powder that, after shaping, is fired at very high temperature. Whilst cooling, the blocks are subjected to an electric field that polarizes the substance.

The sensitivity of these so-called 'PZT materials' is temperature-dependent through the charge sensitivity and the capacitance value, both of which alter with temperature. These changes do not follow simple linear laws. Such materials have a critical temperature, called the 'Curie point'. They must never be taken above it. The Curie point varies from 120 °C for the

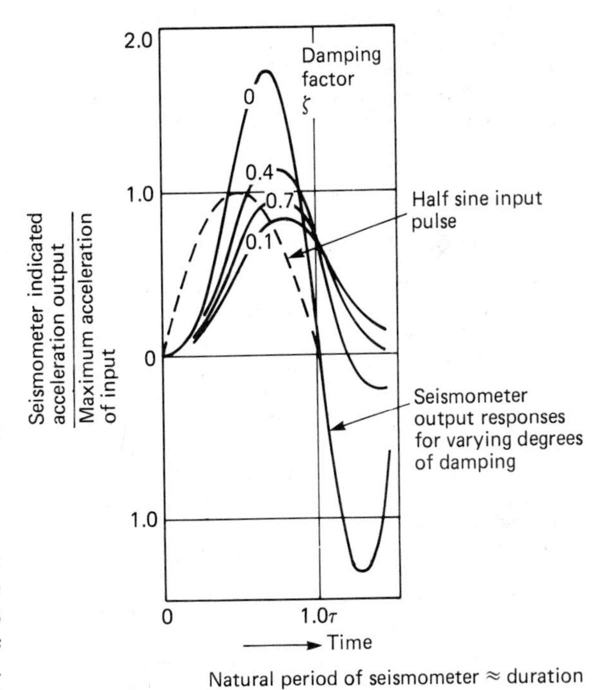

Figure 6.18 Example of response, at various damping factor levels, of a seismic accelerometer to a complex forcing input—a half-sine wave of similar period to that of the natural resonance period of the sensor.

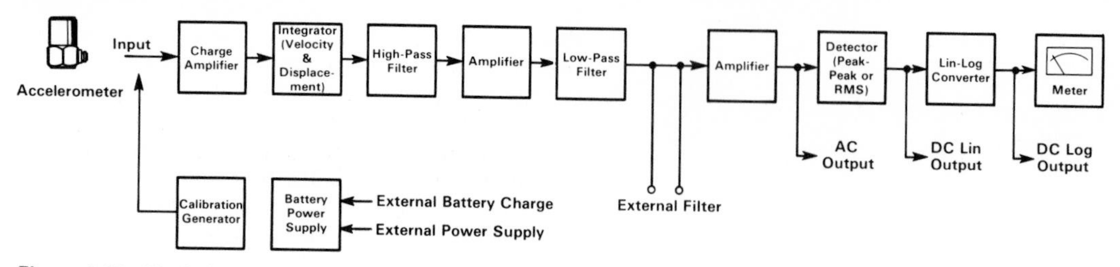

Figure 6.19 Block diagram of vibration measuring system showing functions that may be required. Courtesy, Brüel & Kjaer.

simpler barium titanate forms ranging up to values close to 600 °C. For the interested reader more explanation is to be found in Brüel and Kjaer (1976), Endevco (1980), Harris and Crede (1961), Klaasen (1978) and Trampe-Broch (1980) and in the detailed information provided by the makers of PZT materials.

To read the charge of a PZT sensor an electronic amplifier that converts charge magnitude to a voltage equivalent is used. The nature of the system provides no true d.c. response.

In practice the PZT sensors used to measure acceleration can be operated down to around 0.1 Hz, dependent on the amplitude to be measured. With natural resonant frequency that can be made relatively very high (up to 100 000 Hz in some designs), PZT sensors provide a useful frequency range that can cover most vibration needs. The system response, however, relies not only on the sensor but upon the cables and the pre-amplifier used with the PZT unit.

The PZT material can be used in pure compression, shear or bending, to produce the charge. Figure 6.12 gives some examples of commercially available PZT accelerometers. The sensor design is amenable to the combination of three units giving the three translation components of vibration.

PZT material itself contributes only of the order of 0.03 of critical damping. If no additional damping is added, PZT transducers must not be used too close to their resonant frequency. Mounting arrangements within the case will also add some additional damping. Some designs make use of an additional spring element, some use an additional spring to precompress the PZT element so that it remains biased in compression under all working amplitudes: this makes for more linear operation.

Typical sensor sensitivities range from 0.003 pC/m s^{-2} up to 1000 pC/m s^{-2}, implying that the following pre-amplifier units will also need to vary considerably.

6.3.4.4 *Amplifiers for piezo-electric sensors*

An amplifier for reading out the state of the PZT sensor is one that has very high input impedance, an adequate frequency response and low output impedance. Adjustment of gain and filtering action and integration to yield velocity and displacement are usually also needed to provide easy use for a variety of applications. Figure 6.19 is a typical system incorporating most features that might be needed.

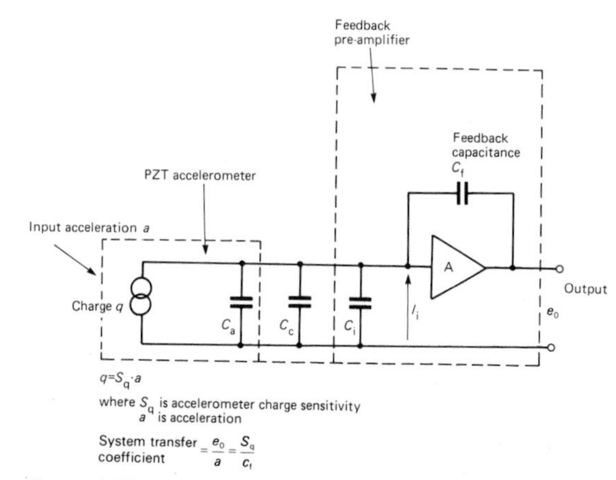

Figure 6.20 Equivalent circuit for piezo-electric sensor when interrogated, as a charge-generating device, by an operational amplifier technique.

The amplifier could be designed to see the sensor either as a voltage source or as a charge source. The latter is preferred for, using modern electronic-feedback operational amplifier techniques, the effect of cable, sensor and amplifier capacitances can be made negligible (which, in the voltage-reading method, is not the case). Cable length is, therefore, of no consequence. This is justified as follows.

Figure 6.20 is the relevant equivalent circuit for a PZT accelerometer that is connected to an operational amplifier (the pre-amplifier) via a cable. It includes the dominant capacitances that occur.

It can be shown, see Trampe-Broch (1980) for example, that the use of feedback in this way and a very high amplifier gain A gives

$$e_0 = \frac{S_q a}{C_f}$$

This shows that the user need only define the sensor charge sensitivity S_q and the feedback capacitance C_f in order to be able to relate output voltage from the pre-amplifier to the acceleration of the sensor.

6.3.5 Measurement of shock

Shock is a sudden short impulse of applied force that generates very large acceleration (100 000 g can arise) and is not recurrent. It can be regarded as a once-only occurrence of a vibration waveform, although sometimes it is used to describe a short burst of oscillation.

Understanding the behaviour of a given vibration sensor requires Fourier analysis of its response to a truncated waveshape. The mathematics becomes more complex. Theoretical study does lead to the generalization that as the waveform becomes more like a single pulse of high magnitude and very short duration the frequency band of the sensor must be widened if the delivered output is to be a satisfactory replica of the actual input vibration parameter. Fidelity increases as the period of the natural frequency of the sensor becomes shorter than the pulse length. An idea of the variation of responses with natural frequency and damping is available in graphs given in Harris and Crede (1961). An example is that in Figure 6.18.

The very large forces exerted on the transducer require a design that recognizes the need to withstand large transient forces without altering mechanical strains in the sensor system.

Well-designed shock sensors can accurately measure single half-sinewave pulses as short as 5 μs. Some amount of ringing in the output is usually tolerated in order to provide measurement of very short duration shocks.

6.4 Literature

There exist many general books on the kinds of transducers that are in use. An IMEKO bibliography, Sydenham (1983), is a useful entry point to the literature of measurement technology.

Of the many general instrument texts that are available, very few actually address the subject of vibration as a distinct chapter. Where included, relevant material will be found under such headings as velocity and acceleration measurement, accelerometers, position sensing and piezo-electric systems. Texts containing a chapter-length introductory discussion include Herceg (1972), Norton (1969) and Oliver (1971).

There are, as would be expected, some (but only a few) works entirely devoted to vibration and related measurands. The following will be of value to readers who require more than the restricted introduction that a chapter such as this provides—Brüel and Kjaer (1975, 1982), Endevco (1980), Harris and Crede (1961), Trampe-Broch (1980) and Wallace (1970).

The various trade houses that manufacture vibration-measuring and -testing equipment also often provide extensive literature and other forms of training aids to assist the uncertain user.

6.5 References

Bently Nevada, *Bently Book One* (Application notes on vibration and machines), Bently Nevada, Minden, USA, (1982)

Brüel & Kjaer, *Vibration Testing Systems*, Brüel & Kjaer, Naerum, Denmark, (1975)

Brüel & Kjaer, *Piezoelectric Accelerometer and Vibration Preamplifier Handbook*, Brüel & Kjaer, Naerum, Denmark, (1976)

Brüel & Kjaer, *Acoustics, Vibration & Shock, Luminance and Contrast, National and International Standards and Recommendations*, Brüel & Kjaer, Naerum, Denmark, (1981)

Brüel & Kjaer, *Measuring Vibration—an Elementary Introduction*, Brüel & Kjaer, Naerum, Denmark, (1982)

Crandall, S. H. *Random Vibration*, Wiley, New York, (1959)

Endevco, *Shock and Vibration Measurement Technology*, Endevco Dynamic Instrument Division, San Juan Capistrano, USA, (1980)

Harris, C. M. and Crede, C. E. *Shock and Vibration Handbook Vol. 1, Basic Theory and Measurements*, McGraw-Hill, New York, (1961, reprinted in 1976)

Herceg, E. E. *Handbook of Measurement and Control*, HB-72, Schaevitz Engineering, Pennsauken, USA, (1972, revised 1976)

Jones, B. E. 'Feedback in instruments and its applications' in *Instrument Science and Technology*, Jones, B. E. (ed.), Adam Hilger, Bristol, (1982)

Klaasen, K. B. 'Piezoelectric accelerometers' in *Modern Electronic Measuring Systems*, Regtien, P. P. L., (ed.), Delft University Press, Delft, (1978)

Norton, H. N. *Handbook of Transducers for Electronic Measuring Systems*, Prentice-Hall, Englewood Cliffs, New Jersey, (1969)

Oliver, F. J. *Practical Instrumentation Transducers*, Pitman, London, (1971)

Sydenham, P. H. *Handbook of Measurement Science—Vol. 2. Fundamentals of Practice*, Wiley, Chichester, (1983)

Trampe-Broch, J. *Mechanical Vibration and Shock Measurements*, Brüel & Kjaer, Naerum, Denmark, (1980)

Wallace, R. H. *Understanding and Measuring Vibrations*, Wykeham Publications, London, (1970)

Wells, P. 'Machine condition monitoring', Proceedings of structured course, Chisholm Institute of Technology, Victoria, Australia, (1981)

7 Measurement of force

C. S. BAHRA

7.1 Basic concepts

If a body is released, it will start to fall with an acceleration due to gravity or acceleration of free fall of its location. We denote by g the resultant acceleration due to attraction of the earth upon the body and the component of acceleration due to rotation of the earth about its axis. The value of g varies with location and height and this variation is about 0.5 per cent between the equator and the poles. The approximate value of g is $9.81\ m/s^2$. A knowledge of the precise value of g is necessary to determine gravitational forces acting on known masses at rest, relative to the surface of the earth in order to establish practical standards of force. Practical standards of dead-weight calibration of force-measuring systems or devices are based on this observation.

It is necessary to make a clear distinction between the units of weight-measuring (mass-measuring) and force-measuring systems. The weight-measuring systems are calibrated in kilograms while the force-measuring systems are in newtons. Mass, force and weight are defined as follows:

Mass. The mass of a body is defined as the quantity of matter in that body and it remains unchanged when taken to any location. The unit of mass is the kilogram (kg).

Force. Force is that which produces or tends to produce a change of velocity in a body at rest or in motion. Force has magnitude, direction and a point of application. It is related to the mass of a body through Newton's second law of motion which gives: force = mass × acceleration.

Unit of force. In the International System of units, the unit of force is the newton (N) and it is that force which when applied to a mass of one kilogram, gives it an acceleration of one metre per second per second (m/s^2).

Weight. Weight F of a body of mass m at rest relative to the surface of the earth is defined as the force exerted on it by gravity: $F = mg$, where g is the acceleration due to gravity.

The main purpose of this chapter is to review the most commonly used force measurement methods and to discuss briefly the principles employed in their design, limitations and use. It is not intended to give a too detailed description of mathematical and physical concepts, but enough information to allow an interested reader to read further.

7.2 Force measurement methods

Force measurement methods may be divided into two categories, direct comparison and indirect comparison. In a direct comparison method, an unknown force is directly compared with a gravitational force acting on a known mass. A simple analytical balance is an example of this method. An indirect comparison method involves the use of calibrated masses or transducers and a summary of indirect comparison methods is given below:

(a) Lever-balance methods.
(b) Force-balance method.
(c) Hydraulic pressure measurement.
(d) Acceleration measurement.
(e) Elastic elements.

Note that the lever-balance methods include examples of both direct and indirect comparisons, but to maintain continuity of information, they are described under one heading.

7.3 Lever-balance methods

7.3.1 Equal-lever balance

A simple analytical balance is an example of an equal-lever balance which consists of a 'rigid' beam pivoted on a knife-edge, as shown in Figure 7.1. An unknown force F_1 is compared directly with a known force F_2. When the beam is in equilibrium the sum of moments about the pivot is zero.

$$F_1 a - F_2 a = 0$$
$$\therefore \quad F_1 = F_2$$

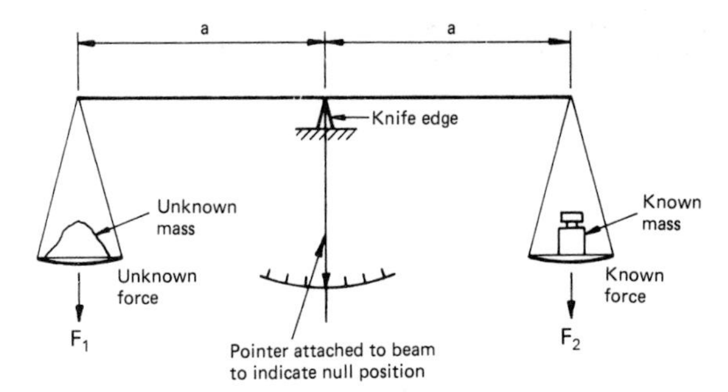

Figure 7.1 Equal-lever balance.

This type of balance is mainly used for weighing chemicals. It gives direct reading, and can weigh up to about 1000 kg with high accuracy if required.

7.3.2 Unequal-lever balance

Figure 7.2 shows a typical arrangement of an unequal-lever balance which can be used for measuring large masses or forces. The balance is obtained by sliding a known mass along the lever. At equilibrium, we have

$$F_1 a = F_2 b$$

$$F_1 = F_2 b/a$$

$$\therefore \quad F_1 \propto b$$

The right-hand side of the beam can therefore be used as a measure of force.

This type of balance is extensively used in materials-testing machines and weight measurement. The balance is normally bulky and heavy, but can be made very accurate.

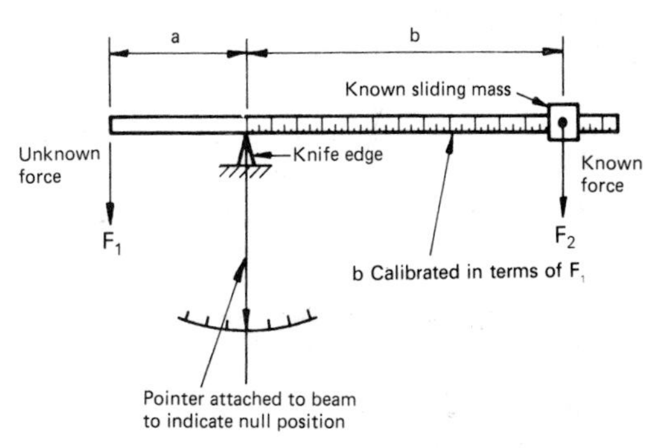

Figure 7.2 Unequal-lever balance.

7.3.3 Compound lever balance

Figure 7.3 shows a compound lever balance which is used for measuring very large masses or forces. Using a number of ratio levers, the applied force is reduced to a level which is just sufficient to actuate a spring within the indicator dial head. The balance is calibrated in units of mass.

7.4 Force-balance methods

Figure 7.4 shows an electronic force-balance type force-measuring system. The displacement caused by the applied force is sensed by a displacement transducer. The displacement transducer output is fed to a servo amplifier to give an output current which flows through a restoring coil and exerts a force on the permanent magnet. This force adjusts itself always to balance the applied force. In equilibrium, the current flowing through the force coil is directly proportional

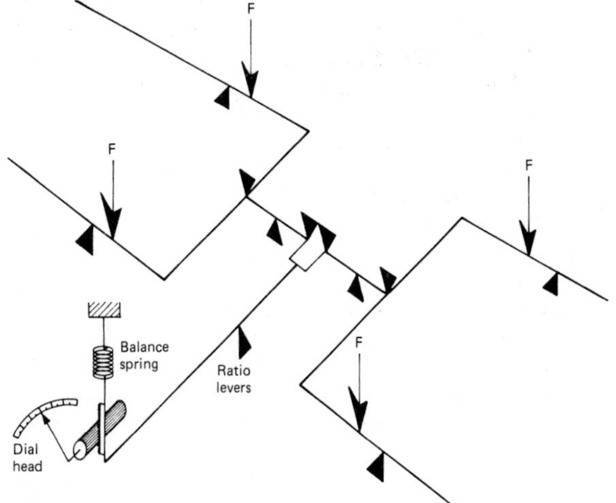

Figure 7.3 Compound-lever balance.

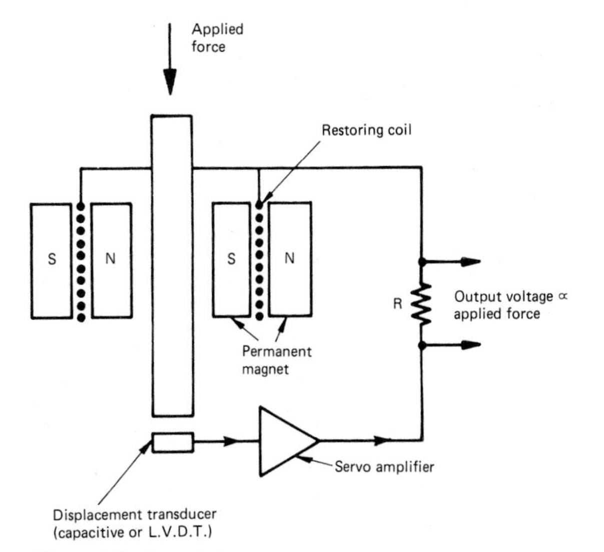

Figure 7.4 Force-balance system.

to the applied force. The same current flows through the resistor R and the voltage drop across this resistor is a measure of the applied force. Being a feedback system, such a device must be thoroughly checked for stability.

The force-balance system gives high stability, high accuracy, negligible displacement and is suitable for both static and dynamic force measurement. The range of this type of instrument is from 0.1 N to about 1 kN. It is normally bulky and heavy and tends to be expensive.

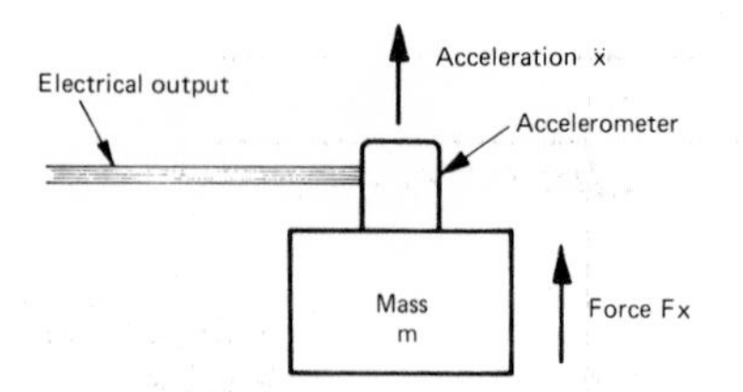

Figure 7.6 Force measurement using accelerometer.

7.5 Hydraulic pressure measurement

The change in pressure due to the applied force may be used for force measurement. Figure 7.5 shows a general arrangement of a hydraulic load cell. An oil-filled chamber is connected to a pressure gauge and is sealed by a diaphragm. The applied force produces a pressure increase in the confined oil and is indicated on the pressure gauge calibrated to give direct reading of force. If an electrical output is required, an electrical pressure transducer may be used in place of the pressure gauge.

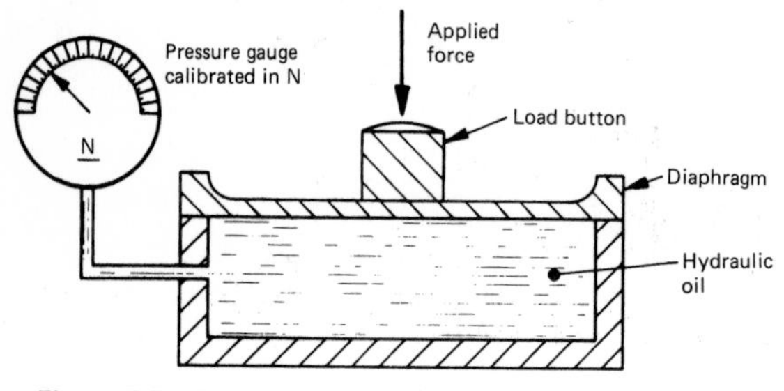

Figure 7.5 Force measurement using hydraulic load cell.

Hydraulic load cells are stiff, with virtually no operational movement, and they can give local or remote indication. They are available in force ranges up to 5 MN with system accuracy of the order of 0.25 to 1.0 per cent.

7.6 Acceleration measurement

As mentioned earlier, force is a product of mass and acceleration. If the acceleration $\ddot{x}$ of a body of known mass m is known, then the force Fx causing this acceleration can be found from the relationship:

$$Fx = m\ddot{x}$$

The acceleration is measured by using a calibrated accelerometer as shown in Figure 7.6. In practice, this method may be used for measuring dynamic forces associated with vibrating masses, and is discussed further in Chapter 6.

7.7 Elastic elements

A measuring system basically consists of three elements; a transducer, a signal conditioner and a display or recorder. In this section, we will discuss various types of transducers, based on small displacements of elastic elements. In general, a transducer is defined as a device which changes information from one form to another. For the purpose of this discussion, a force transducer is defined as a device in which the magnitude of the applied force is converted into an electrical output, proportional to the applied force. The transducers are divided into two classes: active and passive. A passive transducer requires an external excitation voltage whereas an active transducer does not require an electrical input.

In general, a transducer consists of two parts: a primary elastic element which converts the applied force into a displacement and a secondary sensing element which converts the displacement into an electrical output. The elastic behaviour of the elastic element is governed by Hooke's law which states that the relationship between the applied force and the displacement is linear, provided the elastic limit of the material is not exceeded. The displacement may be sensed by various transducing techniques; some of them are examined in this section.

7.7.1 Spring balances

The extension of a spring may be used as a measure of the applied force and this technique is employed in the design of a spring balance as shown in Figure 7.7. This type of balance is a relatively low cost, low accuracy device and can be used for static force measurement.

7.7.2 Proving rings

A proving ring is a high-grade steel ring-shaped element with integral loading bosses as shown in Figure 7.8. Under the action of a diametral force, the ring tends to distort. The amount of distortion is directly proportional to the applied force. For low accuracy requirements, the distortion is measured using a dial gauge or a micrometer whereas for high accuracy applications, a displacement transducer such

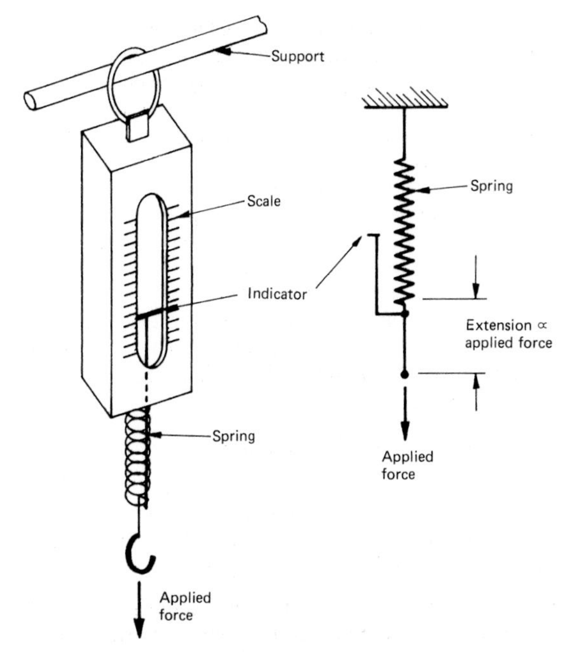

Figure 7.7 Spring balance.

as a linear variable differential transformer may be used. See Chapter 3.

Proving rings are high precision devices which are extensively used to calibrate materials-testing machines. They may be used both in tension and compression, with a compressive force range of the order of 2 kN to 2000 kN with accuracy from 0.2 to 0.5 per cent.

7.7.3 Piezo-electric transducers

A typical arrangement of a piezo-electric transducer is shown in Figure 7.9. When the transducer is subjected to the applied force, a proportional electrical charge appears on the faces of the piezo-electric element. The charge is also a function of force direction. The piezo-electric transducer differs from a conventional (passive) transducer in two respects. First, it is an active system, and secondly, the deflection at rated load is no more than a few thousandths of a millimetre, whereas the corresponding deflection for the conventional system may amount to several tenths of a millimetre.

This type of transducer has high stiffness, resulting in a very high resonant frequency. Because charge can leak away through imperfect insulation, it is unsuitable for measuring steady forces. It is mainly used in vibration studies and is discussed further in Chapter 6. It has small size, rugged construction, is sensitive to temperature changes and is capable of measuring compressive forces from a few kilonewtons to about 1 meganewton with accuracy from 0.5 to 1.5 per cent.

7.7.4 Strain-gauge load cells

7.7.4.1 Design

Bonded strain-gauge load cells are devices producing an electrical output which changes in magnitude when a force or weight is applied, and which may be displayed on a readout instrument or used in a control device. The heart of the load cell is the bonded-foil strain gauge which is an extremely sensitive device, whose electrical resistance changes in direct proportion to the applied force. See Chapter 4.

A load cell comprises an elastic element, normally machined from a single billet of high tensile steel alloy, precipitation hardening stainless steel, beryllium copper or other suitable material, heat-treated to optimize thermal and mechanical properties. The element may take many forms, such as hollow or solid column, cantilever, diaphragm, shear member, or ring. The design of the element is dependent on the load range, type of loading and operational requirements. The gauges are bonded on to the element to measure the strains generated and are usually connected into a four-arm Wheatstone bridge configuration. On larger elements, to get a true average of the strains, often 8, 16

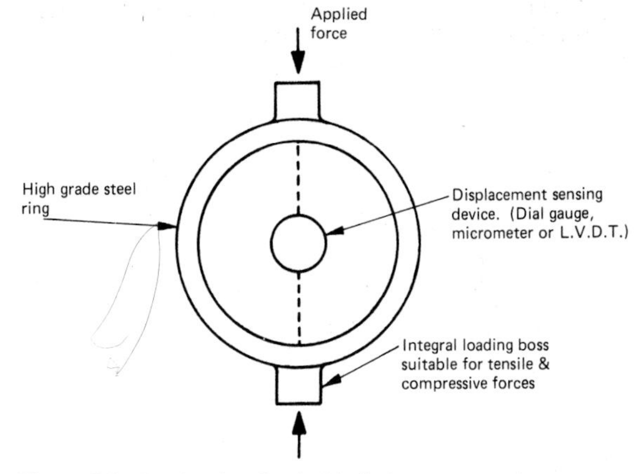

Figure 7.8 Proving ring fitted with displacement-sensing device.

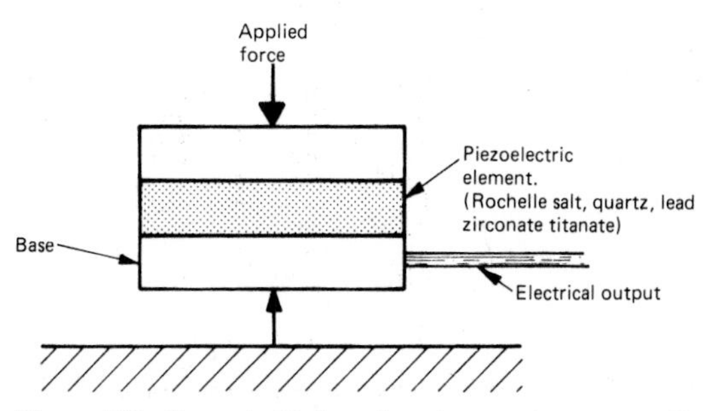

Figure 7.9 Piezo-electric force transducer.

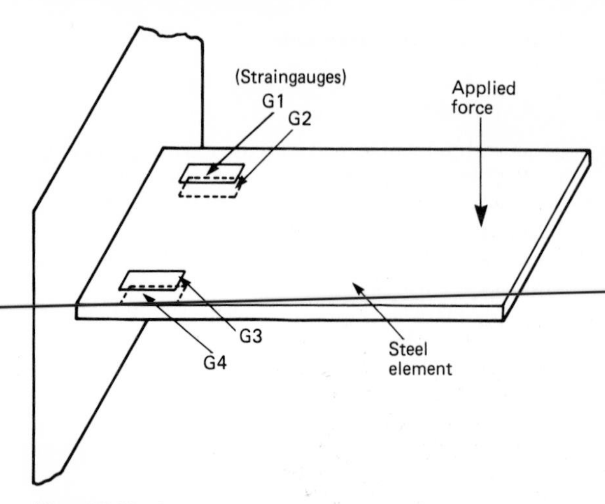

Figure 7.10 Cantilever load cell.

or even 32 gauges are used. To illustrate the working principle, a cantilever load cell is shown in Figure 7.10. Figure 7.11 shows a bridge circuit diagram that includes compensation resistors for zero balance and changes of zero and sensitivity with temperature. To achieve high performance and stability and to minimize glue line thickness, the gauges are often installed on flat-sided elements.

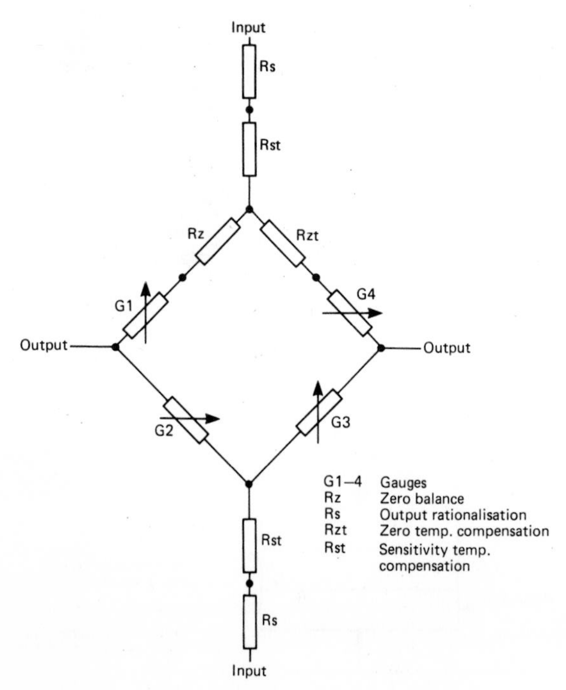

Figure 7.11 Load cell bridge circuit with compensation resistors.

The complete assembly is housed within a protective case with sealing sufficient to exclude the external environment, but capable of allowing the deformation of the element to occur when the force is applied. In some cases, restraining diaphragms minimize the effect of side-loading.

After assembly, the elements are subjected to a long series of thermal and load cycling to ensure that remaining 'locked-up' stresses in the element and bonding are relieved, so that the units will give excellent long-term zero stability.

Figure 7.12 shows some commercially available compression load cells that have been successfully used for monitoring the tension in the mooring legs of a North Sea platform.

7.7.4.2 *Selection and installation*

There are five basic types of cell on the market: compression, tension, universal (both compression and tension), bending and shear. The main factors influencing the selection of cell type are:

(a) The ease and convenience (and hence the cost) of incorporating a cell into the weigher structure.
(b) Whether the required rated load and accuracy can be obtained in the type of cell.

Other considerations include low profile, overload capacity, resistance to side-loads, environmental protection and a wide operating temperature range.

To retain its performance, a cell should be correctly installed into the weigher structure. This means the structure of the weigher, such as vessel, bin, hopper or platform, is the governing factor in the arrangement of the load cells. The supporting structure is also to be considered since it will carry the full weight of the vessel and contents. Difficulties caused by mis-application leading to poor performance and unreliability fall into three main headings:

(a) A non-axial load is applied.
(b) Side-loads are affecting the weight reading.
(c) Free-axial movement of the load is restricted.

Figure 7.13 shows how normal, non-axial and side-loading affects a column stress member. Under normal loading conditions (A) the active strain gauges go into equal compression; however, under non-axial (B) or side-loading (C) conditions, asymmetrical compression results, causing readout errors.

Examples of correct and incorrect fitments are shown in Figure 7.14. The support bracket D is cantilevered out too far and is liable to bend under load. The bracket is applying a load to the side of the vessel, which itself exaggerates this effect as the vessel is not strong enough to support it. The beam also deflects under load, rotating the load cell away from the vertical. The correct example E shows how the errors can be overcome.

Figure 7.12 Compression load cells.

In weighing installations it is important that there is unimpeded vertical movement of the weigh vessel. Obviously this is not possible where there are pipe fittings or stay rods on the vessel, but the vertical stiffness must be kept within allowable limits. One of the most satisfactory ways of reducing the spring rates is to fit flexible couplings in the pipework, preferably in a horizontal mode, and after (for example) the discharge valve so that they are not subject to varying stiffness due to varying pressure (see F and G in Figure 7.14). Where possible, entry pipes should be free of contact with the vessel (refer to H and I).

7.7.4.3 Applications

Load cells have many applications including weight and force measurement, weigh platforms, process control systems, monorail weighing, beltweighers, aircraft, freight and baggage weighing and conversion of a mechanical scale to an electronic scale. Over the past few years, the industrial weighing field has been dominated by load cells because electrical outputs are ideal for local and remote indication and to interface with microprocessors and minicomputers.

Key features of load cells are:

(a) Load range 5 N to 40 MN.

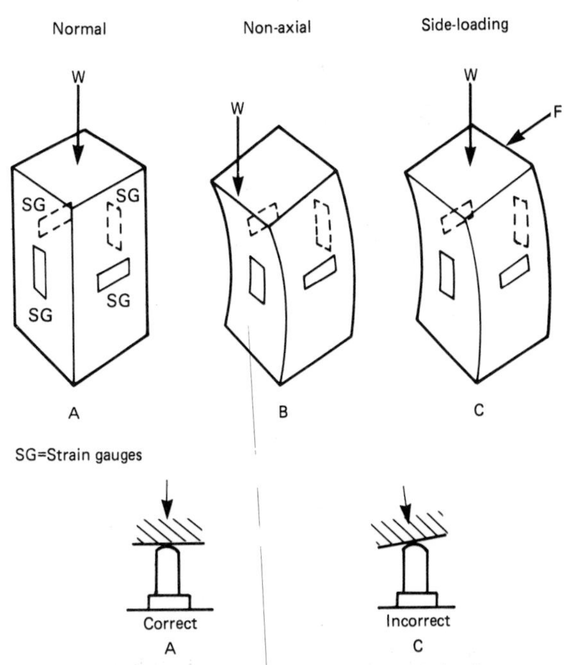

Figure 7.13 Effects of normal, non-axial and side-loading.

(b) Accuracy 0.01 to 1.0 per cent.
(c) Rugged and compact construction.
(d) No moving parts and negligible deflection under load.
(e) Hermetically sealed and thermal compensation.
(f) High resistance to side-loads and withstand overloads.

7.7.4.4 Calibration

Calibration is a process that involves obtaining and recording the load cell output while a direct known input is applied in a well-defined environment. The load cell output is directly compared against a primary or secondary standard of force. A primary standard of force includes dead-weight machines with force range up to about 500 kN; higher forces are achieved with machines having hydraulic or mechanical amplification.

A secondary standard of force involves the use of high precision load cells and proving rings with a calibration standard directly traceable to the National Standard at the National Physical Laboratory in Teddington, Middlesex, or the equivalent standards in other countries. The choice of the standards to be used for a particular calibration depends on the range and the location of the device to be calibrated.

The foregoing has indicated some force-measurement methods. Others are many and varied and no attempt has been made to cover all types. To simplify the selection of a method for a particular application, the main parameters of the methods discussed are summarized in Table 7.1.

7.8 Further developments

Advancing technology, improvements in manufacturing techniques and new materials have permitted increased accuracy and improved design of bonded strain-gauge load cells since their introduction about 30 years ago. Now the microprocessor is available, and therefore further design improvements in these devices are expected.

New transducing techniques are being constantly researched; a number of them have been well studied or are being considered, including gyroscopic force transducers, fibre optics, microwave cavity resonator and thin-film transducing techniques. The thin-film techniques are well documented and therefore are briefly discussed.

Pressure transducers based on vacuum-deposited thin-film gauges are commercially available and attempts are being made to apply these techniques to load cells. The advantages of these techniques are as follows:

(a) Very small gauge and high bridge resistance.
(b) Intimate contact between the element and gauge. No hysteresis or creep of a glue line.
(c) Wide temperature range (−200 °C to +200 °C).

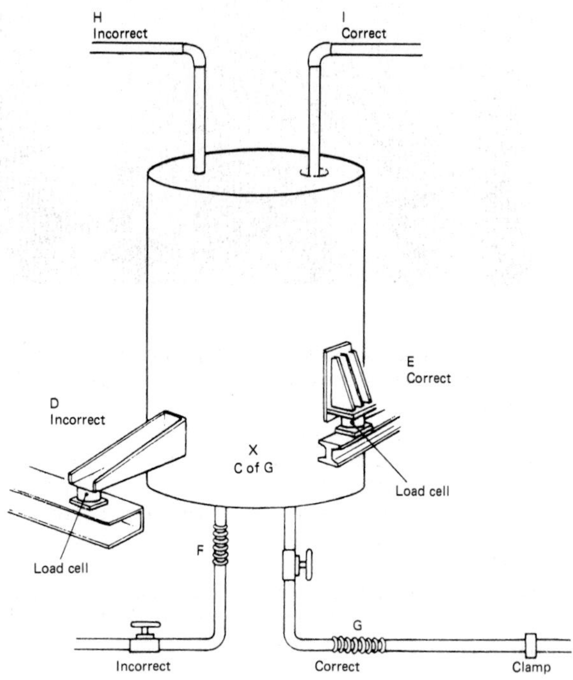

Figure 7.14 Examples of correct and incorrect fitments.

Table 7.1 Summary of main parameters of force-measuring methods

Method	*Type of loading*	*Force range, N (approx.)*	*Accuracy % (approx.)*	*Size*
Lever balance	Static	0.001 to 150 k	Very high	Bulky and heavy
Force-balance	Static/dynamic	0.1 to 1 k	Very high	Bulky and heavy
Hydraulic load cell	Static/dynamic	5 k to 5 M	0.25 to 1.0	Compact and stiff
Spring balance	Static	0.1 to 10 k	Low	Large and heavy
Proving ring	Static	2 k to 2 M	0.2 to 0.5	Compact
Piezo-electric transducer	Dynamic	5 k to 1 M	0.5 to 1.5	Small
Strain-gauge load cell	Static/dynamic	5 to 40 M	0.01 to 1.0	Compact and stiff

(d) Excellent long-term stability of the bridge.
(e) Suitability for mass production.

The techniques are capital-intensive and are generally suitable for low force ranges.

7.9 References

Adams, L. F. *Engineering Measurements and Instrumentation*, The English Universities Press, (1975)

Cerni, R. H. and Foster, L. E. *Instrumentation for Engineering Measurement*, John Wiley and Sons, (1962)

Mansfield, P. H. *Electrical Transducers for Industrial Measurement*, Butterworth, (1973)

Neubert, H. K. P. *Instrument Transducers*, Clarendon Press, (2nd edition, 1975)

WEIGHTECH 79, Proceedings of the Conference on Weighing and Force Measurement; Hotel Metropole, Brighton, England 24–26 September 1979

8 Measurement of density

E. H. HIGHAM

8.1 General

The measurement (and control) of liquid density is critical to a great number of industrial processes. But although density in itself can be of interest, it is usually more important as a way of inferring composition, or concentration of chemicals in solution, or of solids in suspension. Because the density of gases is very small, the instruments for that measurement have to be very sensitive to small changes. They will be dealt with separately at the end of the chapter.

In considering the measurement and control of density or relative density* of liquids, the units used in the two factors should be borne in mind. Density is defined as the mass per unit volume of a liquid and is expressed in such units as kg/m^3, g/l or g/ml.

Relative density, on the other hand, is the ratio of the mass of a volume of liquid to the mass of an equal volume of water at 4 °C (or some other specified temperature), the relative density of water being taken as 1.0. Both density and relative density are temperature-dependent and, for high precision, the temperature at which a measurement is made will have to be known, so that any necessary compensation can be introduced.

The majority of industrial liquid-density instruments are based on the measurement of: weight, buoyancy or hydrostatic head, but measuring systems based on resonant elements or radiation techniques are also used.

8.2 Measurement of density using weight

The actual weighing of a sample of known volume is perhaps the simplest practical application of this principle. Various methods for continuous weighing have been devised, but the most successful involves the use of a horizontal U-shaped tube with flexible couplings at a pivot point.

One example of this type of instrument is the Fisher Controls Company Mark V Gravitrol Density Meter shown in Figure 8.1. In it, the process fluid passes via flexible connectors into the tube loop which is supported towards the curved end on a link associated with the force-balance measuring system. In the pneumatic version of the instrument, the link is attached towards one end of the weighbeam which itself is supported on cross flexure pivots and carries an adjustable counterbalance weight on the opposite side. Also attached to the weighbeam is a dash-pot to reduce the effect of vibration induced by the flow of the process fluid or by the environment in which the instrument is located.

In operation, the counterbalance weight is positioned to achieve balance with the tube loop filled with fluid having a density within the desired working range and the span adjustment is set to its mid position. Balance is achieved when the force applied by the feedback bellows via the pivot and span-adjustment mechanism to the weighbeam causes it to take up a position in which the feedback loop comprising the flapper nozzle and pneumatic relay generates a pressure which is both applied to the feedback bellows and used as the output signal. A subsequent increase in the density of the process fluid causes a minute clockwise rotation of the weighbeam with the result that the flapper is brought closer to the nozzle and so

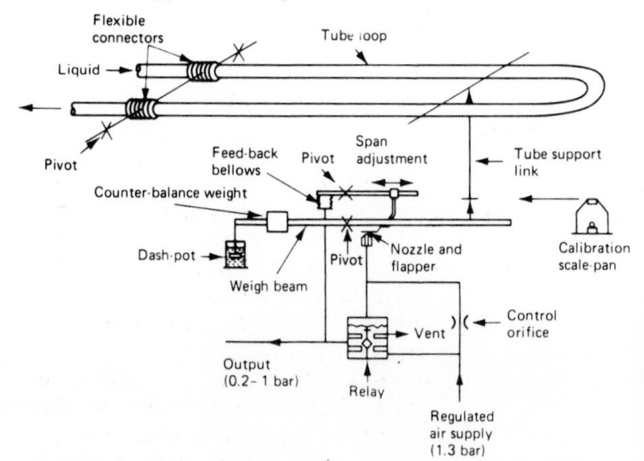

Figure 8.1 Gravitrol density meter. Courtesy, Fischer Controls Ltd.

* The term 'specific gravity' is often used for relative density. However it is not included in the SI System of Units and BS350 points out that it is commonly used when the reference substance is water

increases the back pressure. This change is amplified by the relay and applied to the feedback bellows which in turn applies an increased force via the span-adjustment system until balance is restored.

An electronic force-balance system is also available which serves the same function as the pneumatic force-balance system just described. The basic calibration constants for each instrument are determined at the factory in terms of the weight equivalent to a density of 1.0 kg/dm^3. To adjust the instrument for any particular application, the tube loop is first emptied. Then weights corresponding to the lower range value are added to the calibration scale-pan and the counter-balance weight is adjusted to achieve balance.

Further weights are then added, representing the required span and the setting of the span adjustment is varied until balance is restored. The two procedures are repeated until the required precision is achieved. The pneumatic output, typically 20–100 kPa, then measures the change in density of the flowing fluid. It can be adjusted to operate for spans between 0.02 and 0.5 kg/dm^3 and for fluids having densities up to 1.6 kg/dm^3. The instrument is of course suitable for measurement on 'clean' liquids as well as slurries or fluids with entrained solid matter. In the former case a minimum flow velocity of 1.1 m/s is recommended and in the latter case at least 2.2 m/s to avoid deposition of the entrained solids.

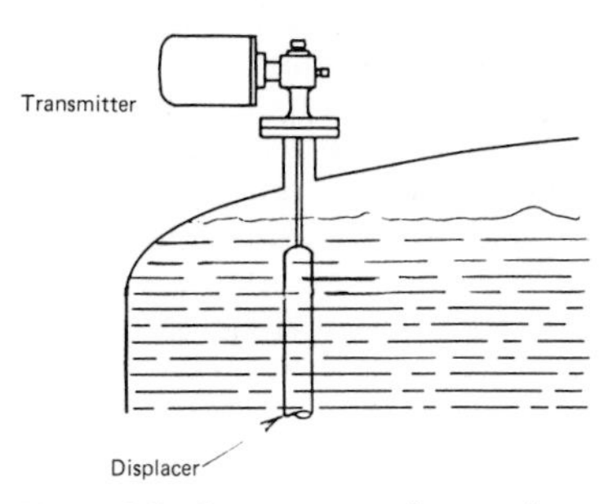

Figure 8.2 Buoyancy transducer and transmitter with tank.

8.3 Measurement of density using buoyancy

Buoyancy transmitters operate on the basis of Archimedes' principle: that a body immersed in a liquid is buoyed upward by a force equal to the weight of the liquid displaced. The cross-sectional area of a buoyancy transmitter displacer is constant over its working length, so that the buoyant force is proportional to the liquid density, see Figure 8.2.

With the arrangement of the force-balance mechanism shown in Figure 8.3, the force on the transmitter force bar must always be in the downward direction. Thus, the displacer element must always be heavier than the liquid it displaces. Displacers are available in a wide selection of lengths and diameters to satisfy a variety of process requirements.

Buoyancy transmitters are available for mounting either on the side of a vessel or for top entry and can be installed on vessels with special linings such as glass, vessels in which a lower connection is not possible. They are also suitable for density measurements in enclosed vessels where either the pressure or level may fluctuate and they avoid the need for equalizing legs or connections for secondary compensating instrumentation, such as repeaters. These transmitters are also suitable for applications involving high temperatures.

Turbulence is sometimes a problem for buoyancy transmitters. When this occurs, the most simple (and often the least expensive) solution is the installation of a stilling well or guide rings. Another alternative is to use a cage-mounted buoyancy transmitter, as shown in Figure 8.4. With this configuration, the measurement is outside the vessel and therefore isolated from the turbulence.

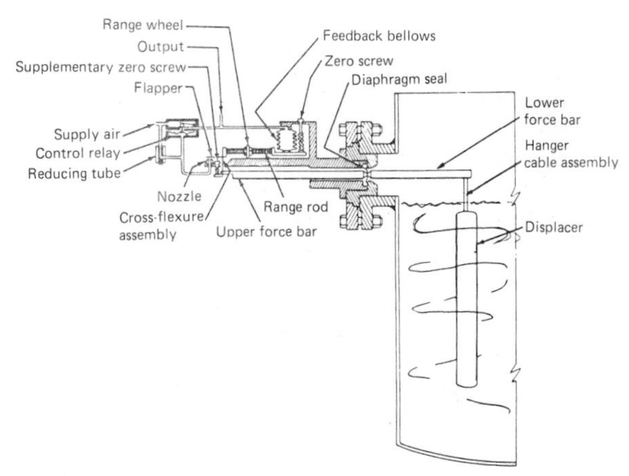

Figure 8.3 Buoyancy transducer and transmitter installation. Courtesy, The Foxboro Company.

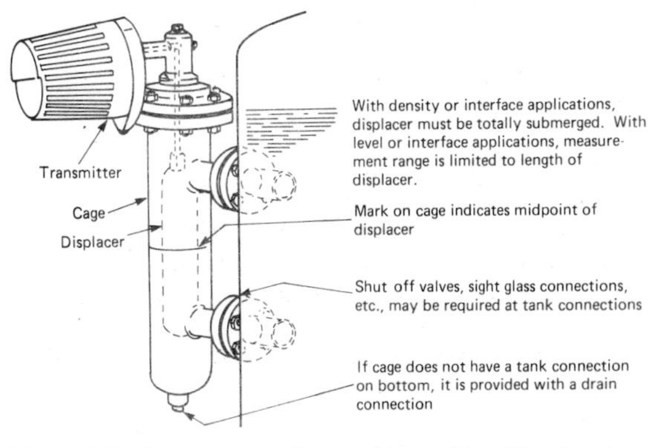

Figure 8.4 Buoyancy transducer and transmitter with external cage. Courtesy, The Foxboro Company.

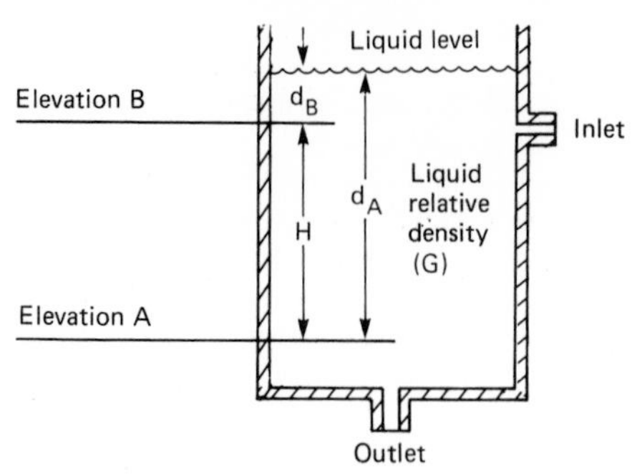

Figure 8.5 Density measurement—hydrostatic head.

8.4 Measurement of density using hydrostatic head

The hydrostatic-head method, which continuously measures the pressure variations by a fixed height of liquid, has proved to be suitable for many industrial processes. Briefly, the principle, illustrated in Figure 8.5, is as follows.

The difference in pressure between any two elevations (A and B) below the surface is equal to the difference in liquid head pressure between these elevations. This is true regardless of variation in liquid level above elevation B. This difference in elevation is represented by dimension H. Dimension H must be multiplied by the relative density of the liquid to obtain the difference in head. This is usually measured in terms of millimetres of water.

To measure the change in head resulting from a change in relative density from G_1 to G_2, it is necessary only to multiply H by the difference between G_1 and G_2. Thus

$$P = H(G_2 - G_1)$$

and if both H and P are measured in millimetres then the change in density is

$$(G_2 - G_1) = P/H$$

It is common practice to measure only the span of actual density changes. Therefore, the instrument 'zero' is 'suppressed' to the minimum head pressure to be encountered; this allows the entire instrument measurement span to be devoted to the differential caused by density changes. For example, if G_1 is 0.6 and H is 3 metres, then the zero suppression value should be 1.8 metres of water. The two principal relationships which must be considered in selecting a measuring device are:

$$\text{span} = H(G_2 - G_1)$$
$$\text{zero suppression value} = H \,.\, G_1$$

For a given instrument span, a low density span requires a greater H dimension (a deeper tank). For a given density span, a low span measuring device permits a shallower tank. Figure 8.6 shows values of H plotted against gravity spans.

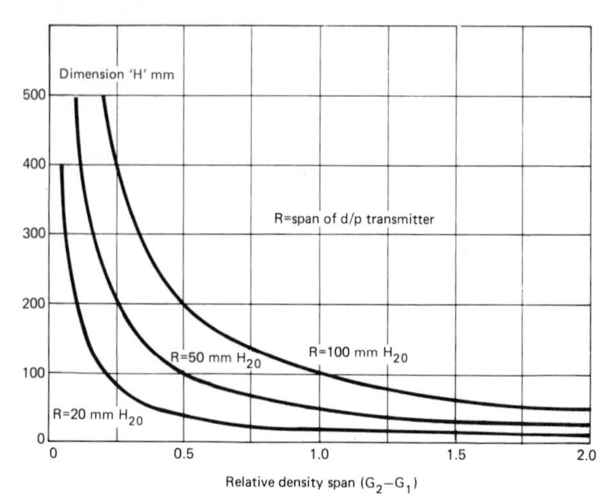

Figure 8.6 Relative density span versus H for various spans.

8.4.1 General differential-pressure (d/p) transmitter methods

There is a variety of system arrangements for determining density from measurements of hydrostatic head using differential-pressure (d/p) transmitters. Although flange-mounted d/p transmitters are often preferred, pipe-connected transmitters can be used on liquids where crystallization or precipitation in stagnant pockets will not occur.

These d/p transmitter methods are usually superior to those in which the d/p transmitter operates in conjunction with bubble tubes and can be used in either pressure or vacuum systems. However, all require the dimensions of the process vessel to provide a sufficient change of head to satisfy the minimum span of the transmitter.

8.4.2 D/p transmitter with overflow tank

Constant-level, overflow tanks permit the simplest instrumentation, as shown in Figure 8.7. Only one d/p transmitter is required. With H as the height of liquid above the transmitter, the equations are still:

$$\text{span} = H(G_2 - G_1)$$
$$\text{zero suppression value} = H \,.\, G_1$$

8.4.3 D/p transmitter with a wet leg

Applications with level or static pressure variations require compensation. There are three basic arrangements for density measurement under these conditions. First, when a seal fluid can be chosen that is always denser than the process fluid and will not mix

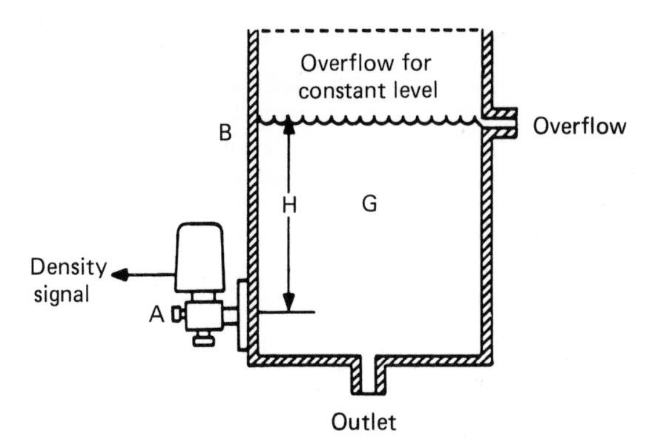

Figure 8.7 Density measurement with constant head.

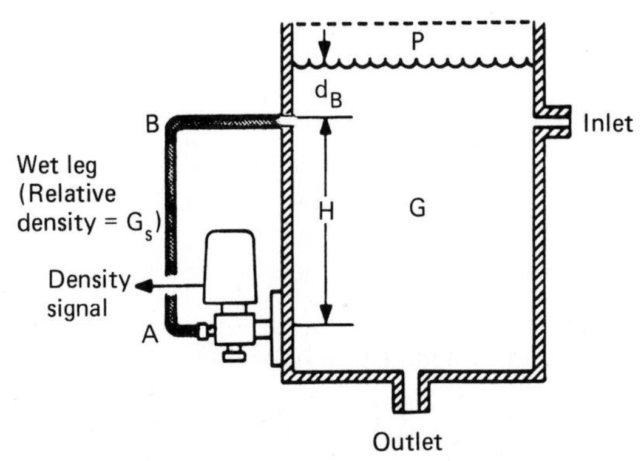

Figure 8.8 Density measurement with wet leg.

with it, the method shown in Figure 8.8 is adequate. This method is used extensively on hydrocarbons with water in the wet leg. For a wet-leg fluid of specific gravity G_S, an elevated zero transmitter must be used. The equations become:

$$\text{span} = H(G_2 - G_1)$$
$$\text{zero elevation value} = H(G_S - G_1)$$

When there is no suitable wet-leg seal fluid, but the process liquid will tolerate a liquid purge, the method shown in Figure 8.9 can be used. To ensure that the process liquid does not enter the purged wet leg, piping to the process vessel should include an appropriate barrier, either gooseneck or trap, as shown in Figure 8.10. Elevation or suppression of the transmitter will depend on the difference in specific gravity of the seal and process liquids. Here, the equations are:

$$\text{span} = H(G_2 - G_1)$$
$$\text{zero suppression value} = H(G_1 - G_S), \quad \text{when } G_1 > G_S$$
$$\text{zero elevation value} = H(G_S - G_1), \quad \text{when } G_S > G_1$$

Ideally, the purge liquid has a specific gravity equal to G, which eliminates the need for either suppression or elevation.

8.4.4 D/p transmitter with a pressure repeater

When purge liquid cannot be tolerated, there are ways to provide a 'mechanical seal' for the low-pressure leg, or for both legs if needed. Figure 8.11 shows the use of a pressure repeater for the upper connection. In one form, this instrument reproduces any pressure existing at the B connection from full vacuum to about 250 Pa positive pressure. In another form this instrument will reproduce any pressure from 7 kPa to 700 kPa. The repeater transmits the total pressure at elevation B to the low-pressure side of the d/p transmitter. In this way, the pressure at elevation B is subtracted from the pressure at elevation A.

The lower transmitter, therefore, measures density (or $H \cdot G$, where G is the specific gravity of the liquid). The equations for the lower transmitter are:

$$\text{span} = H(G_2 - G_1)$$
$$\text{zero suppression value} = H \cdot G_1$$

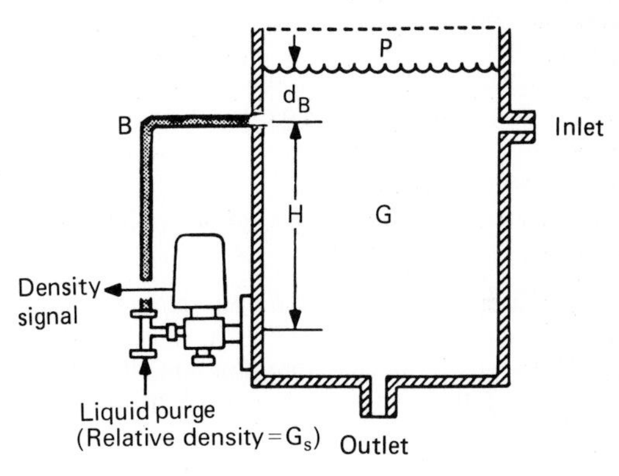

Figure 8.9 Density measurement with purge liquid.

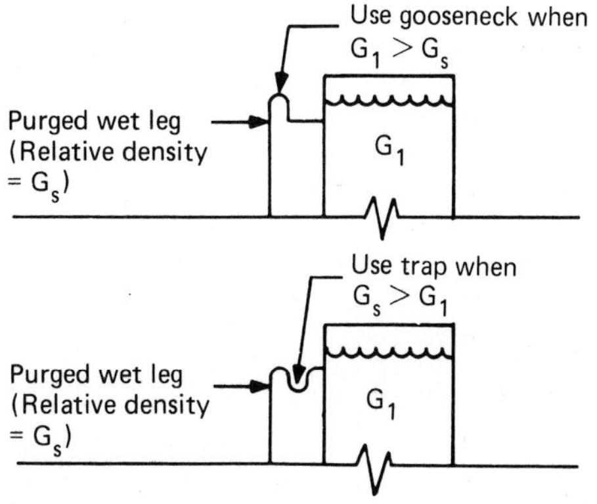

Figure 8.10 Purge system with gooseneck and trap.

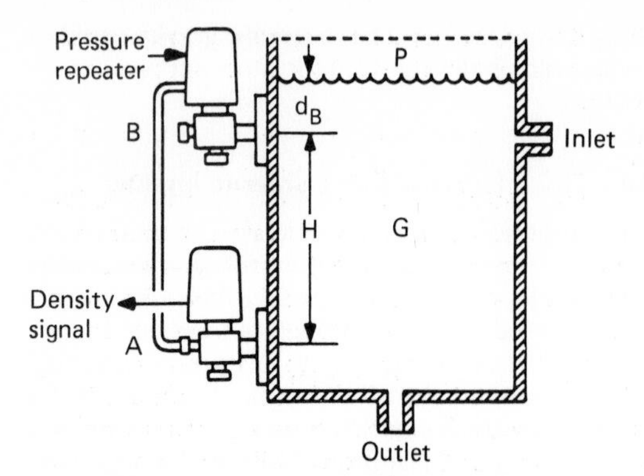

Figure 8.11 Density measurement with pressure repeater.

The equation for the upper repeater is:

$$\text{output (maximum)} = (d_B \text{ max})/(G_2) + P \text{ max}$$

where d_B is the distance from elevation B to the liquid surface, and P is the static pressure on the tank, if any.

Special consideration must be given when the repeater method is used for vacuum applications, where the total pressure on the repeater is less than atmospheric. In some instances density measurement is still possible. Vacuum application necessitates biasing of the repeater signal or providing a vacuum source for the repeater relay. In this case, there are restrictions on allowable gravity spans and tank depths.

8.4.5 D/p transmitter with flanged or extended diaphragm

Standard flanged and extended diaphragm transmitter applications are illustrated in Figure 8.12(a) and (b), respectively. An extended diaphragm transmitter may be desirable in order to place the capsule flush with or inside the inner wall of the tank. With this instrument, pockets in front of the capsule where build-up may occur are eliminated.

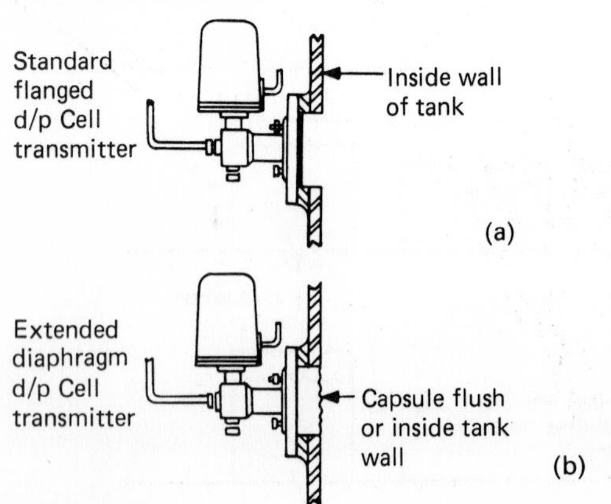

Figure 8.12 D/p cell with flanged or extended diaphragm.

8.4.6 D/p transmitter with pressure seals

If the process conditions are such that the process fluid must not be carried from the process vessel to the d/p transmitter then a transmitter fitted with pressure seals can be used as shown in Figure 8.13. Apart from the additional cost, the pressure seals reduce the sensitivity of the measurement and any mismatch in the two capillary systems can cause further errors. However, the system can be used for either open or closed vessels.

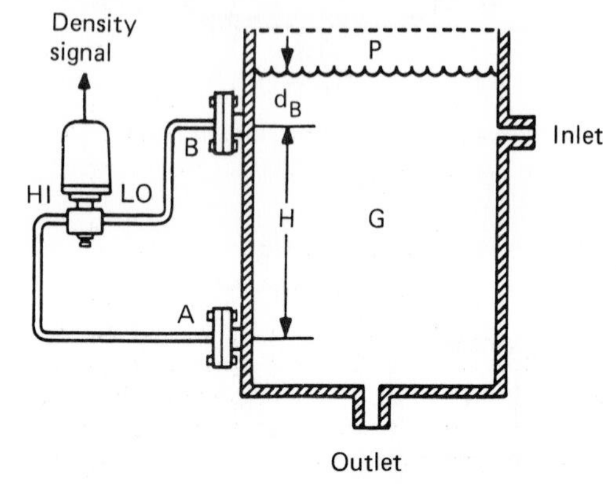

Figure 8.13 D/p cell with pressure seals.

8.4.7 D/p transmitter with bubble tubes

This very simple system, illustrated in Figure 8.14, involves two open-ended tubes, terminated with 'V'

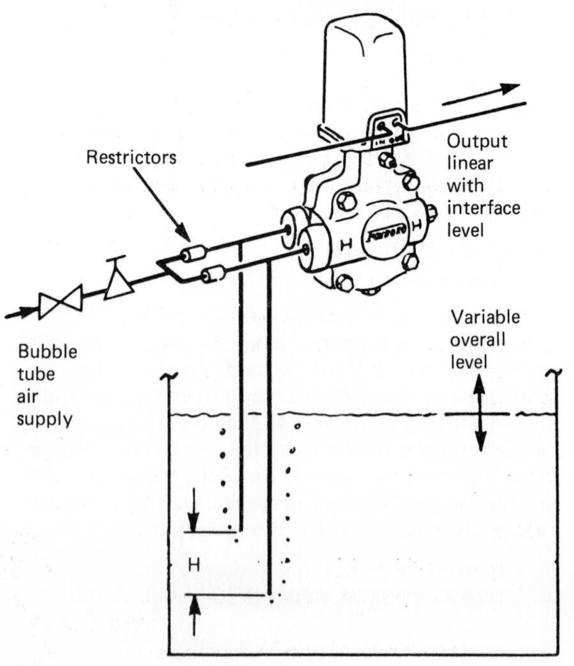

Figure 8.14 D/p cell with bubble tubes.

notches. These are immersed in the liquid with the 'V' notches separated by a known fixed vertical distance H and purged with a low but steady flow of air (or inert gas) at a suitable pressure.

A d/p transmitter connected between these tubes with the higher-pressure side associated with the lower 'V' notch, measures the difference P in hydrostatic pressure at the two points. This is equal to the density × the vertical distance between the two 'V' notches:

$$\text{density} = P/H$$

Although this method is very simple and effective, it is unsuitable for closed vessels or for liquids that may crystallize or involve precipitation which might block the bubble tubes and so give rise to erroneous results.

8.4.8 Other process considerations

Agitation in a process tank where density measurement is made must be sufficient to ensure uniformity of the liquid. But the velocity of fluid at the points where head pressure is measured must be sufficiently low to avoid a significant measurement error. Locations of side-mounted transmitters should be sufficiently high above the bottom of the tank to avoid errors due to them becoming submerged in the sediment that tends to collect there.

8.5 Measurement of density using radiation

Density measurements by this method are based on the principle that absorption of gamma radiation increases with increasing specific gravity of the material measured. These are discussed in Volume 3.

The principal instrumentation includes: a constant gamma source, a detector, and an indicating or recording instrument. Variations in radiation passing through a fixed volume of flowing process liquid are converted into a proportional electrical signal by the detector.

8.6 Measurement of density using resonant elements

Several density-measuring instruments are based on the measurement of the resonant frequency of an oscillating system such as a tube filled with the fluid under test or a cylinder completely immersed in the medium. Examples of each are described in the succeeding sections.

8.6.1 Liquid density measurement

The Solartron Liquid Density Transducer Type 7830 is shown in Figure 8.15. The sensing element comprises a single smooth bore tube through which flows the fluid to be measured. The tube is fixed at each end into heavy nodal masses which are isolated from the outer case by bellows and ligaments. Located along the tube are the electromagnetic drive and pick-up coil assemblies. In operation, the amplifier maintains the tube oscillating at its natural frequency.

Since the natural frequency of oscillation of the tube is a function of the mass per unit length, it must also be a function of the density of the flowing fluid. It also follows that the tube should be fabricated from material having a low and stable coefficient of expansion. If for reasons of corrosion or wear this is not possible, it is important that the temperature is

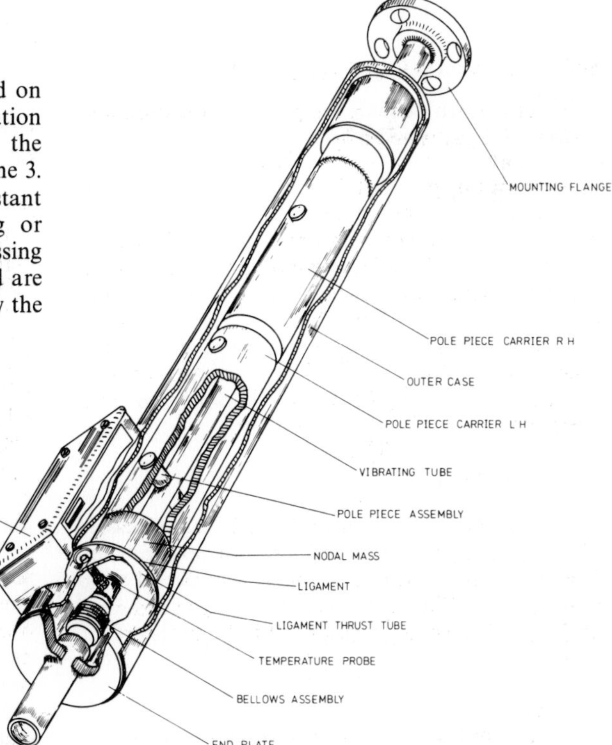

Figure 8.15 Solartron liquid density transducer. Courtesy, Schlumberger Electronics (UK) Ltd.

measured and a suitable correction applied to the density value determined from the resonant frequency.

Typically, the tube vibrates at about 1.3 kHz (when filled with water) and with an amplitude of about 0.025 mm. Densities up to 3000 kg/m^3 can be measured with an accuracy of 0.2 kg/m^3 and a repeatability of 0.02 kg/m^3. This contrasts with accuracies of only about 1 per cent of span that can be achieved with other methods, unless extreme care is taken.

The response is continuous throughout its operating range with no adjustments of span or zero. Recalibration is effected by adjustment of the constants in the associated readout or signal conditioning circuits. The density–frequency relation is given by

$$d = K_0\left(\frac{T^2}{T_0} - 1\right)$$

where P is the density of the measured fluid, K_0 is constant for the transducer, T_0 is the time period of oscillation under vacuum conditions, and T is the time period of oscillation under operating conditions.

It is noteworthy that, although the relation between density and the period of the oscillation strictly obeys a square law, it is linear within 2 per cent for a change in density of 20 per cent. For narrower spans the error is proportionally smaller.

8.6.2 Gas density measurements

The relationship between temperature, pressure and volume of a gas is given by

$$PV = nZR_0T$$

where P is the absolute pressure, V is the volume, n is the number of moles, Z is the compressibility factor, R_0 is the Universal gas constant and T is the absolute temperature. Use of the mole in this equation eliminates the need for determining individual gas constants, and the relationship between the mass of a gas m, its molecular weight Mw and number of moles is given by

$$n = m/Mw$$

When the compressibility factor Z is 1.0 the gas is called *ideal* or *perfect*. When the specific heat is assumed to be only temperature dependent the gas is referred to as *ideal*. If the *ideal* relative density RD of a gas is defined as the ratio of molecular weight of the gas to that of air, then

$$RD = \frac{Mw_{gas}}{Mw_{air}}$$

whereas the *real* relative density is defined as the ratio of the density of the gas to that of air, which is

$$RD = \frac{\rho_{gas}}{\rho_{air}}$$

for a particular temperature and pressure.

The above equation can be rearranged as a density equation thus

$$\rho = \frac{m}{V} = \frac{SGMw_{air}P}{ZR_0T}$$

Most relative density measuring instruments operate at pressures and temperatures close to ambient conditions and hence measure *real* relative density rather than the *ideal* relative density which is based on molecular weights and does not take into account the small effects of compressibility. Hence

$$\underset{(real)}{RD} = \left(\frac{\rho_{gas}}{\rho_{air}}\right)_{TP}$$

where T and P are close to ambient conditions.

Substituting the equation leads to P

$$\underset{(ideal)}{RD} = \left(\frac{ZT}{P_{gas}}\right) \times \left(\frac{P}{ZT_{air}}\right)_{TP} \times \underset{(real)}{RD}$$

For most practical applications this leads to

$$RD = \left(\frac{Z_{gas}}{Z_{air}}\right)_{TP} \underset{(real)}{RD}$$

Thus, the signal from the density transducer provides an indication of the molecular weight or specific gravity of the sampled gas.

The measurement can be applied to almost any gas provided that it is clean, dry and non-corrosive. The accuracy is typically 0.1 per cent of reading and the repeatability 0.02 per cent.

To measure the lower densities of gases, a more sensitive sensing element than that described for measurements on liquids is required. The Solartron Gas Density Transducer Type 7810 shown in Figure 8.16 achieves this by using a thin-walled cylinder resonated in the hoop or radial mode. The maximum amplitude of vibration occurs at the middle of the cylinder with nodes at each end and it is therefore clamped at one end with a free node-forming ring at the other end.

The cylinder is immersed in the gas whose density is to be measured, and it is thus not stressed due to the pressure of the gas. Gas in contact with the cylinder is brought into oscillation and effectively increases the mass of the vibrating system, thereby reducing its resonant frequency.

Oscillation is maintained electromagnetically by positioning drive and pick-up coils inside the cylinder

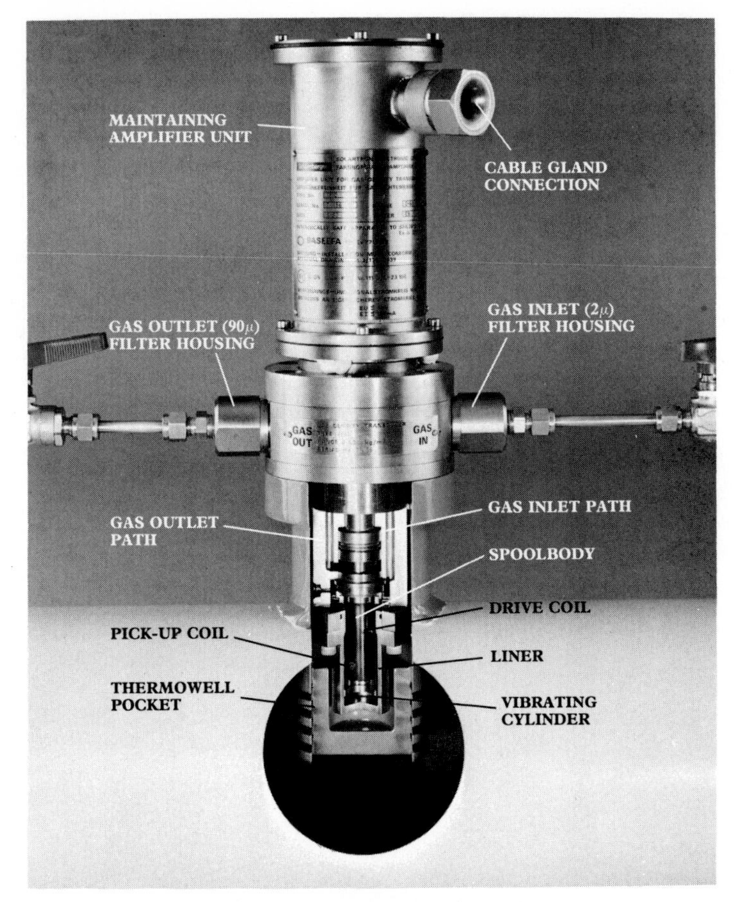

Figure 8.16 Solartron gas density transducer type 7810. Courtesy, Schlumberger Electronics (UK) Ltd.

and connecting them to a maintaining amplifier. The coils are mounted at right angles to each other to minimize stray coupling and phased so that the induced signal is proportional to the velocity, thereby reducing the effect of viscous damping.

A low temperature coefficient is obtained by constructing the cylinder from material having a low temperature coefficient of expansion. The cylinder wall thickness varies from 0.05 to 0.15 mm according to the required density range, the corresponding density ranges varying from 0 to 60 kg/m^3 and 40 to 400 kg/m^3.

The relation between the time period of oscillation of the transducer and gas density d is given by

$$d = 2d_0 \frac{(\tau - \tau_0)}{\tau_0}\left[1 + \frac{K}{2}\left(\frac{\tau - \tau_0}{\tau_0}\right)\right]$$

where τ is the measured time period of oscillation, τ_0 is the time period of oscillation under vacuum conditions, and d_0 and K are the calibration constants for each transducer.

An alternative method for measuring gas density involves a cylindrical test cell in which a hollow spinner is rotated at constant speed. This develops a differential pressure between the centre and ends of the spinner which is directly proportional to the density of the gas and can be measured by any standard differential pressure measuring device. A calibration constant converts the differential pressure to density for the actual conditions of temperature and pressure in the cell.

A sample flow of gas through the cell is induced by connecting it across a small restriction inserted in the main line to create an adequate pressure drop. The restriction could be determined from the square root of the differential pressure across the orifice plate multiplied by the differential pressure developed in the density cell. However, it is important to ensure that the flow of the gas through the density cell is not a significant proportion of the total flow. It is also important to apply a correction if there is any difference between the temperature and pressure of the gas in the density transducer and that in the main stream.

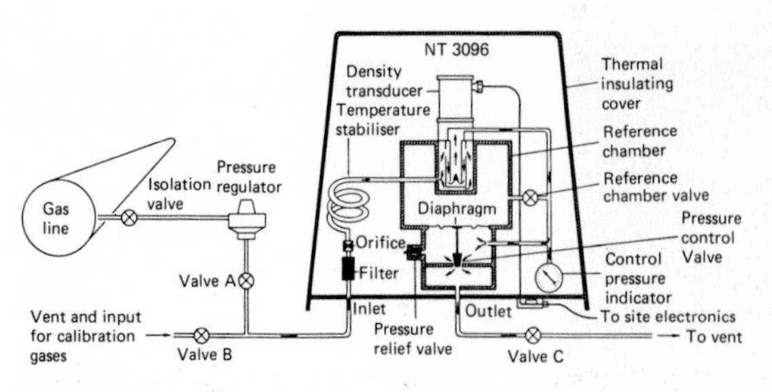

Figure 8.17 Relative density measurement using resonant element. Courtesy, Schlumberger Electronics (UK) Ltd.

8.6.3 Relative density of gases

The Solartron Specific Gravity Transducer Type 3096, shown in Figure 8.17 utilizes the density sensor described in the previous section to measure relative density of gases. In it, the sample of gas and the reference gas are stabilized at the same temperature by coils within thermal insulation. The reference chamber is a constant volume containing a fixed quantity of gas, any variation in temperature is compensated by a change in pressure which is transmitted to the sample gas by a flexible diaphragm. Having achieved pressure and temperature equalization by using a reference gas, a direct relationship between density and relative density can be realized.

9 Measurement of pressure

E. H. HIGHAM

9.1 What is pressure?

When a fluid is in contact with a boundary it produces a force at right angles to that boundary. The force per unit area is called the pressure. In the past, the distinction between mass and force has been blurred because we live in an environment in which every object is subjected to gravity and is accelerated towards the centre of the earth unless restrained. As explained in Chapter 8, the confusion is avoided in the SI system of units (Système International d'Unites) where the unit of force is the newton and the unit of area is a square metre so that pressure, being force per unit area, is measured in newtons per square metre and the unit, known as the pascal, is independent of the acceleration due to gravity.

The relation between the pascal and other units used for pressure measurements is shown in Table 9.1.

There are three categories of pressure measurements, namely absolute pressure, gauge pressure and differential pressure. The absolute pressure is the difference between the pressure at a particular point in a fluid and the absolute zero of pressure, i.e. a complete vacuum. A barometer is one example of an absolute pressure gauge because the height of the column of mercury measures the difference between the atmospheric pressure and the 'zero' pressure of the Torricellian vacuum that exists above the mercury column.

When the pressure-measuring device measures the difference between the unknown pressure and local atmospheric pressure the measurement is known as gauge pressure.

When the pressure-measuring device measures the difference between two unknown pressures, neither of which is atmospheric pressure, then the measurement is known as the differential pressure.

A mercury manometer is used in Figure 9.1 to illustrate these three measurements.

9.2 Pressure measurement

There are three basic methods for pressure measurement. The simplest method involves balancing the unknown pressure against the pressure produced by a column of liquid of known density. The second method involves allowing the unknown pressure to act on a known area and measuring the resultant force either directly or indirectly. The third method involves allowing the unknown pressure to act on an elastic member (of known area) and measuring the resultant stress or strain. Examples of these methods are described in the following sections.

9.2.1 Pressure measurements by balancing a column of liquid of known density

The simplest form of instrument for this type of measurement is the U-tube.

Consider a simple U-tube containing a liquid of density ρ as shown in Figure 9.2. The points A and B are at the same horizontal level and the liquid at C stands at a height h mm above B.

Then the pressure at A
= the pressure at B
= atmospheric pressure + pressure due to column of liquid BC
= atmospheric pressure $+h\rho$

If the liquid is water the unit of measure is mmH_2O and if the liquid is mercury then the unit of measure is mmHg. The corresponding SI unit is the pascal and

$$1\ mmH_2O = 9.806\,65\ Pa$$
$$1\ mmHg = 133.322\ Pa$$

For a system such as this it must be assumed that the density of the fluid in the left-hand leg of the manometer (Figure 9.2) is negligible compared with

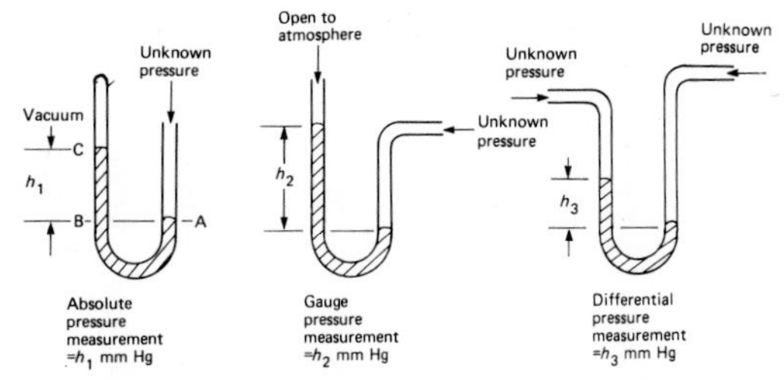

Figure 9.1 Comparison of types of pressure measurements.

Table 9.1 Pressure measurements

	Pascal *Pa*	*Bar* *bar*	*Millibar* *mbar*	*Standard atmosphere* *atm*	*Kilogram force per square cm* *kgf/cm²*	*Pound force per square inch* *lbf/in²*	*Torr*	*Millimetre of water* *mmH₂O*	*Millimetre of mercury* *mmHg*	*Inch of water* *inH₂O*	*Inch of mercury* *inHg*
Pa	1	10^{-5}	10^{-2}	9.869 23 $\times 10^{-6}$	1.019 72 $\times 10^{-5}$	1.450 38 $\times 10^{-4}$	7.500 62 $\times 10^{-3}$	1.019 72 $\times 10^{-1}$	7.500 62 $\times 10^{-3}$	4.014 63 $\times 10^{-3}$	2.953 00 $\times 10^{-4}$
bar	10^{5}	1	10^{3}	9.869 23 $\times 10^{-1}$	1.019 72	14.5038	7.500 62 $\times 10^{-2}$	1.019 72 $\times 10^{-2}$	7.500 62 $\times 10^{-2}$	4.014 63 $\times 10^{-8}$	29.5300
mbar	10^{2}	10^{-3}	1	9.869 23 $\times 10^{-4}$	1.019 72 $\times 10^{-3}$	1.450 38 $\times 10^{-2}$	7.500 62 $\times 10^{-1}$	1.019 72 $\times 10$	7.500 62 $\times 10^{-5}$	4.014 62 $\times 10^{-1}$	2.953 00 $\times 10^{-2}$
atm	1.013 25 $\times 10^{5}$	1.013 25	1.013 25 $\times 10^{3}$	1	1.033 23	1.469 59 $\times 10$	7.600 00 $\times 10^{2}$	1.033 23 $\times 10^{5}$	760	4.067 83 $\times 10^{2}$	29.9213
kgf/cm²	98 066.5	0.980 665	980.665	0.967 841	1	14.2233	735.559 $\times 10^{2}$	10^{4}	7.355 59 $\times 10^{2}$	3.937 00 $\times 10^{2}$	28.9590
lbf/in²	6894.76	0.068 947 6	68.9476	6.804 60 $\times 10^{-2}$	7.030 70 $\times 10^{-2}$	1	51.7149	7.030 69 $\times 10^{2}$	51.7149	27.6798	2.036 02
torr	133.322	1.333 22 $\times 10^{-3}$	1.333 22	1.315 79 $\times 10^{-3}$	1.359 51 $\times 10^{-3}$	1.933 68 $\times 10^{-2}$	1	13.5951	1	53.5240	3.937 01 $\times 10^{-2}$
mmH₂O	9.806 65	9.806 65 $\times 10^{-5}$	9.806 65 $\times 10^{2}$	9.678 41 $\times 10^{-5}$	10^{-4}	1.422 33 $\times 10^{-3}$	7.355 59 $\times 10^{-2}$	1	7.355 59 $\times 10^{-2}$	3.937 01 $\times 10^{-2}$	2.895 90 $\times 10^{-3}$
mmHg	133.322	1.333 22 $\times 10^{-3}$	1.333 22	1.315 79 $\times 10^{-3}$	1.359 51 $\times 10^{-3}$	1.933 68 $\times 10^{-2}$	1	13.5951	1	53.5240	3.937 01 $\times 10^{-2}$
inH₂O	249.089	2.490 89 $\times 10^{-3}$	2.490 89	2.458 31 $\times 10^{-3}$	2.54 $\times 10^{-3}$	3.612 72 $\times 10^{-2}$	1.868 32	25.4	1.868 32	1	7.355 59 $\times 10^{-2}$
inHg	3386.39	3.386 39 $\times 10^{-2}$	33.8639	3.342 11 $\times 10^{-2}$	3.453 16 $\times 10^{-2}$	0.491 154	25.4000	3.453 16 $\times 10^{-2}$	25.4000	13.5951	1

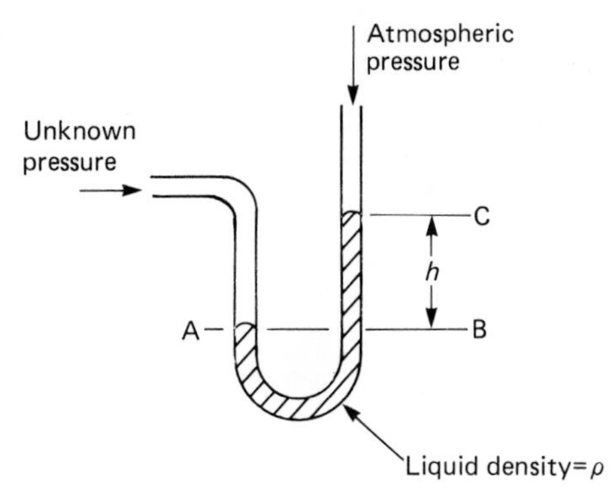

Figure 9.2 Simple U-tube manometer.

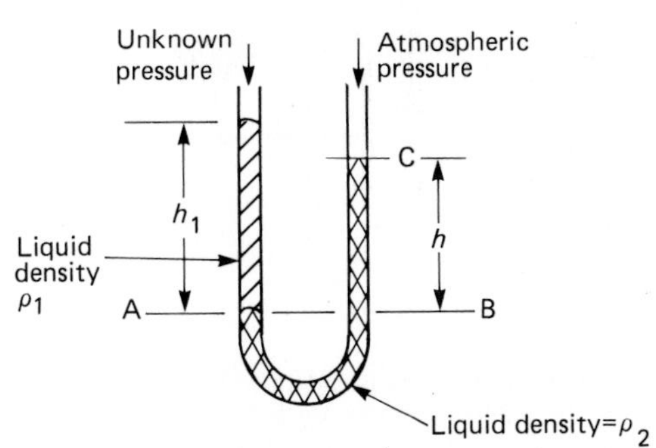

Figure 9.3 Manometer with wet leg connection.

the manometer liquid. If this is not so then a correction must be applied to allow for the pressure due to the fluid in the gauge and connecting pipes. Referring to Figure 9.3, we have

Pressure at A = pressure at B

$$P\,(\text{gauge pressure}) = \rho_1 h_1 + \text{atmospheric pressure}$$
$$= \rho_2 h + \text{atmospheric pressure}$$

or

$$P = \rho_2 h - \rho_1 h_1$$

(Gauge pressure because the atmospheric pressure is superimposed on each manometer leg measurement.)

If the manometer limbs have different diameters as in the case for a well-type manometer, shown in Figure 9.4, then the rise in one leg does not equal the fall in the other. If the well has a cross-sectional area A and the tube has an area a, then the loss of liquid in one unit must equal the gain of liquid in the other. Hence $h_m A = h_2 a$ so that $h_2 = h_m A/a$.

For a simple U-tube measurement the applied pressure $P = (h_2 + h_m)\rho$. If the left-hand leg of the manometer becomes a wet leg with fluid density then

$$P + (h_1 + h_2)\rho_2 = (h_2 + h_m)\rho_1$$

so that

$$P = (h_2 + h_m)\rho_1 - (h_1 + h_2)\rho_2$$

If both manometer legs are wet then

$$P + (h_1 + h_2)\rho_2 = (h_2 + h_m)\rho_1 + (h_1 - h_m)\rho_2$$
$$P = (h_2 + h_m)\rho_1 + (h_1 - h_m)\rho_2 - (h_1 + h_2)\rho_2$$
$$= h_2\rho_1 + h_m\rho_1 + h_1\rho_2 - h_m\rho_2 - h_1\rho_2 - h_2\rho_2$$
$$= \rho_1(h_2 + h_m) - \rho_2(h_m + h_2)$$
$$= (h_2 + h_m)(\rho_1 - \rho_2)$$
$$= h_m(A/a + 1)(\rho_1 - \rho_2)$$

Effect of temperature The effect of variations in temperature have been neglected so far but for accurate work the effect of temperature on the densities of the fluids in the manometer must be taken into account and the effect of temperature on the scale should not be overlooked. For most applications it is sufficient to consider the effect of temperature only on the manometer liquid, in which case the density ρ at any temperature T can be taken to be:

$$\rho = \frac{\rho_0}{1 + \beta(T - T_0)}$$

where ρ_0 is the density at base conditions, β is the coefficient of cubic expansion, T_0 is the base temperature, and T is the actual temperature.

9.2.2 Pressure measurements by allowing the unknown pressure to act on a known area and measuring the resultant force

9.2.2.1 Dead-weight testers

The simplest technique for determining a pressure by measuring the force that is generated when it acts on a known area is illustrated by the dead-weight tester, but

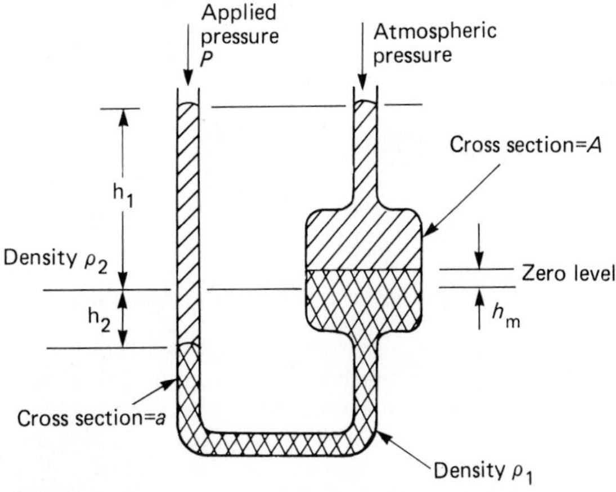

Figure 9.4 Manometer with limbs of different diameters.

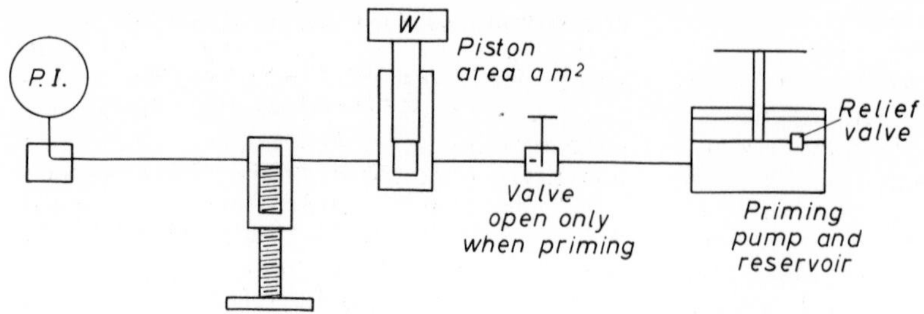

Figure 9.5 Basic system of dead weight tester.

this system is used for calibrating instruments rather than measuring unknown pressures.

The basic system is shown diagrammatically in Figure 9.5. It comprises a priming pump and reservoir, an isolating valve, the piston carrying the weight, a screw press and the gauge under test. In operation, the screw press is set to its zero position, weights representing the desired pressure are applied to the piston and the priming pump is operated to pressure the system. The valve is then shut and the screw press is adjusted until the pressure in the system is sufficient to raise the piston off its stops. If the frictional forces on the piston are neglected then the pressure acting on it is p newtons per square metre and if its area is a square metres, then the resultant force is pa N. This will support a weight $W = pa$ N.

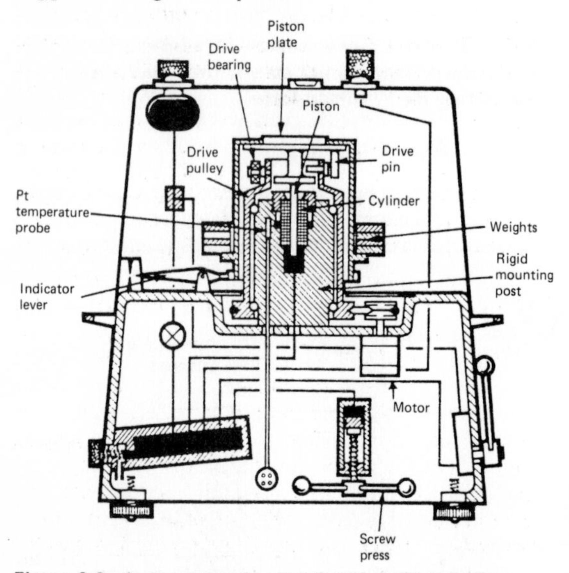

Figure 9.6 Arrangement of a precision dead weight tester. Courtesy, Desgranges and Hout.

The accuracy depends on the precision with which the piston and its associated cylinder are manufactured and on eliminating the effect of friction by rotating the piston whilst the reading is taken.

The Desgranges and Huot range of primary pressure standards is a very refined version of the dead-weight testers. Figure 9.6 shows a sectional drawing of an oil-operated standard. For this degree of precision it is important to ensure that the piston area and gravitational forces are constant so that the basic relation between the mass applied to the piston and the measured pressure is maintained. The instrument therefore includes levelling screws and bubble indicators.

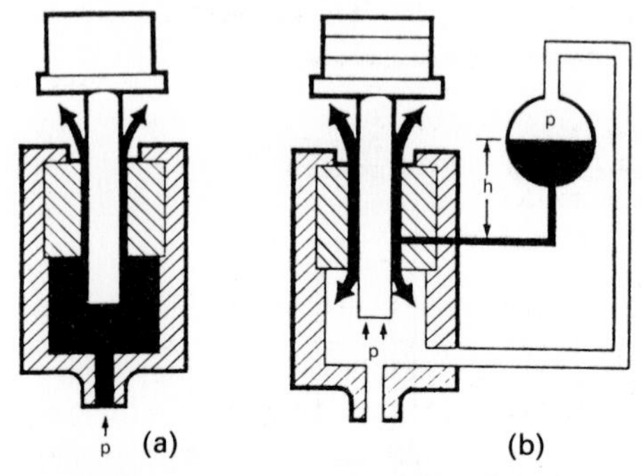

Figure 9.7 Lubrication of the piston. (a) Oil-operated system. (b) Gas-operated system. Courtesy, Desgranges and Hout.

Side stresses on the piston are avoided by loading the principal weights on a bell so that their centre of gravity is well below that of the piston. Only the fractional weights are placed directly on the piston plate and the larger of these are designed to stack precisely on the centre line.

The mobility of the piston in the cylinder assembly determines the sensitivity of the instrument and this requires an annulus that is lubricated by liquid even when gas pressures are being measured. Figure 9.7(a) and (b) show how this is achieved.

The system for liquids is conventional but for gases lubricant in the reservoir passes into the annulus between the piston and cylinder. The gas pressure is applied both to the piston and to the reservoir so that there is always a small hydraulic head to cause lubricant to flow into the assembly.

Rotation of the piston in the cylinder sets up radial forces in the lubricating fluid which tend to keep the piston centred, but the speed of rotation should be constant and the drive itself should not impart vibration or spurious forces. This is achieved by arranging the motor to drive the cylinder pulley via an oval drive pulley which is therefore alternatively accelerating and decelerating. The final drive is via the bearing on to the pin secured to the piston plate. In this way, once the piston is in motion, it rotates freely until it has lost sufficient momentum for the drive bearing to impart a small impulse which accelerates the piston. This ensures that it is rotating freely for at least 90 per cent of the time.

The piston and cylinder are machined from tungsten carbide to a tolerance of 0.1 micrometre so that the typical clearance between them is 0.5 micrometre. A balance indicator which tracks a soft iron band set in the bell shows the position of the piston and allows fluid head corrections for the most precise measurements.

The principal weights are fabricated in stainless steel and supplied in sets up to 50 kg according to the model chosen. The mass of the bell (typically 0.8 kg) and the piston plate assembly (typically 0.2 kg) must be added to the applied mass.

A complete set of piston and cylinder assemblies allows measurements to be made in the ranges from 0.1 to 50 bar to 2.0 to 1000 bar, the uncertainty of measurement being $\pm 5 \times 10^{-4}$ or less for the 'N' class instruments and $\pm 1 \times 10^{-4}$ or less for the 'S' class instruments.

Another type of dead-weight tester is the pneumatic dead weight tester. This is a self-regulating primary pressure standard. An accurate pressure is generated by establishing equilibrium between the air pressure on the underside of a spherical ball on top of which are loaded weights of known mass. The arrangement is shown in Figure 9.8.

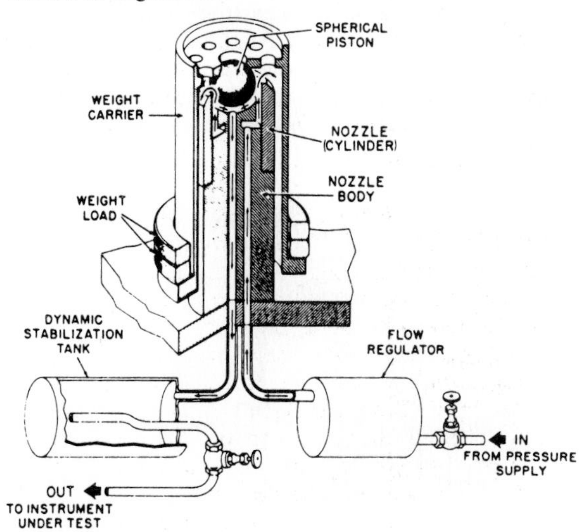

Figure 9.8 Self-regulating primary pressure standard. Courtesy, Amatek Inc.

The precision spherical ball is floated within a tapered stainless-steel nozzle. A regulated flow of air is introduced below the ball and the tapered nozzle so that it is lifted towards the annulus. Equilibrium is established as soon as the ball floats and the vented flow equals the fixed flow and the pressure is proportional to the weight loaded on the ball. In operation the ball is centred by the dynamic film of air which eliminates contact between the ball and nozzle.

When the weights are changed, the position of the ball also changes and in so doing it affects the air flow. The input regulator responds to this change by adjusting the flow of air so that pressure under the sphere and hence the output pressure is regulated at the new value.

9.2.3 Pressure measurement by allowing the known pressure to act on a flexible member and measuring the resultant motion

The great majority of pressure gauges utilize a Bourdon tube, stacked diaphragms, or a bellows to sense the pressure. The applied pressure causes a change in the shape of the sensor that is used to move a pointer with respect to a scale.

9.2.3.1 Bourdon tubes

The simplest form of Bourdon tube comprises a tube of oval cross-section bent into a circle. One end is sealed and attached via an adjustable connecting link to the lower end of a pivoted quadrant. The upper part of the quadrant is the toothed segment which engages in the teeth of the central pinion which carries the pointer that moves with respect to a fixed scale. Backlash between the quadrant and pinion is minimized by a delicate hair-spring. The other end of the tube is open so that the pressure to be measured can be applied via the block to which it is fixed and which also carries the pressure connection and provides the datum for measurement of the deflection.

If the internal pressure exceeds the external pressure the shape of the tube changes from oval towards circular with the result that it becomes straighter. The movement of the free end drives the pointer mechanism so that the pointer moves with respect to the scale. If the internal pressure is less than the external pressure, the free end of the tube moves towards the block, causing the pointer to move in the opposite direction.

The tube may be made from a variety of elastic materials depending on the nature of the fluid whose pressure is to be measured (phosphor bronze, beryllium copper and stainless steel are used most widely but for applications involving particularly corrosive fluids alloys, such as K-Monel, are used). The thickness of the tube and the material from which it is

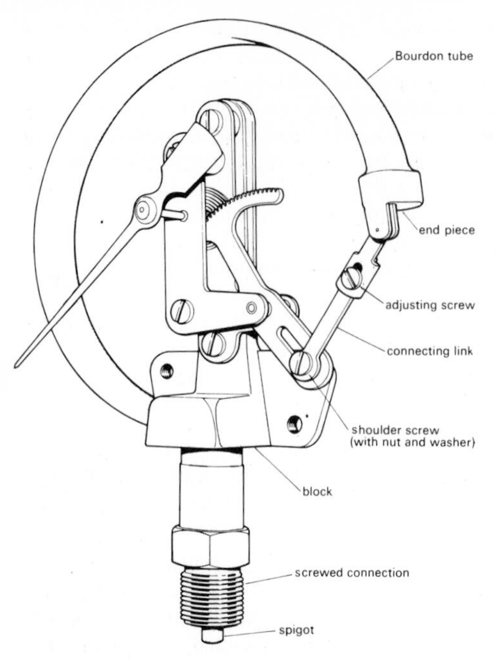

Figure 9.9 Mechanism of Bourdon tube gauge. Courtesy, Budenberg Gauge Co. Ltd.

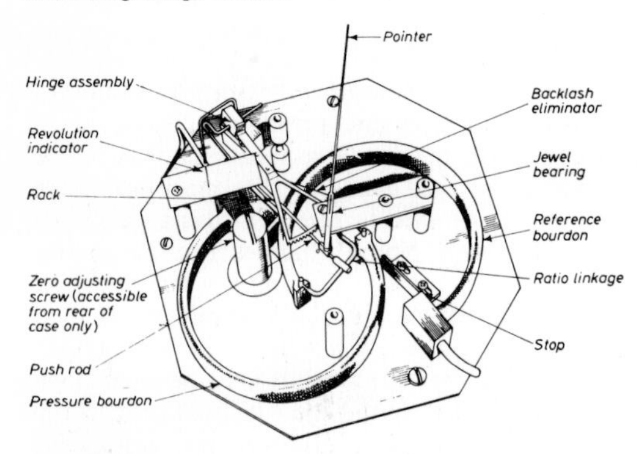

Figure 9.10 Precision absolute pressure gauge. Courtesy, Wallace & Tiernan Ltd.

to be fabricated are selected according to the pressure range, but the actual dimensions of the tube determine the force available to drive the pointer mechanism. The construction of a typical gauge is shown in Figure 9.9.

The performance of pressure gauges of this type varies widely, not only as a result of their basic design and materials of construction, but also because of the conditions under which they are used. The principal sources of error are hysteresis in the Bourdon tube, changes in its sensitivity due to changes of temperature, frictional effects, and backlash in the pointer mechanism. A typical accuracy is ± 2 per cent of span.

Much higher precision can be achieved by attention to detail and one example is illustrated in Figure 9.10 which shows a gauge for measuring absolute pressure. It includes two Bourdon tubes, one being completely evacuated and sealed to provide the reference whilst the unknown pressure is applied to the other Bourdon tube. The free ends of the Bourdon tubes are connected by a ratio linkage which through a push rod transmits the difference in the movement of the free ends to a rack assembly which in turn rotates the pinion and pointer. Jewel bearings are used to minimize friction and backlash is eliminated by maintaining a uniform tension for all positions of the rack and pinion through the use of a nylon thread to connect a spring on the rack with a grooved pulley on the pinion shaft.

The Bourdon tubes are made of Ni-Span C which has a very low coefficient of expansion and good resistance to corrosion. As both Bourdon tubes are subjected to the same atmospheric pressure, the instrument maintains its accuracy for barometric pressure changes of ± 130 mmHg. The dial diameter is 216 mm and the full range of the instrument is covered by two revolutions of the pointer giving an effective scale length of 1.36 m. The sensitivity is 0.0125 per cent and the accuracy 0.1 per cent of full scale. The ambient temperature effect is less than 0.01 per cent of full scale per kelvin.

9.2.3.2 Spiral and helical Bourdon tubes

The amount of the movement of the free end of a Bourdon tube varies inversely as the wall thickness and is dependent on the cross-sectional shape. It also varies directly with the angle subtended by the arc through which the tube is formed. By using a helix or spiral to increase the effective angular length of the tube, the movement of the free end is similarly increased and the need for further magnification is reduced. Examples of these constructions are shown in Figures 9.11 and 9.12. They avoid the necessity for the toothed quadrant with the consequent reduction of backlash and frictional errors. In general, the spiral configuration is used for low pressures and the helical form for high pressures.

Figure 9.11 Helical Bourdon tube. Courtesy, The Foxboro Company.

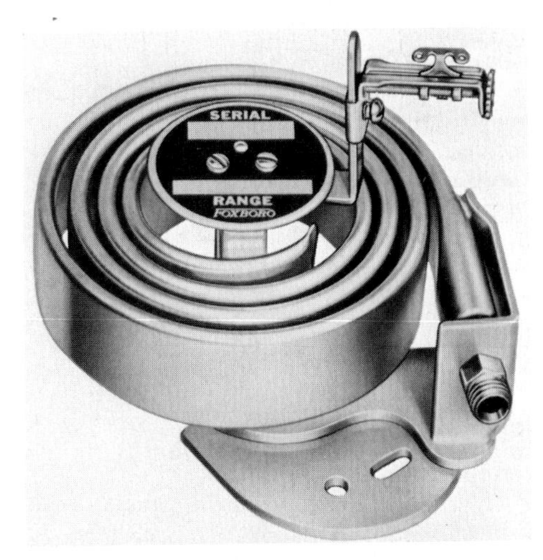

Figure 9.12 Spiral Bourdon tube. Courtesy, The Foxboro Company.

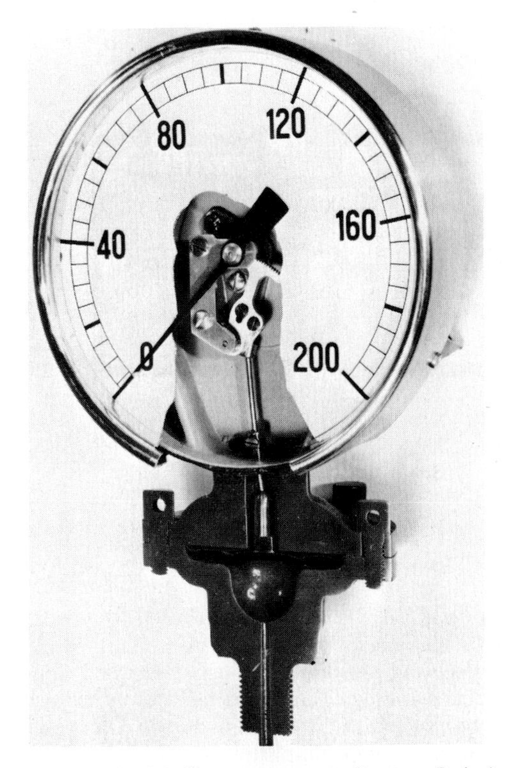

Figure 9.13 Schaffer pressure gauge. Courtesy, Budenberg Gauge Co. Ltd.

9.2.3.3 Diaphragm pressure elements

There are two basic categories of diaphragm elements, namely stiff metallic diaphragms and slack diaphragms associated with drive plates.

The simplest form of diaphragm gauge is the Schaffer gauge shown in Figure 9.13. It consists of a heat-treated stainless-steel corrugated diaphragm about 65 mm in diameter and held between two flanges. The unknown pressure is applied to the underside of the diaphragm and the resultant movement of the centre of the diaphragm is transmitted through a linkage to drive the pointer as in the Bourdon gauge. The upper flange is shaped to provide protection against the application of over-range pressures.

In the Schaffer gauge it is the elastic properties of the metallic diaphragm which govern the range and accuracy of the measurement. An aneroid barometer (Figure 9.14) also uses a corrugated diaphragm but it is supplemented by a spring. The element consists of a flat circular capsule having a corrugated lid and base and is evacuated before being sealed. It is prevented from collapse by a spring which is anchored to a bridge and attached to the top centre of the capsule. Also attached at this point is a lever which acts through a bell crank and lever mechanism to rotate the pointer. When the atmospheric pressure increases the capsule contracts so that the pointer is caused to rotate in one direction. Conversely when the atmospheric pressure falls the capsule expands and the pointer is driven in the opposite direction.

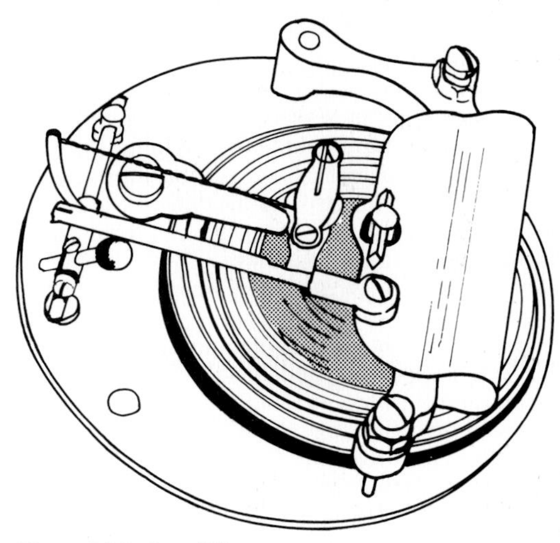

Figure 9.14 Aneroid barometer.

A further example of an instrument employing stiff diaphragms augmented by springs is shown in Figures 9.15 and 9.16. This instrument has largely superseded the bell-type mercury pressure manometer previously widely used for measuring differential associated with orifice-plate flowmeters, partly because of the increased cost, but more particularly because of the health hazards associated with mercury.

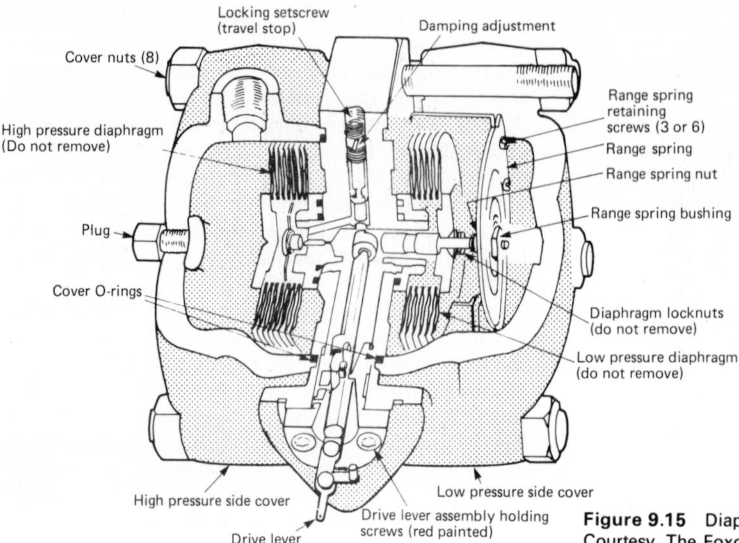

Figure 9.15 Diaphragm type differential pressure transmitter. Courtesy, The Foxoboro Company.

The diaphragm elements (7) and (2) are made up from pairs of corrugated diaphragms with a spacing ring stitch-welded at the central hole. These assemblies are then stitch-welded at their circumference to form a stack. This configuration ensures that when excess pressure is applied to the stack the individual corrugations nest together whilst the stack spacing rings come together to form a metal-to-metal stop.

The diaphragm stacks (7) and (2) are mounted on the central body together with the range spring (3) and drive unit (4). Pressure-tight covers (8) form the high- and low-pressure chambers. The diaphragm stacks (2) and (7) are interconnected via the damping valve (1) and fitted internally with a liquid which remains fluid under normal ambient conditions.

An increase in pressure in the high-pressure chamber compresses the diaphragm stack (7) and in so doing displaces fluid via the damping valve (1) into stack (2) causing it to expand until the force exerted by the range spring balances the initial change in pressure. The deflection of the range spring is transmitted to the inner end of the drive unit, which being pivoted at a sealed flexure (5) transfers the motion to the outer end of the drive shaft (4) where it can be used to operate a pen arm.

A bimetallic temperature-compensator (6) is mounted inside the stack (7) and adjusts the volume of that stack to compensate for the change in volume of the fill liquid resulting from a change of temperature. The instrument is suitable for operating at pressures up to 140 bar and spans between 50 and 500 mbar can be provided by selecting suitable combinations of the range springs which are fabricated from Ni-Span C to make them substantially insensitive to changes of temperature.

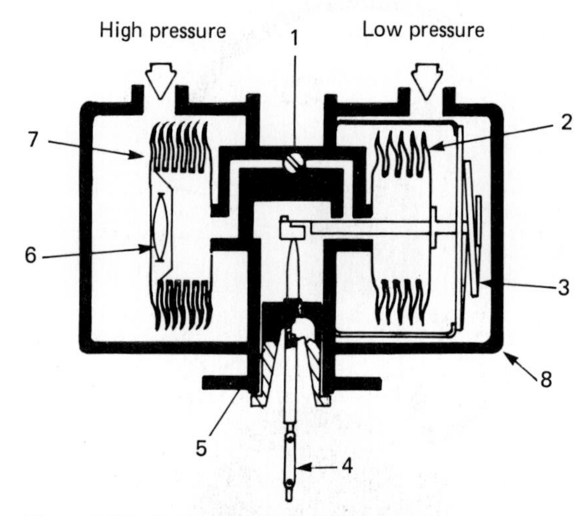

Figure 9.16 Components of the differential pressure transmitter. Courtesy, The Foxboro Company.

Bellows elements With the development of the hydraulic method for forming bellows, many of the pressure-sensing capsules previously fabricated from corrugated diaphragms have been replaced by bellows which are available in a variety of materials. The spring rate or modulus of compression of a bellows varies directly as the modulus of elasticity of the material from which it is formed and proportionally to the third power of the wall thickness. It is also inversely proportional to the number of convolutions and to the square of the outside diameter of the bellows.

The combined effect of variations in the elastic properties of the materials of construction and manufacturing tolerance results in appreciable variations in

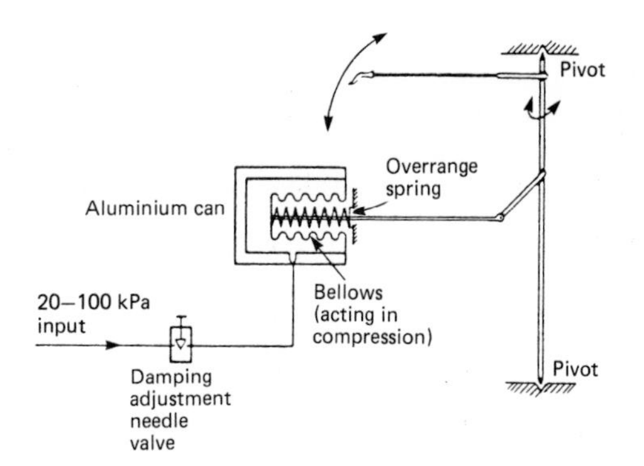

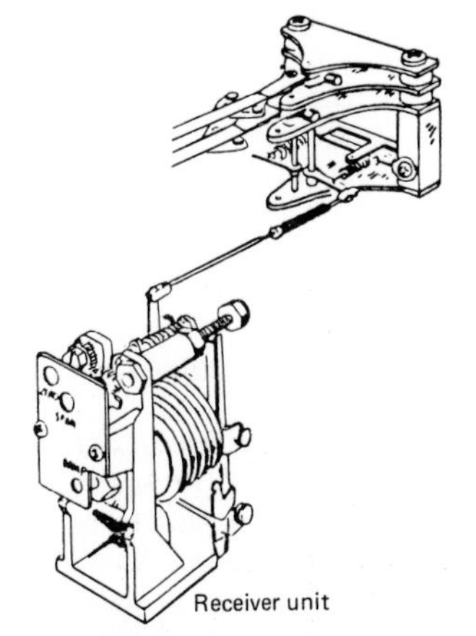

Figure 9.17 Pneumatic receiver using a bellows. Courtesy, The Foxboro Company.

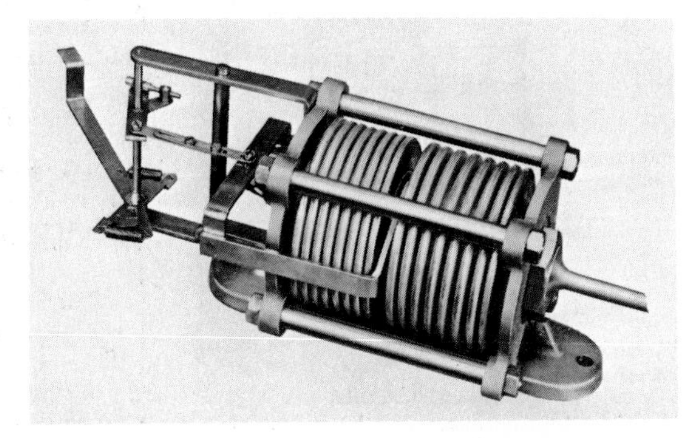

Figure 9.18 Bellows assembly for an absolute pressure gauge. Courtesy, Foxboro-Yoxall Ltd.

the bellows spring rate, not only from one batch to another but also within a batch. For some applications this may not be particularly significant but, when it is, the effect can be reduced by incorporating a powerful spring into the assembly.

Figure 9.17 shows a pneumatic receiver, i.e. a unit specifically designed for measurements in the range 20 to 100 kPa which is one of the standard ranges for transmission in pneumatic systems.

Figure 9.18 shows a bellows assembly for the measurement of absolute pressure. It comprises two carefully matched stainless-steel bellows, one of which is evacuated to a pressure of less than 0.05 mmHg and sealed. The unknown pressure is applied to the other bellows. The two bellows are mounted within a frame and connected together via a yoke which transmits the bellows motion via a link to a pointer or the pen arm of a recorder.

9.2.3.5 Slack-diaphragm pressure elements with drive plates

These are a further example of pressure sensors in which the force produced by the pressure acting on a fixed area is opposed by a spring. The most common application is the measurement of furnace draught where a span between 100 Pa and 2.5 kPa above atmospheric may be required. A typical instrument of this type is shown in Figure 9.19. To respond to such

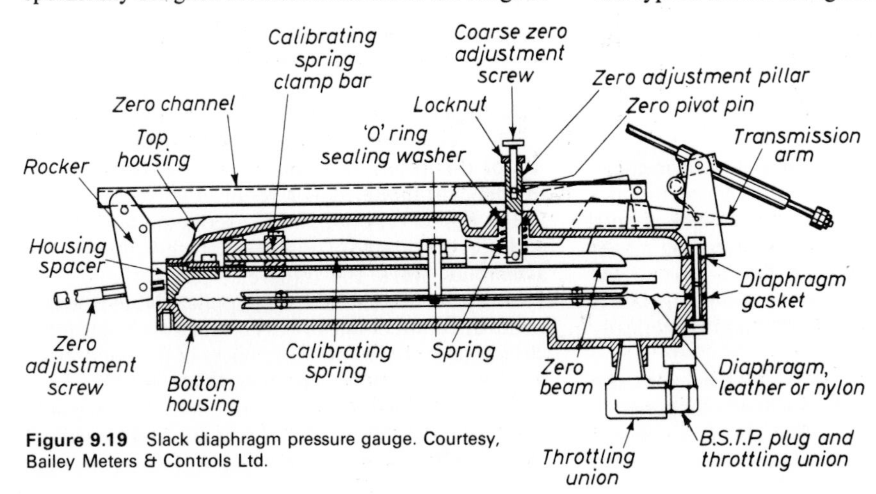

Figure 9.19 Slack diaphragm pressure gauge. Courtesy, Bailey Meters & Controls Ltd.

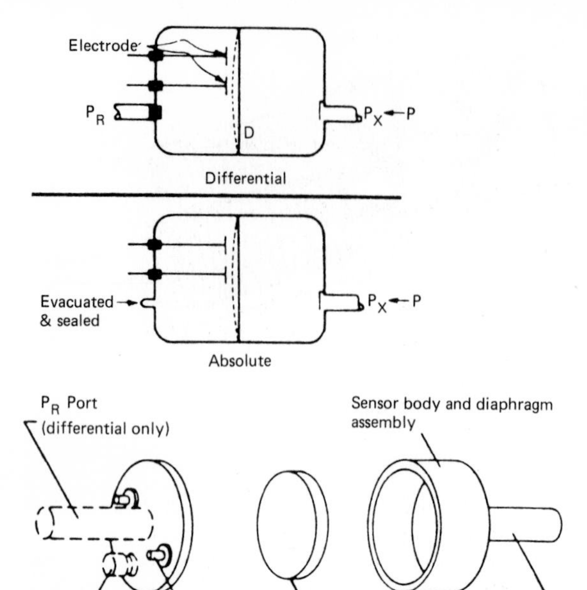

Figure 9.20 Capacitance manometer sensor. Courtesy, MKS Instruments Inc.

small pressures a large-area diaphragm is required. It is made from very thin non-porous material and supported on both sides over a large portion of its area by drive plates. Travel of the diaphragm is limited by the drive plates coming to rest against stops to provide overload protection. Motion of the diaphragm is produced by the difference in pressure across it and is opposed by a flat beryllium copper spring. The span of the instrument is adjusted by varying the effective length of the spring, and hence its rate.

For measuring gauge pressure, the movement of the diaphragm is transmitted to the pointer directly by a suitable mechanism. For measuring differential pressure, both sides of the chamber containing the diaphragm are sealed and the motion is transmitted through the seal by a magnetic coupling.

9.2.3.6 Capacitance manometers

The application of electronic techniques to measure the deflection of a diaphragm and hence to infer pressure has resulted in major improvements in both sensitivity and resolution as well as providing means for compensating for nonlinear effects. One of the devices in which these techniques have been applied is the capacitance manometer shown diagrammatically in Figure 9.20.

For such a sensor it is important that the diaphragm and sensor body are capable of withstanding a wide range of process fluids including those which are highly corrosive. It is also important for them to have thermal coefficients which closely match those of the electrode assembly and screening material. 'Inconel' is a suitable material for the body and diaphragm, whilst 'Fosterite' with either nickel or palladium is used for the electrode assembly. With these materials pressures as low as 10^{-3} Pa can be measured reliably.

The tensioned metal diaphragm is welded into the sensor body and the electrode assembly is located in the body at the correct position with respect to the diaphragm. If the sensor is to be used for absolute pressure measurements, the sensor-body assembly is completed by welding in place a cover which carries the two electrode connections and the getter assembly. If on the other hand the sensor is to be used for differential pressure measurements, then provision is made for connecting the reference pressure.

The hysteresis error for such a sensor is normally less than 0.01 per cent of the reading; for sensors having spans greater than 100 Pa the error is almost immeasurable. The non-linearity is the largest source of error in the system apart from temperature effects and is usually in the order of 0.05 per cent of reading and is minimized by selective adjustments in the associated electronic circuits.

Errors due to ambient temperature changes affect both the zero and span. Selection of the optimum materials of construction results in a zero error of approximately 0.02 per cent of span per kelvin and a span error of approximately 0.06 per cent of span per kelvin. The span error can be reduced to 0.0005 per cent by including a temperature sensor in the body of the pressure sensor and developing a corresponding correction in the measuring circuits. The zero error can be reduced to 0.002 per cent by including a nulling circuit.

9.2.3.7 Quartz electrostatic pressure sensors

There are two principal types of quartz sensors used for pressure measurement. The first are those in which the applied force causes an electrostatic charge to be developed across the crystal which is then measured by a charge amplifier and the resultant signal used to provide an indication of the applied force.

The second category (Section 9.2.3.9) involves the use of the quartz in some form of resonator whose frequency is modified as a result of the applied force.

The Kistler type 601 and 707 series shown in Figure 9.21 are an example of quartz electrostatic sensor. The assemblies utilize the transverse piezo-electric effect illustrated in Figure 9.22. The application of a force F in the direction of one of the neutral axes Y sets up an electrostatic charge on the surfaces of the polar axis x at right angles to it. The magnitude of this charge depends on the dimensions of the quartz crystal and by selecting a suitable shape it is possible to secure a high charge yield combined with good linearity and low

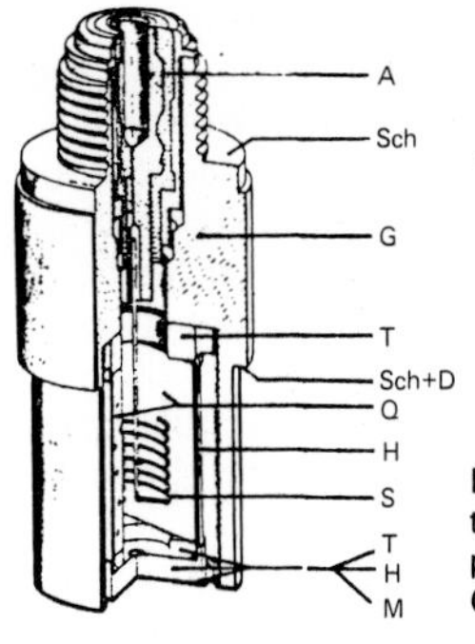

Figure 9.21 Pressure transducer using transverse piezo-electric effect of quartz. Courtesy, Kistler Instruments Ltd.

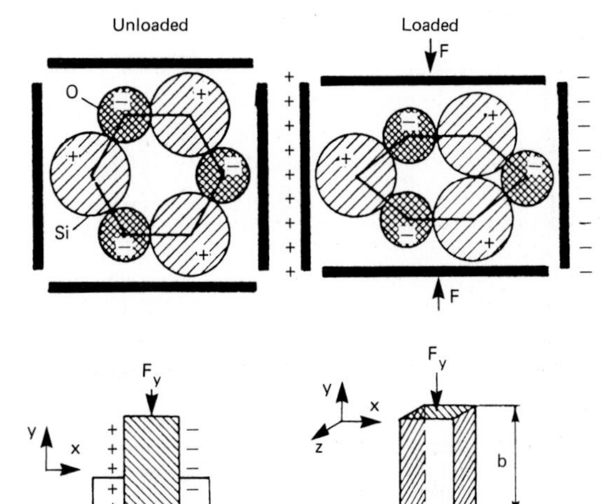

Figure 9.22 Principle of transverse piezo-electric effect. Courtesy, Kistler Instruments Ltd.

temperature sensitivity. Similarly, the principle of the longitudinal piezo-electric effect is illustrated in Figure 9.23.

A typical transducer is assembled from three quartz stacks Q (Figure 9.21) joined rigidly to the holder G by means of a preload sleeve H and temperature compensator T. The pressure to be measured acts on the diaphragm M where it is converted into the force which is applied to the three quartz stacks. The contact faces of the quartz are coated with silver and a central noble metal coil S conducts charge to the connector A.

The outer faces of the quartz are connected to the housing. With this configuration linearities of between 0.2 and 0.3 per cent are achieved for spans up to 25 MPa and the sensors have a uniform response up to about 30 kHz with a peak of about 100 kHz. Because there must be a finite leakage resistance across the

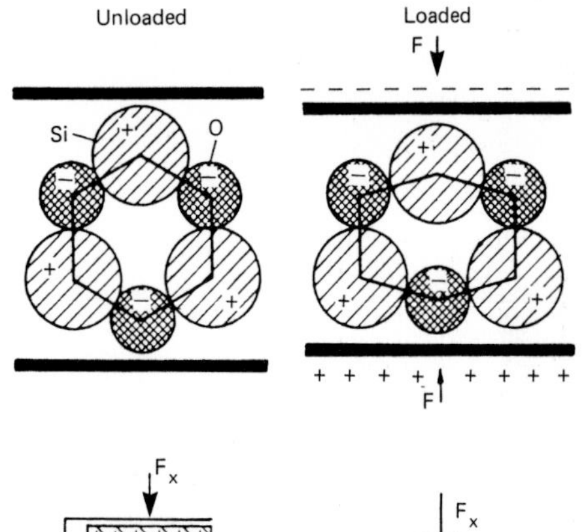

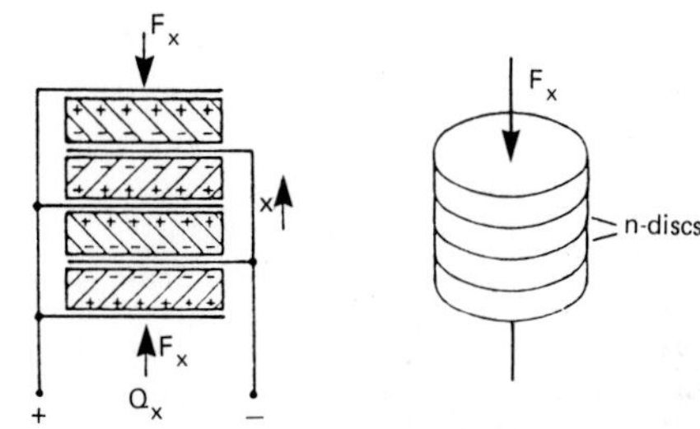

Figure 9.23 Principle of longitudinal piezo-electric effect. Courtesy, Kistler Instruments Ltd.

sensor, such devices cannot be used for static measurements. The low frequency limit is of the order of 1 Hz, depending on the sensitivity. The type of charge amplifier associated with these sensors is shown in Figure 9.24. It comprises a high-gain operational amplifier with MOSFET input stage to ensure that the input impedance is very high, and capacitor feedback to ensure that the charge generated on the quartz transducer is virtually completely compensated. It can be shown that the output voltage from the amplifier is $-Q/C_g$ where Q is the charge generated by the quartz sensor and C_g is the feedback capacitance. Thus the system is essentially insensitive to the influence of the input cable impedance.

Sensors such as these are characterized by their high stability, wide dynamic range, good temperature stability, good linearity and low hysteresis. They are available in a very wide variety of configurations for pressure ranges from 200 kPa to 100 MPa.

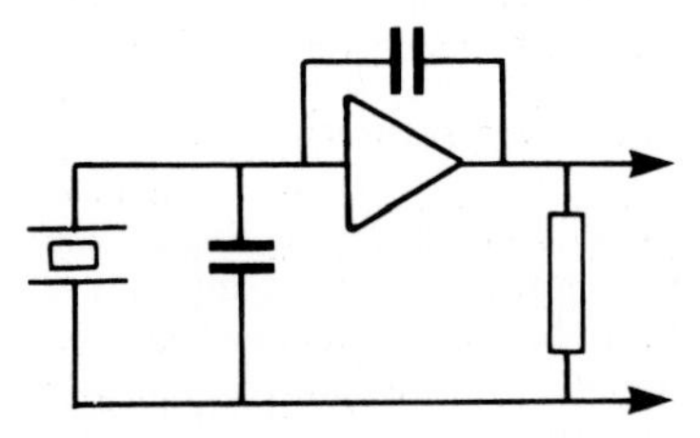

Figure 9.24 Charge amplifier associated with piezo-electric effect sensor.

Figure 9.25 Piezo-resistive pressure transducer. Courtesy, Kistler Instruments Ltd.

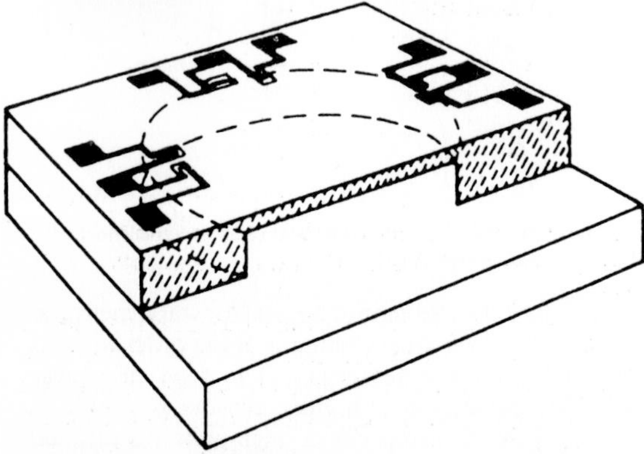

Figure 9.26 Schematic drawing of pressure sensing element. Courtesy, Kistler Instruments Ltd.

9.2.3.8 Piezo resistive pressure sensors

For many metals and some other solid materials, the resistivity changes substantially when subjected to mechanical stress. Strain gauges, as described in Chapter 4, involve this phenomenon, but the particular characteristics of silicon allow construction of a thin diaphragm that can be deflected by an applied pressure and can have resistors diffused into it to provide a means for sensing the deflection. An example of this is the Kistler 4000 series as shown in Figure 9.25 for which the pressure-sensing element is shown in Figure 9.26.

Because the stress varies across the diaphragm, four pairs of resistors are diffused into a wafer of n-type silicon, each pair having one resistor with its principal component radial and one with its principal component circumferential. As described later, this provides means for compensating the temperature-sensitivity of the silicon. Mechanically they form part of the diaphragm but they are isolated electrically by the p–n junction so that they function as strain gauges. The diaphragm is formed by cutting a cylindrical recess on the rear surface of the wafer using initially ultrasonic or high-speed diamond machining and finally chemical etching. This unit is then bonded to a similar unprocessed chip so that a homogeneous element is produced. If it is desired to measure absolute pressures the bonding is effected under a vacuum. Otherwise the cavity behind the diaphragm is connected via a hole in the base chip and a bonded tube to the atmospheric or reference pressure. The schematic arrangements of two such transducers are shown in Figure 9.27.

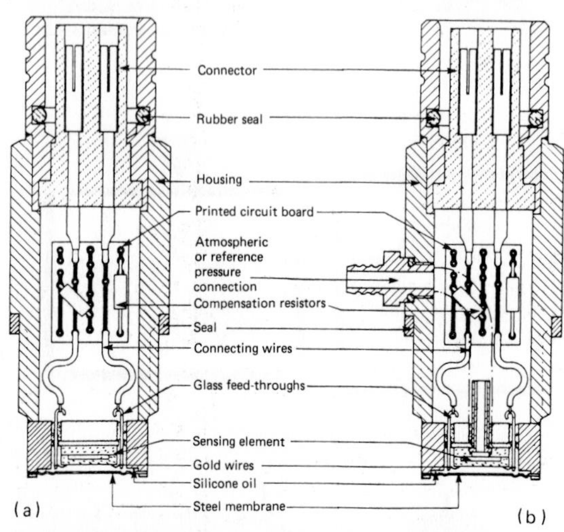

Figure 9.27 Cross section of piezo-resistive pressure transducer. (a) For absolute pressure. (b) For gauge pressure. Courtesy, Kistler Instruments Ltd.

The mechanical strength of silicon depends largely on the state of the surface and in general this imposes an upper limit of about 100 MPa on the pressures that can be measured safely by the sensors. The lower limit is about 100 kPa and is determined by the minimum thickness to which the diaphragm can be manufactured reliably.

Both the gauge factor G and resistance R of the diffused resistors are sensitive to changes of temperature and the sensors need to be associated with some form of compensating circuits. In some instances this is provided by discrete resistors closely associated with the gauge itself. Others utilize hybrid circuits, part of which may be on the chip itself. Individual compensation is always required for the zero offset, the measurement span and temperature stabilization of the zero. Further improvement in the performance can be achieved by compensating for the nonlinearity and the effect of temperature on the span.

9.2.3.9 Quartz resonant pressure sensors

A second method of utilizing the piezo-electric effect is to observe the change in resonant frequency of the

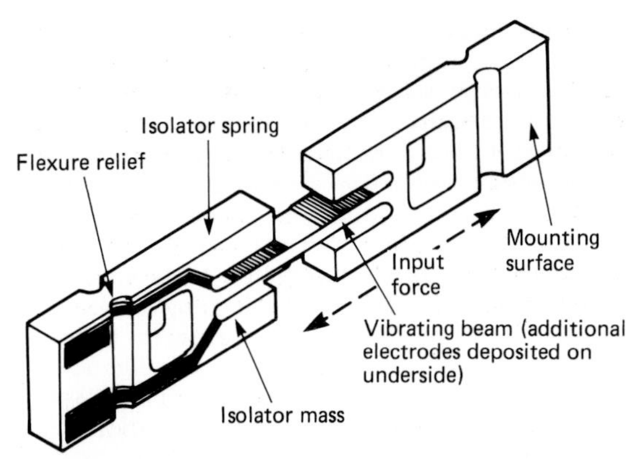

Figure 9.28 Resonant piezo-electric force sensor. Courtesy, Paroscientific Inc.

piezo-electric sensor resulting from application of the force developed by the unknown pressure acting on a flexible diaphragm of fixed area. One such sensor utilizing this principle to measure absolute pressures is shown diagrammatically in Figure 9.28.

It depends for its operation on a fixed beam oscillating in its first flexural mode and mounted in an isolation system that effectively decouples it from the structures to which it is attached. The entire sensor is fabricated from a single piece of quartz to minimize energy loss to the joints and the cut is orientated to minimize the effect of temperature changes. Four electrodes are vacuum-deposited on the beam and, with diagonally opposite pairs of electrodes connected to an oscillator, the beam is maintained in oscillation at its resonant frequency. The response to the imposed electric field is illustrated in Figure 9.29. The Q of the sensor may be as high as 40 000 so that not more than a few milliwatts are needed to sustain the oscillation. Under tension, the resonant frequency increases and under compression it is reduced.

Figure 9.30 shows the embodiment of the sensor in an absolute pressure transducer. The pressure to be measured is applied to a bellows which converts it into an upward force which acts on the force arm causing it to pivot about the centrally located cross-flexures. As a result, a compressive force is applied to the quartz sensor causing its resonant frequency to be reduced. Because the quartz element is essentially rigid the entire mechanical structure is constrained to minute deflections and hysteretic effects are virtually eliminated. If the bellows, together with its associated flexures and levers, is enclosed in a structure which is evacuated, this not only provides the zero pressure reference, it also eliminates the mass loading and damping effects on the quartz resonator (directly increasing the Q) and further minimizes the effect of ambient temperature changes. Balance weights are included in the system of levers so that the centre of gravity of the mechanism coincides with the centre of the flexures. This minimizes errors in response due to vibration or acceleration forces.

The relation between the applied pressure P and the oscillation frequency is given by

$$P = A\left(1 - \frac{T_0}{T}\right) - B\left(1 - \frac{T_0}{T}\right)^2$$

where T_0 is the periodic time when the applied pressure is zero, T is the periodic time when the applied pressure is P, and A and B are calibration constants for the transducer.

The nominal frequency of the sensor at zero pressure is 40 kHz and this changes to about 36 kHz at full-scale pressure. A convenient method of measuring the output is to allow the signal to gate the signal from a 10 MHz clock. Thus by timing 1000 cycles of the resonant sensor the applied pressure can be determined with a resolution of 0.003 per cent of full scale in approximately 25 milliseconds.

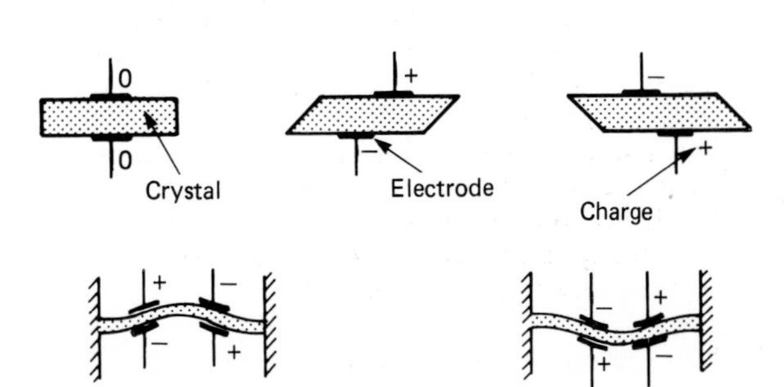

Figure 9.29 Oscillator mode for piezo-electric force sensor. Courtesy, Paroscientific Inc.

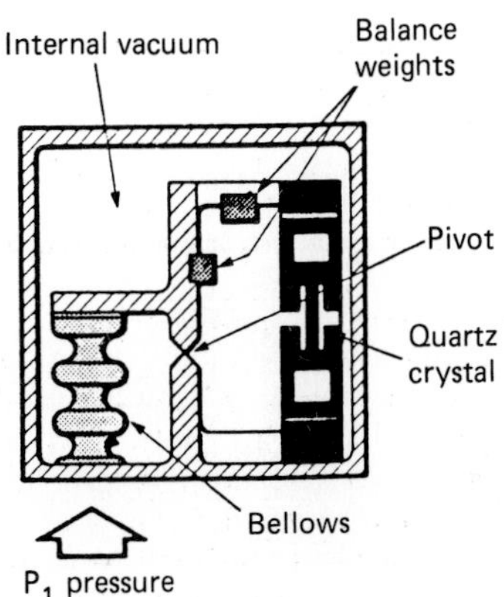

Figure 9.30 Configuration of force sensor in absolute pressure transducer. Courtesy, Paroscientific Inc.

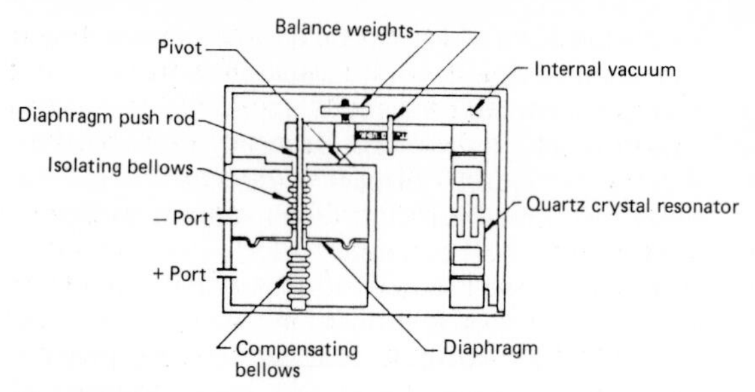

Figure 9.31 Configuration of force sensor in differential pressure transducer. Courtesy, Paroscientific Inc.

The sensor can be adapted to measure differential pressures by mounting a pair of matched bellows in opposition to act on the suspension arm as shown in Figure 9.31. However, additional errors arise from sensitivity to the static pressure due to imperfections in the bellows and their matching. This has led to the development of a transducer similar in many respects to the established designs of differential pressure transmitters.

Typical specifications:

For absolute pressure measurements with spans between 0 to 100 kPa and 0 to 6 MPa or differential pressure measurements with spans between 0 to 40 kPa and 0 to 275 kPa.

Repeatability	0.005% of span
Hysteresis	0.005% of span
Temperature coefficient of zero	0.007% of span/ kelvin
Temperature coefficient of reading	0.0045% of reading/ kelvin
Operating temperature range	−55 to 110 °C
Power requirement	6 milliwatts
Mass	0.17 kg
Approximate size	22 × 40 × 40 mm

A third group of pressure sensors is based on strain-gauge technology (see Chapter 4), in which the resistance-type strain sensors are connected in a Wheatstone bridge network. To achieve the required long-term stability and freedom from hysteresis, the strain sensors must have a molecular bond to the deflecting member which in addition must also provide the necessary electrical isolation over the operating temperature range of the transducer.

This can be achieved by first sputtering the electrical isolation layer on the stainless-steel sensor beam or diaphragm and then sputtering the thin-film strain-gauge sensors on top of this. An example of this type of sensor is the CEC Instrumentation 4201 series shown in Figure 9.32.

The pressure inlet adaptor is fabricated from precipitation-hardened stainless steel and has a deep recess between the mounting thread and diaphragm chamber to isolate the force-summing diaphragm from the mounting and other environmental stresses.

The transducer is modular in construction to allow the use of alternative diaphragm configurations and materials. For most applications the diaphragm is stainless steel and the thickness is selected according to the required measurement range. For some applications, enhanced corrosion resistance is required, in which case Inconel 625 or other similar alloys may be used as the diaphragm material, but to retain the same margin of safety a thicker member is usually required and this in turn reduces the sensitivity.

The sensor is a sputtered thin-film strain gauge in which the strain-gauge pattern is bonded into the structure of the sensor assembly on a molecular basis and the sensor assembly itself is welded into the remaining structure of the transducer. The stainless-steel header which contains the electrical feed-through to the temperature-compensation compartment is also welded into the structure of the transducer.

This welding, in conjunction with the ceramic firing technique used for the electrical feed-through con-

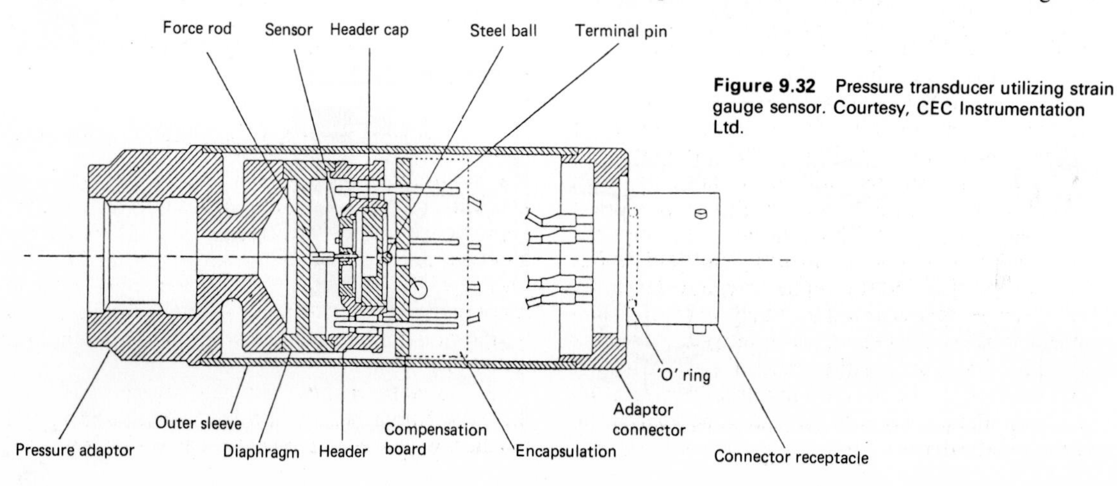

Figure 9.32 Pressure transducer utilizing strain gauge sensor. Courtesy, CEC Instrumentation Ltd.

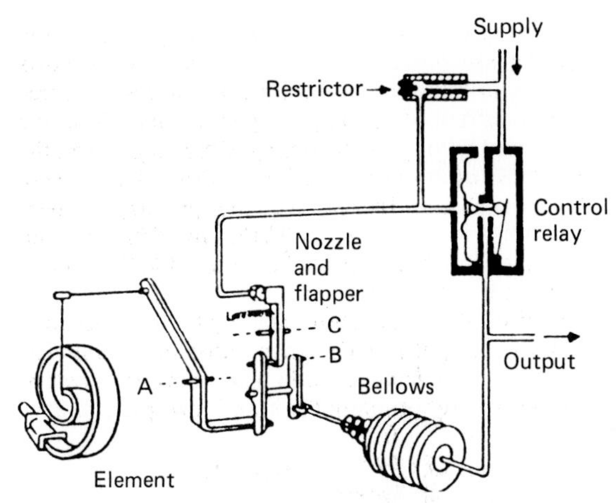

Figure 9.33 Arrangement of pneumatic motion-balance transmitter. Courtesy, The Foxboro Company.

nections, provides secondary containment security of 50 MPa for absolute gauges and those with a sealed reference chamber.

Sensors of this type are available with ranges from 0 to 100 kPa up to 0 to 60 MPa with maximum non-linearity and hysteresis of 0.25 to 0.15 per cent respectively and a repeatability of 0.05 per cent of span. The maximum temperature effect is 0.15 per cent of span per kelvin.

9.3 Pressure transmitters

In the process industries, it is often necessary to transmit the measurement signal from a sensor over a substantial distance so that it can be used to implement a control function or can be combined with other measurement signals in a more complex scheme.

The initial development of such transmission systems was required for the petroleum and petro-chemical industries where pneumatic control schemes were used most widely, because they could be installed in plants where explosive or hazardous conditions could arise and the diaphragm actuator provided a powerful and fast-acting device for driving the final operator. It followed that the first transmission systems to be evolved were pneumatic and were based on the standardized signal range 20 to 100 kPa.

The first transmitter utilized a motion-balance system, i.e. one in which the primary element produces a movement proportional to the measured quantity, such as a Bourdon tube, in which movement of the free end is proportional to the applied pressure. However, these transmitters were rather sensitive to vibration and have, in general, been superseded by force-balance systems. But pneumatic transmission itself is unsuitable when the distance involved exceeds a few hundred metres, because of the time delay and response lag which occur.

Consequently, an equivalent electronic system has been evolved. In this, a current in the range 4 to 20 mA d.c. and proportional to the span of the measured quantity is generated by the sensor and transmitted over a two-wire system. The advantage of this system is that there is virtually no delay or response lag, and the transmitted signal is not affected by changes in the characteristic of the transmission line. Also there is sufficient power below the live zero (i.e. 4 mA) to operate the sensing device. Such systems have the additional advantage that they are more easily con-figurated in complex control schemes than the corre-sponding pneumatic transmitters. Telemetry and pneumatic systems are discussed further in Chapters **00–00** of Volume 4.

9.3.1 Pneumatic motion-balance pressure transmitters

Figure 9.33 shows the arrangement of a typical pneumatic motion-balance transmitter in which the sensor is a spiral Bourdon tube. Changes in the measured variable, which could be pressure, or temperature in the case of a filled thermal system, cause the free end of the Bourdon tube to move. This movement is transmitted via a linkage to the lever that pivots about the axis A. The free end of this lever bears on a second lever that is pivoted at its centre so that the movement is transmitted to a third lever that is free to pivot about the axis C. The initial movement is thus transferred to the flapper of the flapper/nozzle system. If as a result, the gap between the flapper and nozzle is increased, the nozzle back-pressure falls and this in turn causes the output pressure from the control relay to fall. As this pressure is applied to the bellows the change causes the lever pivoted about the axis B to retract so that the lever pivoted about the axis C moves the flapper towards the nozzle. This causes the nozzle back-pressure to rise until equilibrium is established. For each value of the measurement there is a definite flapper/nozzle relationship and therefore a definite output signal.

9.3.2 Pneumatic force-balance pressure transmitters

There are many designs of pneumatic force-balance transmitters, but in the Foxboro Company design the same force-balance mechanism is used in all the pressure and differential pressure transmitters. It is shown in Figure 9.34 and its basic function is to convert a force applied to its input point into a proportional pneumatic signal for transmission, such as 20 to 100 kPa.

The force to be measured may be generated by a Bourdon tube, a bellows or a diaphragm assembly and applied to the free end of the force bar. This is pivoted

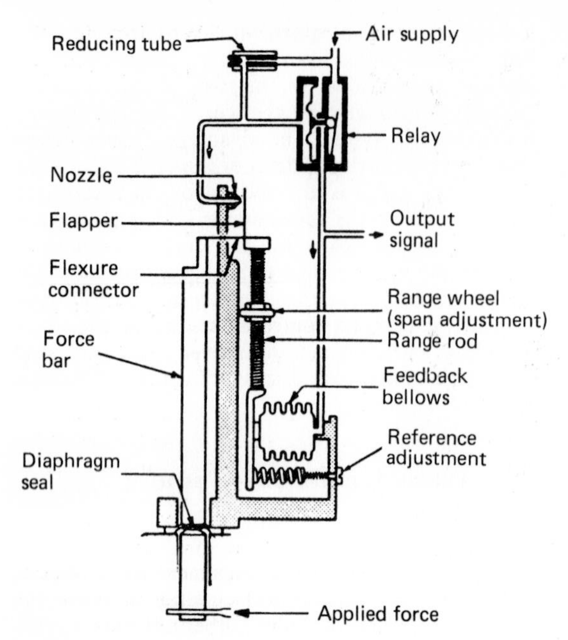

Figure 9.34 Arrangement of pneumatic force-balance transmitter. Courtesy, The Foxboro Company.

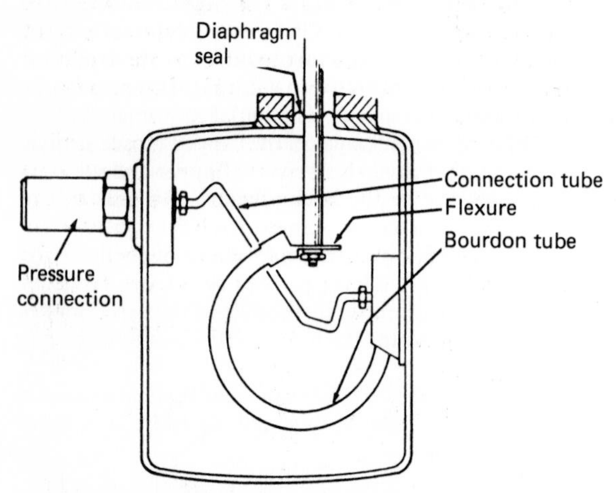

Figure 9.35 Bourdon tube primary element arranged for operation in conjunction with a force-balance mechanism. Courtesy, The Foxboro Company.

at the diaphragm seal, which in some instruments also provides the interface between process fluid and the force-balance mechanism, so that an initial displacement arising from the applied force appears amplified at the top of the force bar where it is transmitted via the flexure connector to the top of the range rod. If the applied force causes movement to the right, the flapper uncovers the nozzle with the result that the nozzle back-pressure falls. This change is magnified by the 'relay' whose output is applied to the feedback bellows thereby producing a force which balances the force applied initially. The output signal is taken from the 'relay' and by varying the setting of the range wheel the sensitivity or span can be adjusted through a range of about 10 to 1. By varying the primary element pressures from about 1.3 kPa to 85 MPa and differential pressures from 1 kPa to 14 MPa may be measured.

Figures 9.35–9.38 show some of the alternative primary elements which can be used in conjunction with this force-balance mechanism to measure gauge differential and absolute (high and low) pressures.

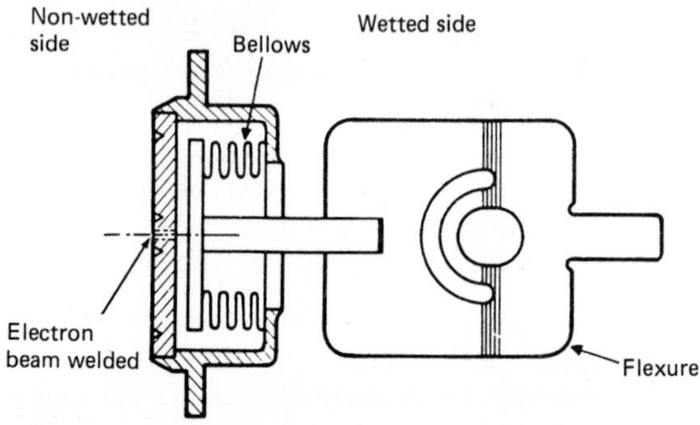

Figure 9.36 Bellows type primary element for absolute pressure measurements. Courtesy, The Foxboro Company.

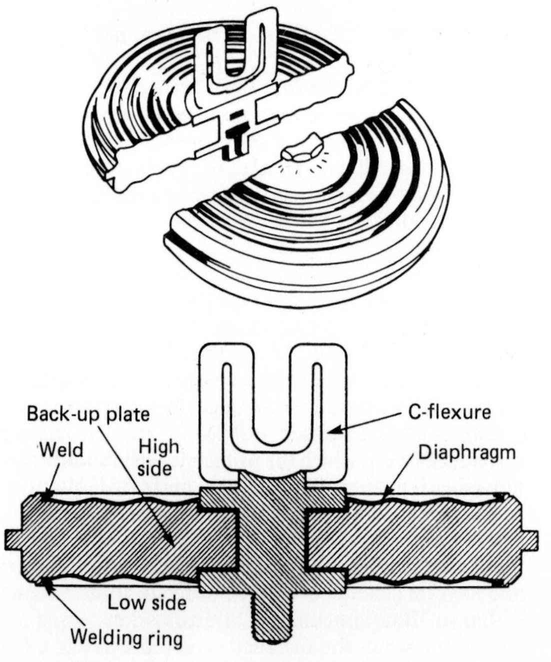

Figure 9.37 Diaphragm assembly for differential pressure measurements. Courtesy, The Foxboro Company.

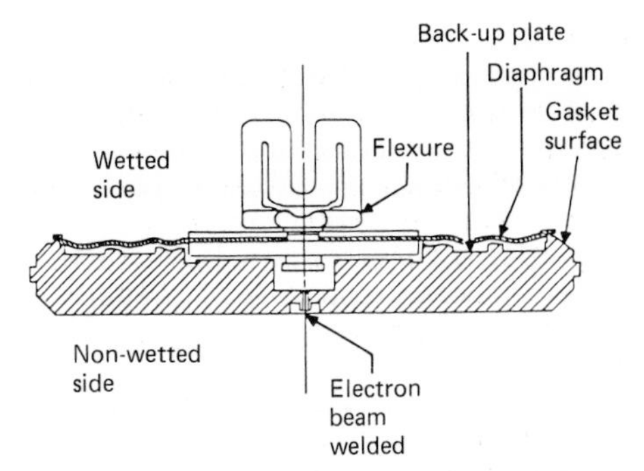

Figure 9.38 Diaphragm assembly for low absolute pressure measurements. Courtesy, The Foxboro Company.

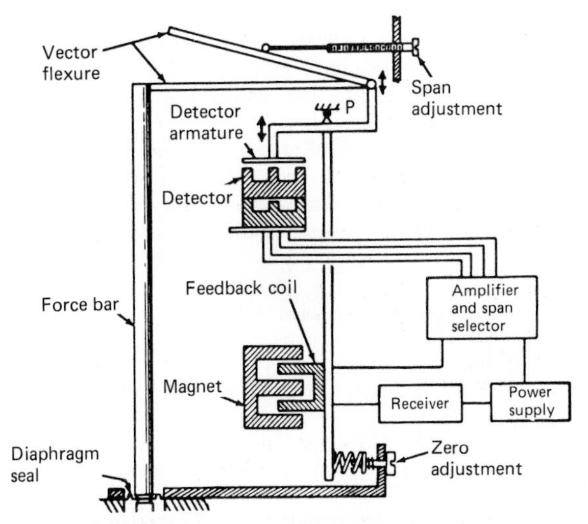

Figure 9.39 Arrangement of electronic force-balance mechanism. Courtesy, The Foxboro Company.

9.3.3 Electronic force-balance pressure transmitters

As with the pneumatic force-balance transmitters, there are many designs of electronic force-balance transmitters, but the Foxboro series serves to illustrate the principal mechanism. Again the mechanism shown in Figure 9.39 is used for a series of transmitters. Its basic function is to measure the force derived by a primary element as a result of applying the pressure to be measured.

The force is applied via a flexure to the lower end of the force bar which pivots on the diaphragm seal that in some instruments also serves to isolate the process fluid from the measuring system. The corresponding force at the top of the force bar is transmitted to the vector assembly, the effective angle of which can be varied by the span adjustment. A secondary lever system, attached at the apex of the vector assembly, is pivoted at the point P and carries both the detector armature and the coil of the feedback motor.

In operation, a change in the force applied to the force bar is applied to the vector assembly, causing a slight movement at the apex. This is transferred to the detector armature, a ferrite disc which moves with respect to the detector coils and so modifies the coupling between the two coils. These coils are connected in an oscillator circuit so that a slight movement of the armature with respect to the coils causes a substantial change in the oscillator output which after rectification is applied to the feedback motor in such a manner that the initial disturbing force is balanced.

The current flowing through the feedback coil is used as the output signal from the transmitter. Fine adjustments of the span are effected by varying the effective angle of the vector flexures. But larger changes are made by changing the effective gain of the oscillator/amplifier circuit shown in Figure 9.40.

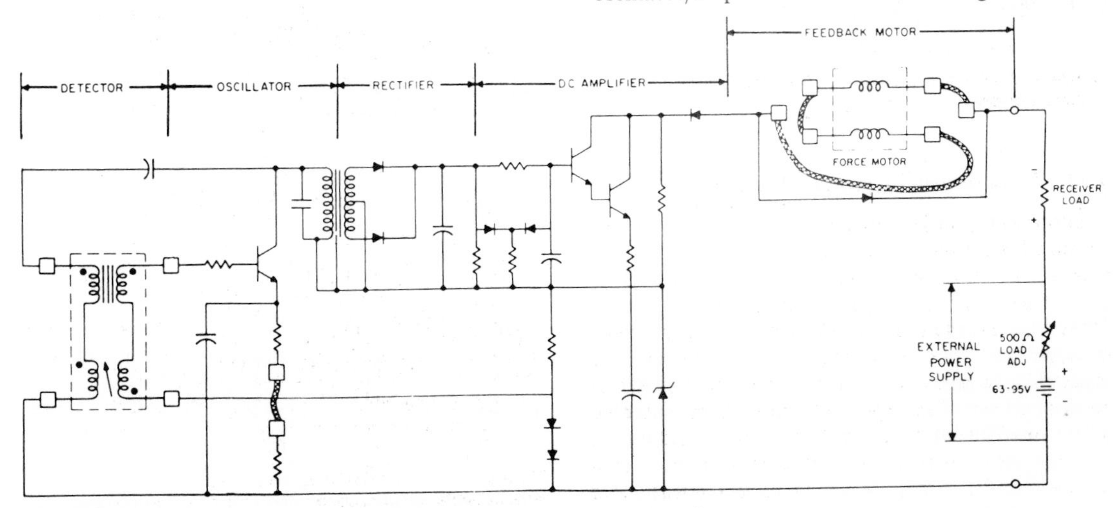

Figure 9.40 Circuit for electronic force-balance system. Courtesy, The Foxboro Company.

As with the pneumatic force-balance transmitters there is a wide range of both gauge and absolute pressure sensors that can be operated in conjunction with the force-balance mechanism as well as differential pressure sensors as shown in Figures 9.41–9.44. These provide absolute and gauge pressure measurements for ranges from 1.3 kPa to 85 MPa and differential pressures from 1 kPa to 14 MPa with an accuracy of 0.5 per cent of span.

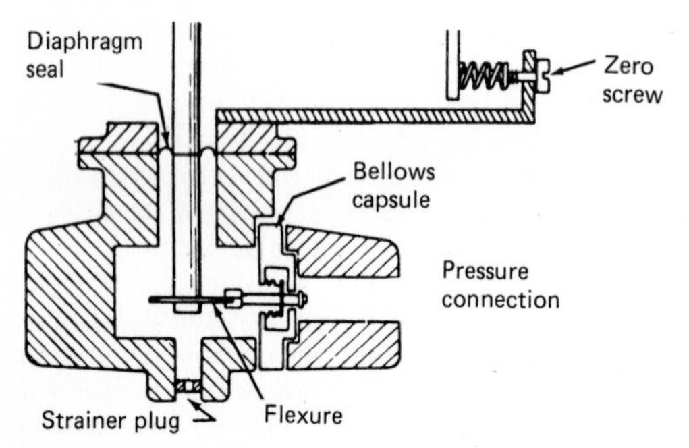

Figure 9.41 Bellows type primary element for gauge pressure measurements. Courtesy, The Foxboro Company.

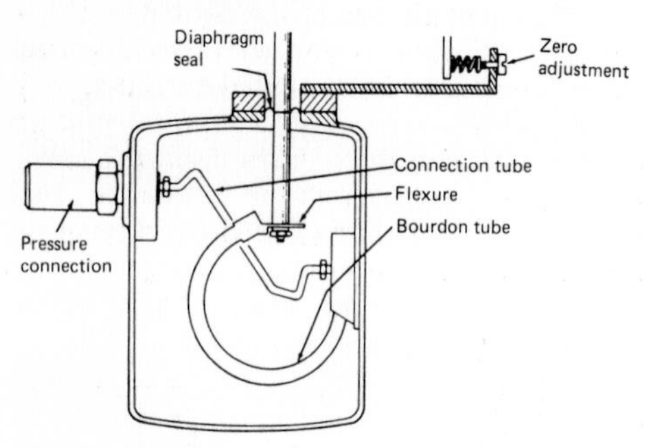

Figure 9.42 Bourdon type primary element. Courtesy, The Foxboro Company.

9.3.4 Force-measuring pressure transmitters

In addition to the force-balance pressure transmitters previously described, there are now transmitters which measure pressure by measuring the deflection of an elastic member resulting from the applied pressure. One of these is the Foxboro 820 series of transmitters, in which the force is applied to a pre-stressed wire located in the field of a permanent magnet. The wire is an integral part of an oscillator circuit which causes the wire to oscillate at its resonant (or natural) frequency. For an ideal system, the resonant frequency is a function of the length, the square root of tension and the mass of the wire.

The associated electronic circuits include the oscillator as well as the components to convert oscillator frequency into a standard transmission signal such as 4 to 20 mA d.c. As shown in Figure 9.45 the oscillator signal passes via a pulse-shaper to two frequency-converters arranged in cascade, each of which produces an output proportional to the product of the applied frequency and its input voltage so that the output of the second converter is proportional to the square of the frequency and therefore to the tension in the wire. The voltage is therefore directly proportional to the force produced by the primary element which in turn is proportional to the measured pressure.

The configuration of the resonant-wire system for primary elements such as a helical Bourdon tube, a gauge pressure, a differential pressure and absolute pressure is shown in Figures 9.46–9.49 respectively. Vibrating wires are also used as strain gauges, as discussed in Chapter 4.

A second category of pressure transmitters involves the measurement of the deflection of a sensing diaphragm which is arranged as the movable electrode between the fixed plates of a differential capacitor. An

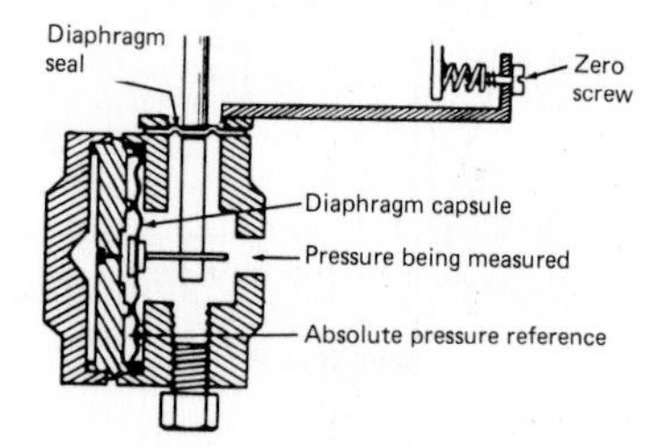

Figure 9.43 Diaphragm assembly for low absolute pressure measurements. Courtesy, The Foxboro Company.

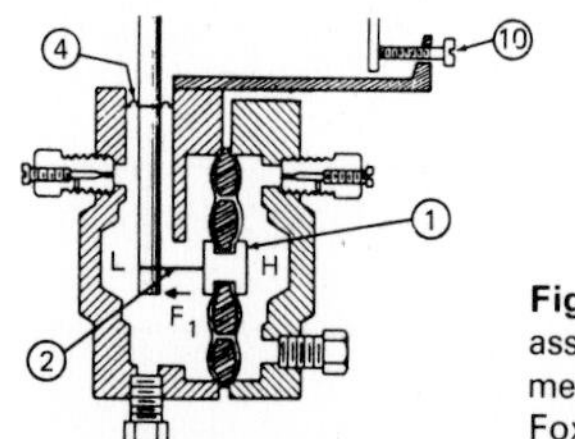

Figure 9.44 Diaphragm assembly for differential pressure measurements. Courtesy, The Foxboro Company.

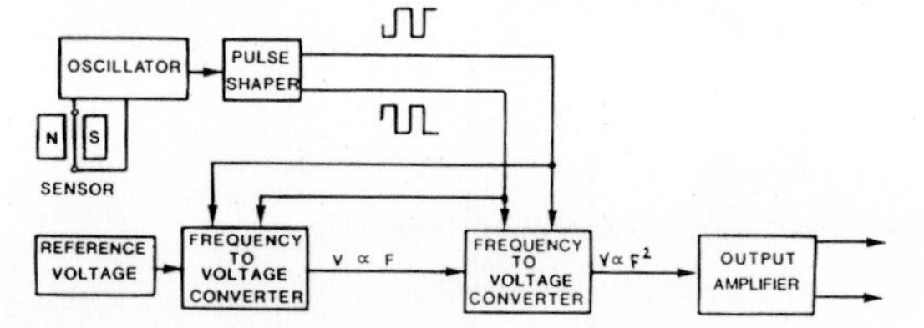

Figure 9.45 Functional diagram of electronic circuit for resonant wire pressure transmitter. Courtesy, The Foxboro Company.

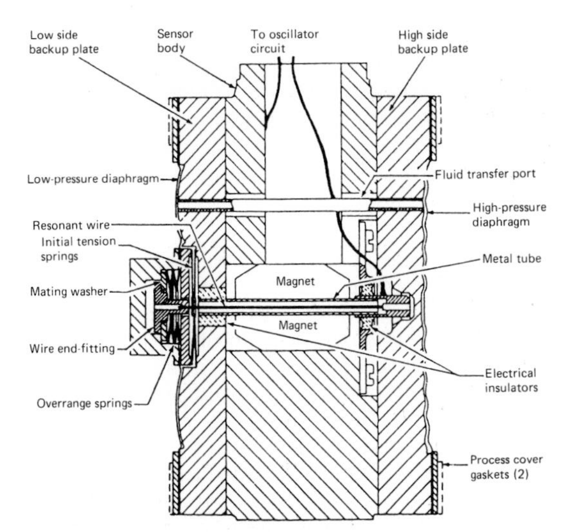

Figure 9.46 Arrangement of diaphragm assembly for differential pressure measurements. Courtesy, The Foxboro Company.

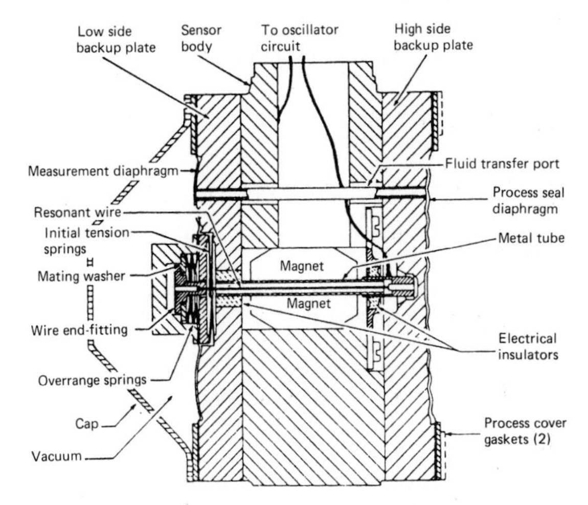

Figure 9.47 Arrangement of diaphragm assembly for absolute pressure measurements. Courtesy, The Foxboro Company.

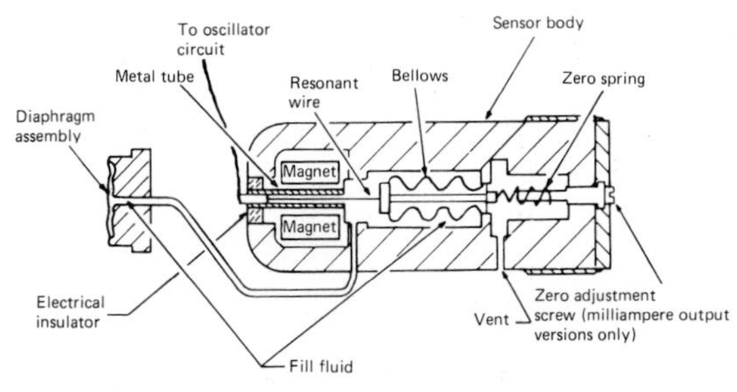

Figure 9.48 Arrangement of gauge pressure element for resonant wire sensor. Courtesy, The Foxboro Company.

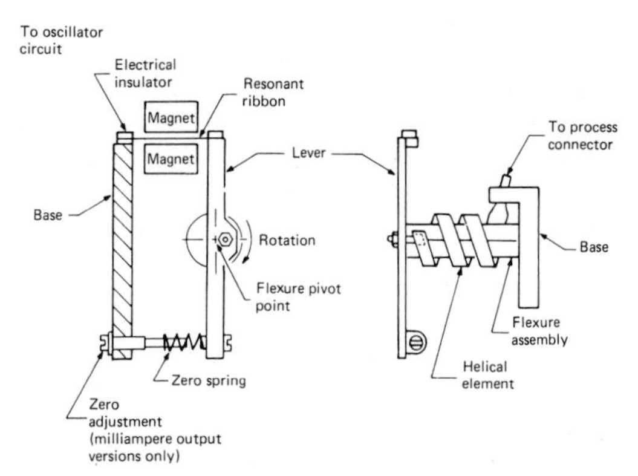

Figure 9.49 Arrangement of helical Bourdon tube for resonant wire sensor. Courtesy, The Foxboro Company.

example of this is the Siemens Teleperm K Transmitter. The arrangement of the measuring cell for differential pressures and absolute pressures is shown in Figure 9.50.

It is a flat cylindrical unit sealed at both ends by flexible corrugated diaphragms which provide the interface between the process fluid and the sensor. Under overload conditions, these seat on matching corrugations machined in the housing. The sensor comprises a hollow ceramic chamber divided into two by the sensing diaphragm. The interiors of the chambers are filled with liquid and sealed by a ring diaphragm. The interior walls of both chambers are metallized and form the fixed plates of the differential capacitor whilst the sensing diaphragm forms the movable plates of the capacitor.

When the measuring cell is subjected to a differential pressure, the sensing diaphragm is displaced slightly,

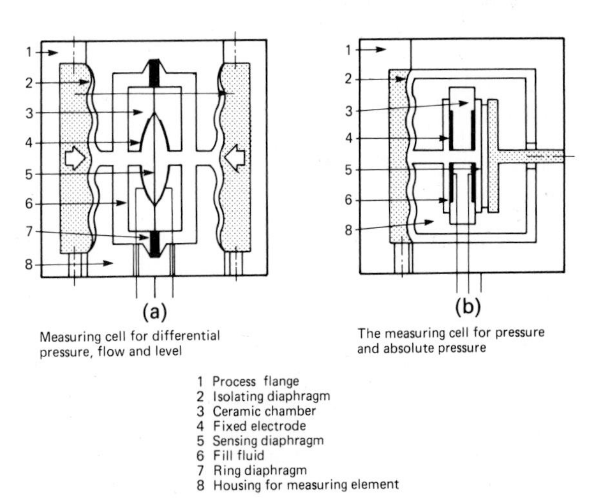

Figure 9.50 Arrangement of capacitance type differential and absolute pressure sensors. Courtesy, Siemens Ltd.

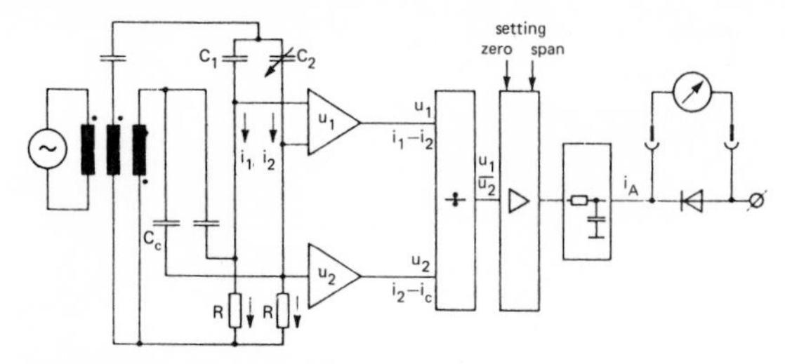

Figure 9.51 Functional diagram of electronic circuit for gauge and absolute pressure capacitance sensor. Courtesy, Siemens Ltd.

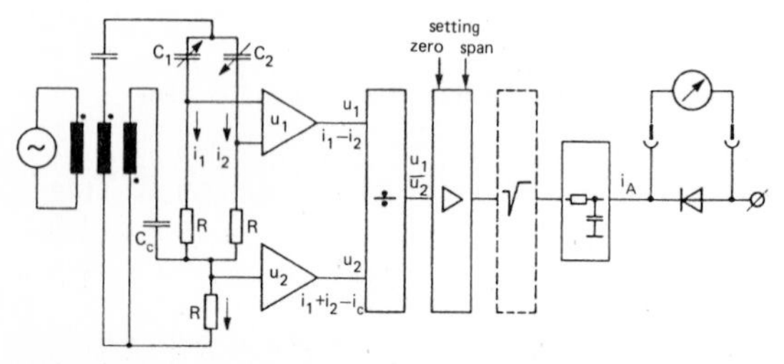

Figure 9.52 Functional diagram of electronic circuit for differential pressure capacitance sensor. Courtesy, Siemens Ltd.

causing a change in capacitance which is converted by the associated measuring circuit into a standard transmission signal such as 4 to 20 mA d.c.

For measuring absolute pressures, one side of the measuring cell is evacuated to provide the reference pressure and for measuring gauge pressures, one side is vented to atmosphere.

Under these conditions the stiffness of the isolating diaphragm determines the range. For high pressures the diaphragm is augmented by a spring.

Figure 9.51 shows the basic circuit for absolute pressure and gauge pressure transmitters whilst Figure 9.52 shows the corresponding details for the differential pressure transmitter which includes a square root extraction circuit.

In both models the sensing diaphragm acts as the moving electrode in the capacitor detector. The effective values of the capacitors are as follows

$$C_1 = \frac{A\varepsilon}{d_0} + C_S$$

$$C_2 = \frac{A\varepsilon}{d_0 + \Delta d} + C_S$$

where A is effective electrode area, ε is permittivity of the dielectric fluid, d_0 is effective distance between fixed electrodes and sensing electrode, Δd is displacement of sensing electrode, and C_S is stray capacitance. From this it follows that

$$\frac{C_1 - C_2}{C_2 - C_S} = \frac{\Delta d}{d_0}$$

which is the same as the deflection constant for the sensing diaphragm so that Δd is proportional to the differential pressure which can therefore be measured by an all-bridge network. To compensate for the effect of stray capacitances a capacitor C is included in the bridge circuit but supplied with a voltage in anti-phase to that applied to C_1 and C_2.

If the impedances of the capacitors C_1, C_2 and C_c are high compared with their associated resistors then the currents flowing through them are proportional to the capacitances, so that the output from amplifier U_1 is proportional to $(i_1 - i_2)$ and from amplifier U_2 $(i_2 - i_C)$. When these two signals are applied to a dividing stage, the resultant signal is proportional to the displacement of the sensing electrode and hence to the applied pressure. For the differential pressure transmitter, both C_1 and C_2 are variable but it can be shown that

$$\frac{\Delta d}{d_0} = \frac{C_1 - C_2}{C_1 + C_2 - 2C_S}$$

Applying the same conditions as before, this leads to

$$\frac{\Delta d}{d_0} = \frac{i_1 - i_2}{i_1 + i_2 - i_C}$$

As $(i_1 - i_2)$ and $(i_1 + i_2 - i_C)$ are proportional to the input signals of amplifier U_1 and U_2 it follows that the output from the dividing stage is proportional to the applied differential pressure.

Most differential pressure transmitters are used in conjunction with orifice plates to measure flow. If therefore the output from the dividing stage is applied to a square root extracting circuit then its output becomes proportional to flow rate.

9.4 References

Hewson, J. E., *Process Instrumentation Manifolds: their Selection and Use.* Instrument Society of America, (1981)

Lyons, J. L., *The Designer's Handbook of Pressure-Sensing.* Van Nostrand Reinhold, (1980)

Neubert, H. K. P., *Instrument Transducers, an Introduction to their Performance and Design.* Clarendon Press, 1975)

10 Measurement of vacuum

D. J. PACEY

10.1 Introduction

10.1.1 Systems of measurement

The term *vacuum* refers to the range of pressures below atmospheric, and the measurement of vacuum is thus the measurement of such pressures. Pressure is defined as force divided by area, and the SI unit is the newton/metre^2 (Nm^{-2}) or pascal (Pa). Pressure may also be stated in terms of the height of a column of a suitable liquid, such as mercury or water, that the pressure will support. The relation between pressure units currently in use is shown in Table 10.1.

In engineering, it has long been customary to take atmospheric pressure as the reference, and to express pressures below this as 'pounds per square inch of vacuum', or 'inches of vacuum' when using a specified liquid. The continual changes in atmospheric pressure, however, will lead to inaccuracy unless they are allowed for. It is preferable to use zero pressure as the reference, and to measure pressures above this. Pressures expressed in this way are called *absolute pressures*.

10.1.2 Methods of measurement

Since pressure is defined to be force/area, its measurement involves directly or indirectly the measurement of the force exerted upon a known area. A gauge which does this is called an *absolute gauge*, and allows the pressure to be obtained from a *reading* and known physical quantities associated with the gauge, such as areas, lengths, sometimes temperatures, elastic constants, etc. The pressure when obtained is independent of the composition of the gas or vapour which is present.

Many technological applications of vacuum use the long free paths, or low molecular incidence rates that vacuum makes available. These require pressures that are only a very small fraction of atmospheric, where the force exerted by the gas is too small to be measured, making absolute gauges unusable. In such cases non-absolute gauges are used which measure pressure indirectly by measuring a pressure-dependent physical property of the gas, such as thermal conductivity, ionizability, or viscosity. These gauges always require calibration against an absolute gauge, for each gas that is to be measured. Commercial gauges are usually calibrated by the manufacturer using dry air, and will give true readings only when dry air is present. In practice it is difficult to be certain of the composition of the gases in vacuum apparatus, thereby causing errors. This problem is overcome in the following way. When a gauge using variation of thermal conductivity indicates a pressure of 10^{-1} Pa, this would be recorded as an *equivalent dry air pressure of* 10^{-1} *Pa*. This means that the thermal conductivity of the unknown gases present in the vacuum apparatus has the same value as that of air at 10^{-1} Pa, and not that the pressure is 10^{-1} Pa.

10.1.3 Choice of non-absolute gauges

Since the gauge referred to above measures thermal conductivity, it is particularly useful for use on vacuum apparatus used for making vacuum flasks, or in which low-temperature experiments are carried out, and in which thermal conductivity plays an important part. Similarly an ionization gauge would be suitable in the case of apparatus used for making radio valves and cathode ray tubes in which the ionizability of the gases is important. In general, it is desirable to match as far

Table 10.1 Relation between pressure units

	N/m^2 (Pa)	*torr*	*mb*	*atm*
N/m^2 (Pa)	1	7.50×10^{-3}	10^{-2}	9.87×10^{-6}
torr	133.3	1	1.333	1.316×10^{-3}
mb	100	0.750	1	9.87×10^{-4}
atm	1.013×10^{5}	760	1.013×10^{3}	1

as possible, the physical processes in the gauge with those in the vacuum apparatus.

10.1.4 Accuracy of measurement

Having chosen a suitable gauge, it is necessary to ensure that the pressure in the gauge head is the same as that in the vacuum apparatus. Firstly the gauge head is connected at a point as close as possible to the point where the pressure is to be measured and by the shortest and widest tube available. Secondly, sufficient time must be allowed for pressure equilibrium to be obtained. This is particularly important when the pressure is below 10^{-1} Pa, and when ionization gauges, which interact strongly with the vacuum apparatus, are used. Times of several minutes are often required. When non-absolute gauges are used, even under ideal conditions, the accuracy is rarely better than ± 20 per cent, and in a carelessly operated ionization gauge worse than ± 50 per cent. Representative values for the mid-range accuracy of various gauges are given in Table 10.2 at the end of this chapter along with other useful information.

10.2 Absolute gauges

10.2.1 Mechanical gauges

These gauges measure the pressure of gases and vapours by making use of the mechanical deformation of tubes or diaphragms when exposed to a pressure difference. If one side of the sensitive element is exposed to a good vacuum, the gauge is absolute.

10.2.1.1 The Bourdon tube gauge

A conventional gauge of this type can be used to measure pressure down to 100 Pa if carefully made. Its construction is described in Chapter 9 on pressure measurement.

10.2.1.2 The quartz spiral gauge

This gauge measures differential pressures over a range of 100 Pa from any chosen reference pressure. It is suitable for use with corrosive gases or vapours.

Construction The sensitive element is a helix of 0.5 mm diameter quartz tubing usually 20 mm in diameter, 30 mm long to which the vacuum is applied internally. The helix coils and uncoils in response to pressure changes, the motion being measured by observing the movement of a light spot reflected from a small mirror attached to its lower end. The whole assembly is mounted in a clear glass or quartz enclosure, which can be brought to any desired reference pressure. If this is zero, the gauge indicates absolute pressure.

10.2.1.3 Diaphragm gauge

This gauge measures pressures of gases and vapours down to 10 Pa. Its construction is described in Chapter 9.

10.2.2 Liquid manometers

These gauges measure the pressure of gases and vapours from atmospheric to about 1 Pa by balancing the force exerted by the gas or vapour against the weight of a column of liquid, usually mercury, water or oil. These devices provide the simplest possible means of pressure measurement.

Construction The construction of various forms of liquid manometer is described in Chapter 9.

Operation For measuring relative pressures, the open manometer shown in Figure 10.1(a) may be used. In this case the difference h in levels may be taken to express the *vacuum* directly in inches of water, or by use of the formula $p=h\rho g$, where ρ is the density of the liquid, and g is the acceleration due to gravity, the

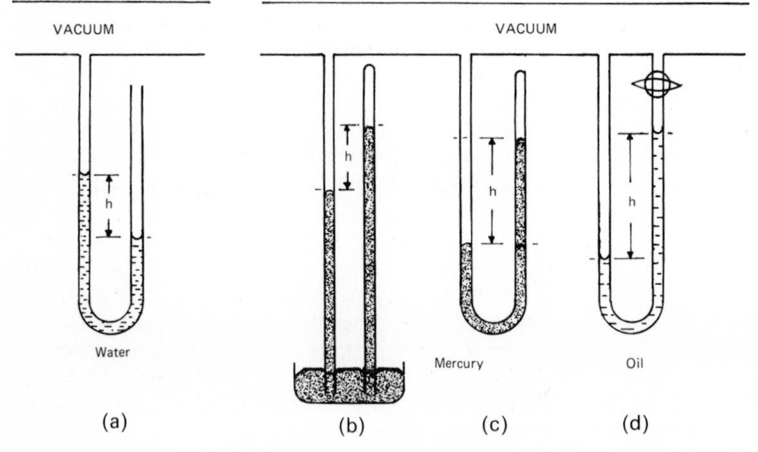

Figure 10.1 Liquid manometers.

vacuum may be expressed in SI units. The measurement of absolute pressures requires a vacuum reference which may be obtained in several ways as shown in Figure 10.1(b), (c), (d). A barometer tube is used in diagram (b), immersed in the same liquid pool, in this case usually mercury, as the manometer tube. A more compact form is provided by the closed manometer, shown in (c). This again uses mercury, and the space in the closed limb is evacuated. A useful version of the closed manometer which can be used with oil is shown in (d), where the tap may be opened when the apparatus is at zero pressure, and closed immediately before taking measurements. When oil is used in vacuum measurement, difficulty will be experienced with the liberation of dissolved gases, which must be removed slowly by slow reduction of the pressure.

10.2.3 The McLeod gauge (1878)

Function This gauge measures the pressure of gases only, from 5×10^{-4} Pa to atmospheric by measuring the force exerted by a sample of the gas of known volume after a known degree of compression.

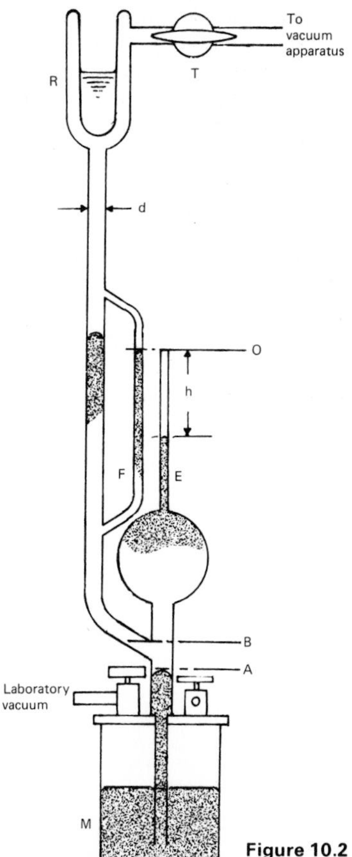

Figure 10.2 The McLeod gauge.

Construction This is of glass as shown in Figure 10.2 and uses mercury as the manometric liquid. The measuring capillary E and the reference capillary F are cut from the same length of tube to equalize capillary effects. A trap R refrigerated with liquid nitrogen or solid carbon dioxide excludes vapours, and prevents the escape of mercury vapour from the gauge. The tap T maintains the vacuum in the gauge when it is transferred to another system.

Operation The mercury normally stands at A, allowing the bulb and measuring capillary to attain the pressure p in the vacuum apparatus; at pressures below 10^{-2} Pa several minutes are required for this. To take a reading, the mercury is raised by slowly admitting air to the mercury reservoir M. When the mercury passes B, a sample of gas of volume V is isolated, and the pressure indicated will be that in the gauge at this instant. The mercury in the reference capillary is then brought to O, the level of the top of the measuring capillary and the length h of the enclosed gas column, of area a, is measured. The mercury is then returned to A, by reducing the pressure in the reservoir M, thus preparing the gauge for a further measurement.

Calculation of the pressure Applying Boyle's law to the isolated sample of gas, we have

original pressure × original volume
= final pressure × final volume

or

$$pV = (h\rho g + p)ah$$

where ρ is the density of mercury and g is the acceleration due to gravity.

Thus

$$p = \frac{ah^2}{V - ah}\rho g$$

When measuring low pressures, the final volume ah is very much less than the original volume v.

Hence

$$P = \frac{a}{V} \cdot \rho g \, . \, h^2$$

Showing that $p \propto h^2$, giving a square law scale.

The value of a is found by weighing a pellet of mercury of known length inserted in the measuring capillary, and V is determined by weighing the quantity of distilled water that fills the bulb and measuring capillary from the level A, to its closed end. Both of these measurements are carried out by the manufacturer, who then calculates values of h corresponding to a series of known pressures, which can then be read directly on the scale.

The Ishii effect The use of a refrigerated trap with this gauge, which is necessary in almost every instance, leads to a serious underestimation of the pressure, which is greater for gases with large molecules. First noted by Gaede in 1915, and thoroughly investigated by Ishii and Nakayama in 1962 the effect arises from the movement of mercury vapour from the pool at A, which passes up the connecting tube, and then condenses in the refrigerated trap. Gas molecules encountered by the mercury vapour stream are carried along with it, and are removed from the bulb, producing a lowering of the pressure there. The effect is greater for large molecules since they provide large targets for the mercury vapour stream. The error may be reduced by reducing the mercury vapour flow, by cooling the mercury pool at A artificially, or by reducing the diameter d of the connecting tube. In the latter case the response time of the gauge to pressure changes will be lengthened.

Approximate errors for a gauge in which $d = 1$ cm, and the mercury temperature is 300 K are -4 per cent for helium, -25 per cent for nitrogen, and -40 per cent for xenon.

10.3 Non-absolute gauges

10.3.1 Thermal conductivity gauges

Function These gauges measure the pressure of gases and vapours from 1000 Pa to 10^{-1} Pa by making use of the changes in *thermal conductivity* which take place over this range. Separate calibration against an absolute gauge is required for each gas. Since the sensitive element used is an electrically heated wire, these gauges are known as *hot-wire gauges.*

10.3.1.1 Thermocouple gauge (Voege 1906)

Construction An electrically heated wire operating at a temperature of about 320 K is mounted inside a glass or metal envelope connected to the vacuum apparatus. A thermocouple attached to the centre of the wire enables its variation in temperature due to pressure changes to be observed. For simplicity the construction shown in Figure 10.3 may be used. Four parallel lead-through wires pass through one end of the envelope, and two noble metal thermocouple wires are fixed across diagonal pairs. The wires are welded at their intersection so that one dissimilar pair forms the hot wire, and the other, the thermocouple.

Operation A stabilized electrical supply S is connected to the hot wire, and adjusted to bring it to the required temperature. The resistance R connected in series with the millivoltmeter M is used to set the zero of the instrument. A rise in the pressure increases the heat loss from the wire, causing a fall of temperature. This results in a reduction of thermocouple output registered by M, which is scaled to read pressure of dry air.

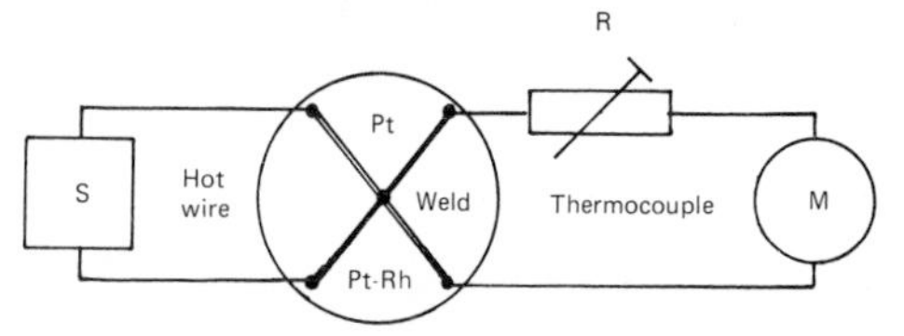

Figure 10.3 The thermocouple gauge.

10.3.1.2 The Pirani gauge (Pirani 1906)

Construction An electrically heated platinum or tungsten wire, operating at a temperature of 320 K is mounted along the axis of a glass or metal tube, which is connected to the vacuum apparatus. Changes in the pressure cause temperature changes in the wire, which are followed by using the corresponding changes in its electrical resistance. The wire temperature may also be affected by variations of room temperature and these are compensated by use of an identical dummy gauge head sealed off at a low pressure. The gauge and dummy heads are shown in Figures 10.4 and 10.5. For reasons of economy, the dummy head is often replaced by a bobbin of wire having the same resistance and temperature coefficient of resistance, mounted close to the gauge head.

Operation The gauge and dummy heads form adjacent arms of a Wheatstone bridge circuit as shown in Figure 10.6. This arrangement also compensates for the effects of temperature changes on the resistance of the leads connecting the gauge head to the control unit, thereby allowing remote indications of pressure. Resistances Y and Z form the other arms of the bridge,

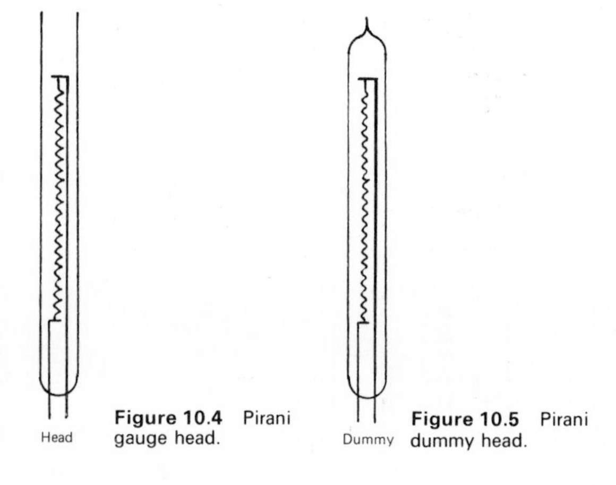

Figure 10.4 Pirani gauge head.

Figure 10.5 Pirani dummy head.

Z being variable for use in zero setting. Power is obtained from a stabilized supply S, and the meter M measures the out-of-balance current in the bridge.

The wire is brought to its operating temperature, and the bridge is balanced giving zero current through M, when the pressure is low. A rise in pressure causes an increase of heat loss and a fall in temperature of the wire. If the power input is kept constant, the wire temperature falls, causing a fall of resistance which produces a current through M, which is calibrated to read pressure of dry air. Alternatively, the fall in wire temperature may be opposed by increasing the input voltage so that the wire temperature remains constant. The input voltage then depends on the pressure, and the meter measuring the voltage can be scaled to read pressure. The constant balance of the bridge is maintained by a simple electronic circuit. This arrangement is effective in extending the high pressure sensitivity of the gauge to 10^4 Pa or higher, since the wire temperature is maintained at this end of the pressure range.

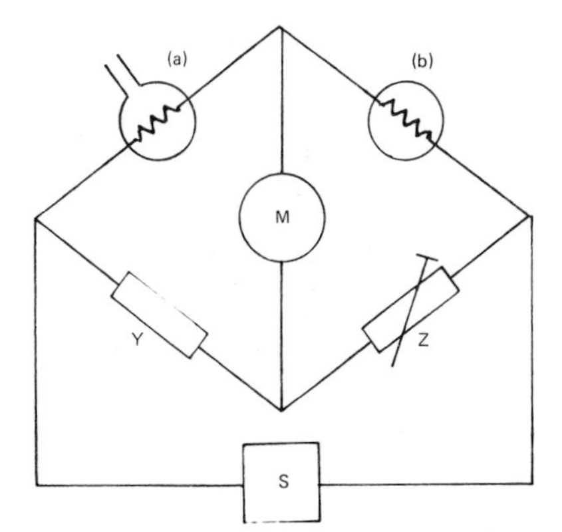

Figure 10.6 Pirani gauge circuit.

10.3.1.3 The thermistor gauge

This gauge closely resembles the Pirani gauge in its construction except that a small bead of semiconducting material takes the place of the metal wire as the sensitive element. The thermistor bead is made of a mixture of metallic oxides, about 0.2 mm in diameter. It is mounted on two platinum wires 0.02 mm in diameter, so that a current may be passed through it. Since the semiconductor has a much greater temperature coefficient of resistance than a metal, a greater sensitivity is obtained. Furthermore, on account of its small size it requires less power, allowing the use of batteries, and it responds more rapidly to sudden changes of pressure.

10.3.2 Ionization gauges

These gauges measure the pressure of gases and vapours over the range 10^3 Pa to 10^{-8} Pa by making use of the current carried by ions formed in the gas by the impact of electrons. In the cold-cathode gauges, the electrons are released from the cathode by the impact of ions, whilst in the hot-cathode gauges the electrons are emitted by a heated filament.

10.3.2.1 The discharge-tube gauge

Construction This is the simplest of the cold-cathode ionization gauges and operates over the range from 10^3 Pa to 10^{-1} Pa. The gauge head shown in Figure 10.7 consists of a glass tube about 15 cm long and 1 cm in diameter, connected to the vacuum apparatus. A flat or cylindrical metal electrode attached to a glass/metal seal is mounted at each end. Aluminium is preferable as it does not readily disintegrate to form metal films on the gauge walls during use. A stable power supply with an output of 2.0 kV at 2.0 mA is connected across the electrodes, in series with a resistor R of about 2 MΩ to limit the current, and a 1 mA meter M scaled to read the pressure.

Operation When the gauge is operating, several distinct luminous glows appear in the tube, the colours of which depend on the gases present. These glows are called the positive column P and negative glow N and result from ionization of the gas. The process is illustrated in Figure 10.8, where a positive ion striking the cathode C releases an electron. The electron is accelerated towards the anode, and after travelling some distance encounters a gas molecule and produces the ionization which forms the negative glow. Ions

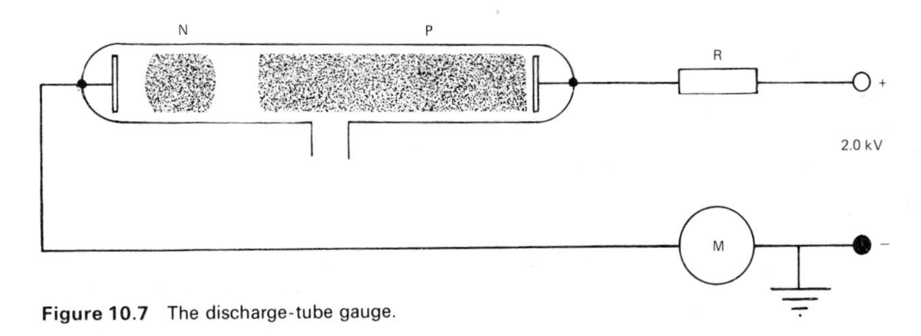

Figure 10.7 The discharge-tube gauge.

from the negative glow are attracted to the cathode where further electrons are emitted. This process, though continuous when established, requires some initial ions to start it. These may be formed by traces of radioactivity in the environment, though some delay may be experienced after switching on. The operating pressure range is determined by the electron path lengths. Above 10^3 Pa the motion of the electrons is impeded by the large number of gas molecules, whilst below about 10^{-1} Pa the electrons travel the whole length of the tube without meeting a gas molecule, and ionization ceases.

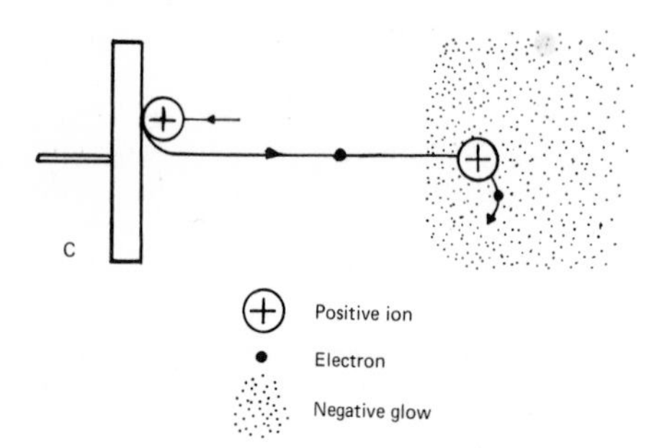

Figure 10.8 The production of carriers in the glow discharge.

10.3.2.2 The Penning ionization gauge (*Penning 1937*)

This cold-cathode gauge is sensitive, simple and robust, and therefore finds wide industrial application. It measures the pressure of gases and vapours over the range from 1 Pa to 10^{-5} Pa. This is shown in Figure 10.9.

Construction A glass or metal envelope connected to the vacuum apparatus houses two parallel cathode plates C of non-magnetic material separated by about 2 cm, and connected together electrically. Midway between these, and parallel to them is a wire anode ring A. Attached to the outside of the envelope is a permanent-magnet assembly which produces a transverse magnetic flux density B of about 0.03 T. This greatly increases the electron path length and enables a glow discharge to be maintained at low pressures. An alternative construction, of greater sensitivity, due to Klemperer (1947) is shown in Figure 10.10. This uses a non-magnetic cylindrical cathode C about 30 mm in diameter and 50 mm long, which may form the gauge envelope, along the axis of which is a stiff wire anode A, 1 mm in diameter. An axial magnetic flux density B of about 0.03 T is provided by a cylindrical permanent magnet or solenoid.

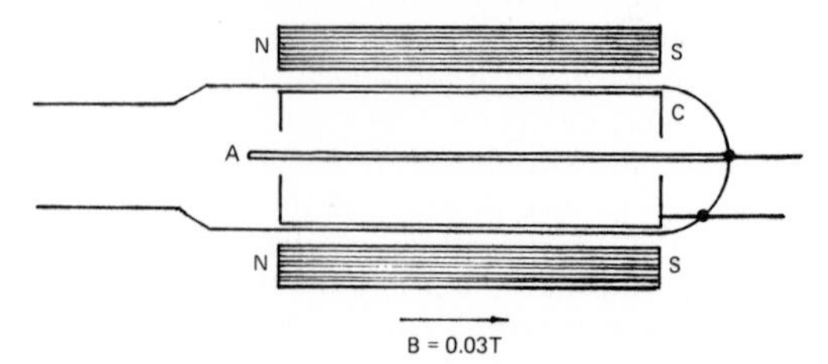

Figure 10.10 Cylindrical form of Penning gauge.

Operation A stable 2.0 kV power supply capable of supplying 2 mA is connected in series with a 1 mA meter M scaled to read pressure. The 2 MΩ ballast resistor R limits the current to 1 mA at the upper end of the pressure range. Electron paths in the gauge are shown in Figure 10.11. The electrode assembly, shown in section, is divided for purposes of explanation into two regions. On the right-hand side the magnetic field is imagined to be absent, and an electron from the cathode oscillates through the plane of the anode ring several times before collection, thereby increasing the electron path length. On the left-hand side, the presence of the magnetic flux causes a helical motion around the oscillatory path causing a still greater increase. The combined effect of these two processes is to bring about electron paths many metres in length, confined within a small volume. All gas discharges are subject to abrupt changes in form when the pressure varies. These mode changes lead to a sudden change in gauge current of 5 to 10 per cent as the pressure rises, which is not reversed until the pressure is reduced below the level at which it occurred. The effect, shown in Figure 10.12, is known as hysteresis, and causes ambiguity since a given pressure p is associated with two slightly different currents i_1 and i_2. By careful

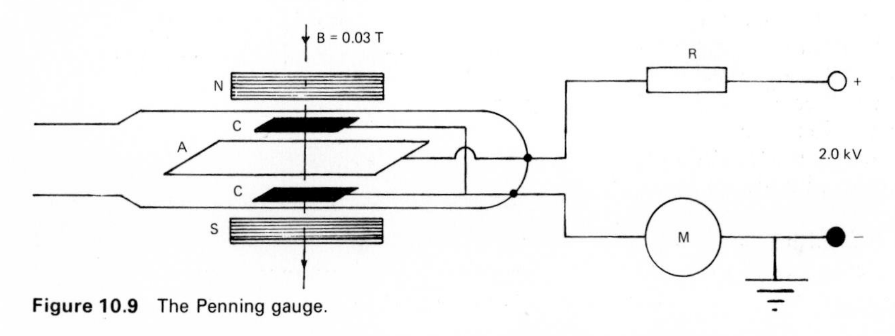

Figure 10.9 The Penning gauge.

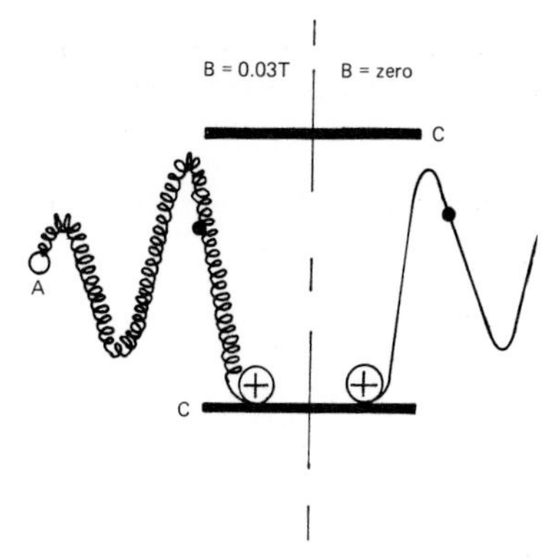

Figure 10.11 Electron paths in the Penning gauge.

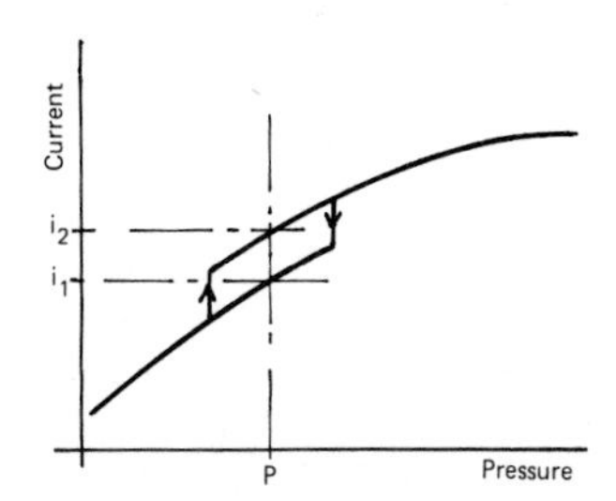

Figure 10.12 Hysteresis in the Penning gauge.

design, the effect may be minimized, and made to appear outside the operating range of the gauge.

10.3.2.3 The hot-cathode ionization gauge (Buckley 1916)

This is the most sensitive available gauge, and has the unique property that its reading is directly proportional to pressure over the range from 100 Pa to 10^{-8} Pa.

Construction The gauge head shown in Figure 10.13 is a special triode valve, usually with a hard glass envelope. Stainless steel may also be used, or a nude form of gauge in which the gauge electrodes are inserted directly into the vacuum vessel. The filament F, of heavy-gauge tungsten, operates at about 2000 K, and may be readily damaged by accidental inrushes of air. A filament of iridium coated with thorium oxide operating at a lower temperature is almost indestructible. Around the filament is a molybdenum or tungsten grid G also heavily constructed, and outside the grid is a cylindrical ion-collector C of nickel. Since the ion current received by this electrode is very small, special care is taken with its insulation.

Operation The gauge head is furnished with stable electrical supplies as shown in Figure 10.14. The filament is heated to produce electrons which are attracted to the grid where a fraction of them is immediately collected. The remainder oscillate several times through the grid wires before collection, forming ions by collision with the gas molecules. The electron current i_- is measured by M_1 and is usually between 0.1 mA and 5.0 mA. Ions formed between the grid and ion-collector constitute an ion current i_+ shown by M_2. Electrons are prevented from reaching the ion-collector by the application of a negative bias of 20 V. Ions formed between the filament and the grid are attracted by the filament where their impact etches its surface and shortens its life. This is particularly the case when the gauge is operated at pressures above 1 Pa, and if active gases such as oxygen are present.

Outgassing Since the gauge is highly sensitive, the gas molecules covering the electrodes and envelope must be removed by heating them to the highest safe temperature. For the filament, the required temperature can be obtained by increasing the filament

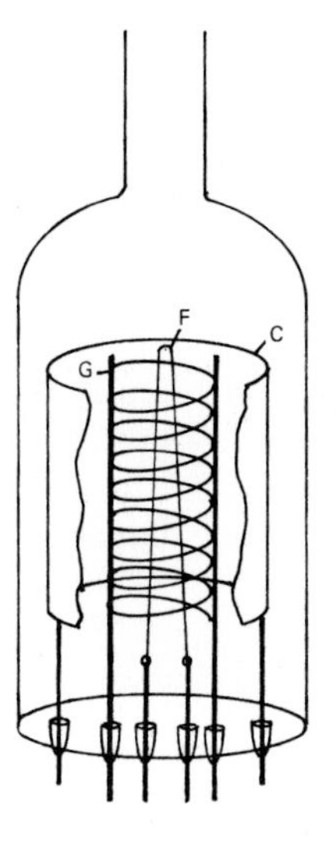

Figure 10.13 The hot-cathode ionization gauge.

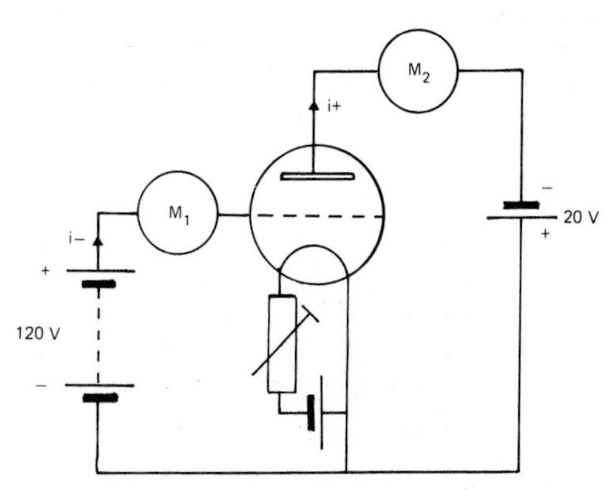

Figure 10.14 Hot-cathode ionization gauge.

current, whilst the grid and ion-collector may be heated by electron bombardment, using the filament as the source. Commercial gauge control units make provision for this treatment. The envelope is heated in an oven, or by means of a hot-air gun.

Pumping During operation, the gauge removes gas molecules from the vacuum apparatus, and thus behaves as a pump. Two processes are involved: at the filament one takes place in which molecules of active gases combine to form stable solid compounds; in the other, at the ion-collector, the positive ions embed themselves beneath its surface. The speed of pumping can be reduced by lowering the filament temperature and by reducing the rate of collection of ions.

Relationship between ion current and pressure If the pressure is p, the ion current i_+, and the electron current i_-, it is found for a given gas, say nitrogen, that

$$i_+ \propto p i_- \qquad (10.1)$$

Therefore

$$i_+ = K p i_- \qquad (10.2)$$

where K is a constant called the *gauge factor* for nitrogen. The SI unit is Pa^{-1}, and its value for an average gauge is 0.1 Pa^{-1}. The value for a particular gauge is given by the maker. For other gases

$$i_+ = C K p i_- \qquad (10.3)$$

where C is the relative sensitivity, with respect to nitrogen. Its approximate value for various gases is as follows:

Gas	He	H_2	N_2	Air	Ar	Xe	Organic vapours
C	0.16	0.25	1.00	1.02	1.10	3.50	>4.0

Equation (10.3) shows that for a given gas and value of i_-

$$i_+ \propto p$$

This valuable property of the gauge is obtained by stabilizing i_- by means of an electronic servo system which controls the filament temperature, and can switch the filament off if the gauge pressure becomes excessive.

10.3.2.4 The Bayard–Alpert ionization gauge (1950)

The soft X-ray effect The conventional ionization gauge described in Section 10.3.2.3 is not able to measure pressures below 10^{-6} Pa, due to the presence of a spurious current in the ion-collector circuit produced by processes occurring in the gauge, and independent of the presence of gas. This current is produced by soft X-rays generated when electrons stike the grid. The phenomenon is called the *soft X-ray effect*. The wavelength λ of this radiation is given by

$$\lambda = 1200/V \text{ nm} \qquad (10.4)$$

where V is the grid potential. If this is 120 volts then $\lambda = 10$ nm. Radiation of this wavelength cannot escape through the gauge envelope, but when absorbed by the ion-collector causes the emission of photoelectrons which are collected by the grid. In the collector circuit the loss of an electron cannot be distinguished from the gain of a positive ion, so that the process results in a steady spurious ion current superimposed on the true ion current. The spurious current is about 10^{-10} A and is of the same order of magnitude as true ion current at 10^{-6} Pa. It is therefore difficult to measure pressures below this value with this type of gauge. A modified design due to Bayard and Alpert shown in Figure 10.15 enables the area of the ion-collector, and hence the spurious current, to be reduced by a factor of 10^3, thereby extending the range to 10^{-9} Pa.

Construction The filament F is mounted outside a cylindrical grid G, having a fine wire collector C of 0.1 mm diameter tungsten mounted along its axis. The electrodes are mounted in a glass envelope which has a transparent conducting coating W on its inner wall to stabilize the surface potential.

Operation The gauge is operated in the same manner as a conventional ionization gauge. Electrons from the filament oscillate through the grid volume and form ions there. These ions are pushed by the positive potential of the grid towards the ion-collector, which forms their only means of escape. Thus despite its small area, the electrode is an extremely good collector of ions.

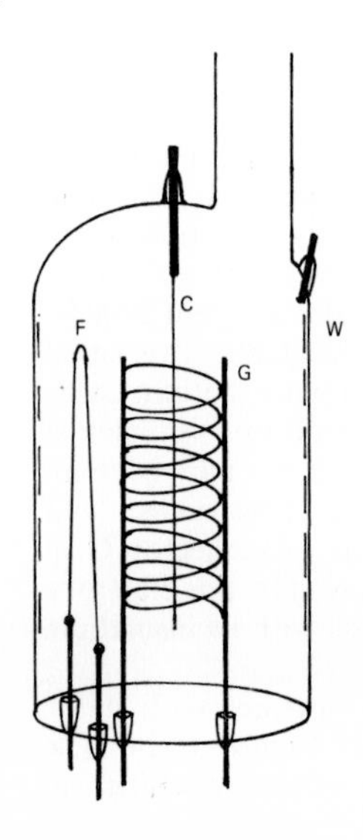

Figure 10.15 The Bayard–Alpert ionization gauge.

Table 10.2 Properties of gauges

Gauge	*Pressure range (Pa)*	*Accuracy ±%*	*Cost**	*Principal advantages*	*Principal limitations*
Bourdon tube	10^5–10^2	10	A	Simple. Robust.	Poor accuracy below 100 Pa.
Quartz spiral	10^5–10	10	B	Reads differential pressures.	Rather fragile.
Diaphragm	10^5–10	5	B	Good general-purpose gauge.	Zero setting varies.
Liquid manometers	10^5–10^2	5–10	A	Simple. Direct reading.	Vapour may contaminate vacuum.
McLeod	10^5–5×10^{-4}	5–10	C	Wide pressure range. Used for calibration.	Intermittent. Measures GAS pressures only.
Thermocouple	10^3–10^{-1}	20	B	Simple. Robust. Inexpensive.	Response not instantaneous.
Pirani	10^3–10^{-2}	10	C	Robust.	Zero variation due to filament contamination.
Thermistor	10^3–10^{-2}	10	C	Fast response. Low current consumption.	—
Discharge tube	10^3–1	20	B	Very simple. Robust.	Limited pressure range.
Penning	1–10^{-5}	10–20	C	Sensitive. Simple. Robust.	Large pumping effect. Hysteresis.
Hot-cathode ion	10^2–10^{-6}	10–30	D	Sensitive. Linear scale. Instantaneous response.	Filament easily damaged. Needs skilful use.
Bayard–Alpert	1–10^{-8}	10–30	D	As above, with better low-pressure performance.	As above.

* Scale of costs (£): A 0–50; B 50–200; C 200–400; D 400–600.

10.4 References

B.S.I. 1951, *Glossary of Terms Used in Vacuum Technology. Part I Terms of General Application*, British Standards Institution, (1969)

Carpenter, L. G., *Vacuum Technology*, Hilger, (1970)

Leck, J. H., *Pressure Measurement in Vacuum Systems*, Institute of Physics, (1964)

Pirani, M. and Yarwood, J., *Principles of Vacuum Engineering*, Chapman & Hall, (1961)

Ward, L. and Bunn, J. P., *Introduction to the Theory and Practice of High Vacuum Technology*, Butterworth, (1967)

11 Particle sizing

W. L. SNOWSILL

11.1 Introduction

The size of particles is an extremely important factor in their behaviour. To name but a few examples, it affects their chemical reactivity, their optical properties, their performance in a gas stream, and the electrical charge they can acquire. The methods used for assessing size are often based on one or more of these effects.

Particulate technology is a complex subject, and the major factor in this complexity is the variety of the physical and chemical properties of the particles. What appears to the naked eye as a simple grey powder can be a fascinating variety of shapes, colours and sizes when viewed under a microscope. Particles can be solid or hollow, or filled with gas. The surface structure, porosity, specific gravity etc. can have a profound effect on their behaviour. Their ability to absorb moisture or to react with other chemicals in the environment or with each other can make handling very difficult as well as actually affecting the size of the particles. The size analyst has to combat the problem of particles adhering to each other because of chemical reactions, mechanical bonding or electrostatic charging, and the problem increases as the size decreases. At the same time he must be aware that the forces applied to keep them separate may be enough with friable particles to break them.

Sampling is a crucial factor when measurements are made on particles. The essential points are:

(a) To be of any value at all, the sample must be representative of the source.
(b) Steps must be taken to avoid the sample changing its character before or during analysis.
(c) Particulate material when poured, vibrated or moved in any way tends to segregate itself. The coarser particles tend to flow down the outside of heaps, rise to the top of any vibrating regime, and be thrown to the outside when leaving a belt feeder. These factors need to be given careful consideration especially when attempting to subdivide samples.

11.2 Characterization of particles

Most particles are not regularly shaped so that it is not possible to describe the size uniquely. To overcome this problem, the standard procedure is to use the diameter of equivalent spheres. However, an irregularly shaped particle can have an almost limitless number of different equivalent spheres depending on the particular parameter chosen for equivalence.

For example, the diameter of a sphere with an equivalent volume would be different from that with an equivalent surface area.

Consider a cubic particle with edge of length x. The diameter of an equivalent volume sphere would be $x(6/\pi)^{1/3}$, i.e. $1.24x$. The diameter of an equivalent surface area sphere would be $x(6/\pi)^{1/2}$, i.e. $1.38x$. The chosen equivalent is usually related to the method of analysis. It is sensible to select the method of analysis to suit the purpose of the measurement but in some cases this is complicated by practical and economic considerations.

Sometimes, the equivalent diameter is not particularly relevant to the process, whereas the actual measurement made is relevant. In such cases, the size is sometimes quoted in terms of the parameter measured. A good example of this is terminal velocity (see Section 11.3). If, for example, information is required to assess the aerodynamic effect of a gas stream on particles, terminal velocity is more relevant than particle size. Even if the particles are spherical, conversion can be complicated by the possible variations in particle density. The term 'vel' is sometimes used to denote particle size. A 1 vel particle has a free falling speed of 10 mm s^{-1} in still dry air at s.t.p.

It is important when equivalent diameters are quoted that the basis (equivalent mass, volume, surface area, projected area, etc.) is clearly stated.

11.2.1 Statistical mean diameters

Microscopic examination of an irregularly shaped particle suggests other methods of assessing the mean

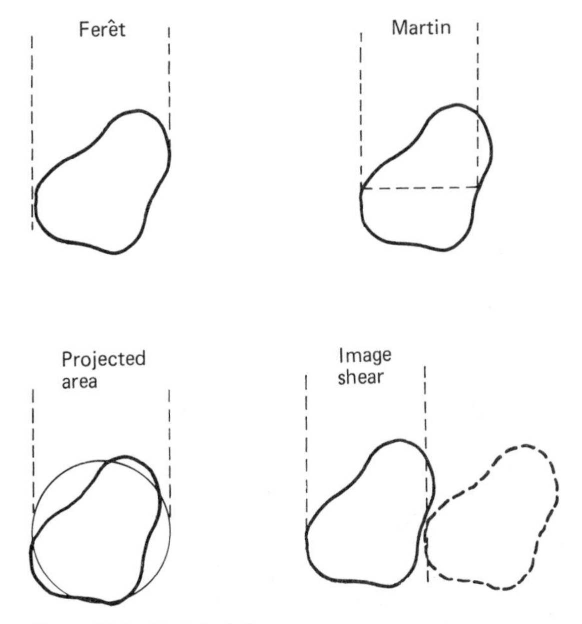

Figure 11.1 Statistical diameters.

diameter. Consider a large number of identical particles, 'truly' randomly orientated on a microscope slide. The mean of a given measurement made on each of the particles but in the same direction (relative to the microscope) would yield a statistical mean diameter. The following is a series of statistical mean diameters that have been proposed (see Figure 11.1):

(a) Ferêt's diameter: the mean of the overall width of a particle measured in all directions.
(b) Martin's diameter: the mean of the length of a chord bisecting the projected area of the particle measured in all directions.
(c) Projected area diameter: the mean of the diameters of circles having the same area as the particle viewed in all directions.
(d) Image shear diameter: the mean of the distances that the image of a particle needs to be moved so that it does not overlap the original outline of the particle, measured in all directions.

In microscopy, because particles tend to lie in a stable position on the slide, measurements as above of a group of particles would not be 'truly' randomly orientated. In these circumstances, the above diameters are 'two-dimensional statistical mean diameters'.

11.3 Terminal velocity

The terminal velocity of a particle is that velocity resulting from the action of accelerating and drag forces. Most commonly it is the free falling speed of a particle in still air under the action of gravity. The relationship between the terminal velocity of a particle and its diameter depends on whether the flow local to the particle is laminar or turbulent. In laminar flow, the particle falls more quickly than in turbulent flow where particles tend to align themselves for maximum drag and the drag is increased by eddies in the wake of the particles.

The general equation for the drag force F on a particle is:

$$F = Kd^n V^n \eta^{2-n} \rho_0^{n-1}$$

where K is the drag coefficient depending on shape, surface, etc., d is the particle dimension (diameter of a sphere), V is relative velocity, η is fluid viscosity, ρ_0 is fluid density, and n varies from 1 for laminar flow to 2 for turbulent flow.

For some regularly shaped particles K can be calculated. For example for a sphere in laminar flow, $K = 3\pi$.

Hence from the above, we find for laminar flow spheres

$$F = 3\pi d V \eta$$

and this is known as Stokes's law.

By equating drag force and gravitational force we can show

$$3\pi d V_T \eta = \frac{\pi d^3}{6}(\rho - \rho_0)g$$

where ρ is particle density, and V_T is terminal velocity. Thus,

$$V_T = (\rho - \rho_0)\frac{gd^2}{18\eta}$$

If the terminal velocity of irregularly shaped particles is measured together with ρ and η, the value obtained for d is the Stokes diameter. Sometimes the term 'aerodynamic' diameter is used, denoting an equivalent Stokes sphere with unit density. Stokes diameters measured with spheres are found to be accurate (errors <2 per cent) if the Reynolds number

$$Re = \frac{\rho_0 V d}{\eta}$$

is less than 0.2. At higher values of Re, the calculated diameters are too small. As Re increases, n increases progressively to 2 for $Re > 1000$ when the motion is fully turbulent and according to Newton the value of K for spheres reduces to $\pi/16$.

For very small particles where the size approaches the mean free path of the fluid molecules ($\sim 0.1\ \mu$m for dry air at s.t.p.) the drag force is less than that predicted by Stokes. Cunningham devised a correction for Stokes's equation:

$$F=3\pi dV\eta\,\frac{1}{1+(b\lambda/d)}$$

where λ is the mean free path and b depends on the fluid (e.g. for air at s.t.p. dry, $b \simeq 1.7$).

11.4 Optical effects caused by particles

When light passes through a suspension of particles, some is absorbed, some scattered and a proportion is unaffected, the relative proportions depending on the particle size, the wavelength of the light and the refractive indices of the media. The molecules of the fluid also scatter light.

Some optical size-analysis methods infer size from measurements of the transmitted, i.e. unaffected light, others measure the scattered light. Some operate on suspensions of particles, others on individual particles.

The theory of light-scattering by particles is complicated. Rayleigh's treatment which applies only to particles whose diameter $d \ll \lambda$ (the wavelength) shows that the intensity of scattered light is proportional to d^6/λ^4. It also shows that the scattering intensity varies with the observation angle and this also depends on d. As size d approaches λ however, the more rigorous treatment of Mie indicates that the scattering intensity becomes proportional to d^2, i.e. particle cross-sectional area, but that the effective area is different from the geometrical area by a factor K, known as the scattering coefficient or efficiency factor, which incorporates d, λ and the refractive index. Where $d \ll \lambda$ the two theories are similar. In the region around $d=\lambda$, however, K oscillates (typically between about 1.5 and 5) tending towards a mean of 2. Beyond about $d=5\lambda$, the value of K becomes virtually 2, i.e. the effective cross-sectional area of a particle is twice the geometrical area. As d/λ increases the preferred scattering angle reduces and becomes more distinct and forward scattering predominates (diffraction).

If the light is not monochromatic, the oscillation of K is smoothed to a mean of about 2.

The ratio of the intensity of the transmitted light I_T to the incident light I_0 is given by the Lambert–Beer law

$$\frac{I_T}{I_0}=\exp\left(-K\frac{a}{A}\right)$$

where a is the total projected area of the particles in the light beam, A is the area of the beam and again K is the scattering coefficient. This is often simplified to

$$\text{optical density } D=\log_{10} I_0/I_T =0.4343K(a/A)$$

The scattering coefficient is sometimes called the 'particle extinction coefficient'. This should not be confused with extinction coefficient ξ. If the transmission intensity of a beam of light changes from I_0 to I_t in a path length L

$$I_T/I_0=\xi L$$

where K is contained within ξ.

Extinction $=\ln I_0/I_t$ is the Napierian equivalent of optical density.

Although the value of K has been shown to be virtually 2, the scattering angle for larger particles ($\sim 30\,\mu$m) is small and about half the light is forward-scattered. It follows that depending on the observation distance and the size of the sensor, much of the forward-scattered light could be received and the effective value of K in the above expression could be as low as 1. It will be apparent that the effect of a distribution of particles on light transmission is not a simple function of the projected area.

Bearing in mind the above limitations on K, it is possible to estimate the transmitted light intensity through a distribution of particles by summing the area concentrations within size bands. In each band of mean diameter d, the effective area a/A is $1.5KcL/\rho d$, where c is the mass concentration, L is the optical path length, and ρ is the particle density.

11.5 Particle shape

Although we can attribute to a particle an equivalent diameter, for example a Ferêt diameter d_F, this does not uniquely define the particle. Two particles with the same Ferêt diameter can have a very different shape. We can say that the volume of an equivalent sphere is

$$\frac{\pi}{6}(d_F)^3$$

but we must recognize that the actual volume V is probably very different. Heywood has proposed the use of shape coefficients. We can assign a coefficient $\alpha_{V,F}$ to a particle such that

$$V=\alpha_{V,F}(d_F)^3$$

Thus, if we use another method of size analysis which in fact measures particle volume V, knowing d_F we can calculate $\alpha_{V,F}$. Similarly, by measuring particle surface area S, we can assign a coefficient $\alpha_{S,F}$ so that

$$S=\alpha_{S,F}(d_F)^2$$

$\alpha_{V,F}$ is called the volume shape coefficient (based on Ferêt diameter) and $\alpha_{S,F}$ is called the surface shape coefficient (based on Ferêt diameter).

Clearly, there are other shape coefficients, and they can be associated with other diameters.

The ratio $\alpha_S/\alpha_V=\alpha_{S,V}$ is called the surface volume shape coefficient.

The subject is covered by BS 4359 (1970) Pt. III which includes definitions and tables of the various coefficients for a number of regular shapes: cubes, ellipsoids, tetrahedra, etc., and a number of commonly occurring particles. The coefficients α_S, α_V and $\alpha_{S,V}$ together provide a very good indication of particle shape, in a quantified form.

11.6 Methods for characterizing a group of particles

We have already established a number of alternative 'diameters' to be used to characterize particles. There are also several ways of characterizing groups of particles. They are all assessments of the quantities of particles within 'diameter' bands, but the quantities can be numbers of particles, mass of particles, volume, surface area, etc. As with particle equivalent diameters, it is important that the basis of the analysis is made clear.

There are also several methods for expressing the results of a size analysis. Perhaps the most obvious is tabulation and a contrived example of this is given in Table 11.1 which shows the masses of particles

Table 11.1 Alternative methods of tabulating the same size analysis

(a)

Size band (μm)	*% mass in band*
0–5	0.1
5–10	2.4
10–15	7.5
15–20	50.0
20–25	27.0
25–30	12.5
>30	0.5

(b)

Stated size	*% less than stated size*
5	0.1
10	2.5
15	10.0
20	60.0
25	87.0
30	99.5

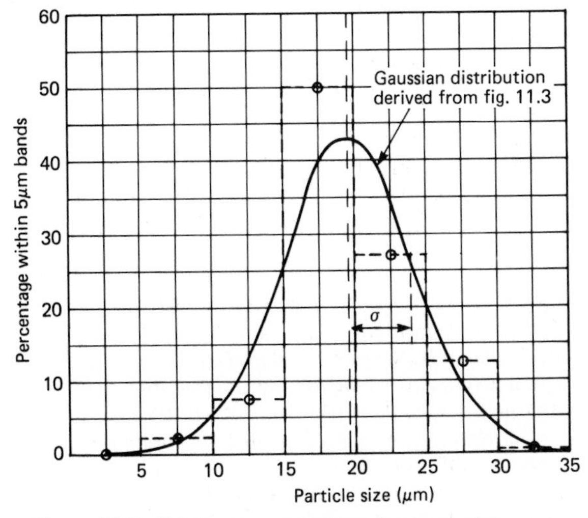

Figure 11.2 Relative percentage mass–frequency plot.

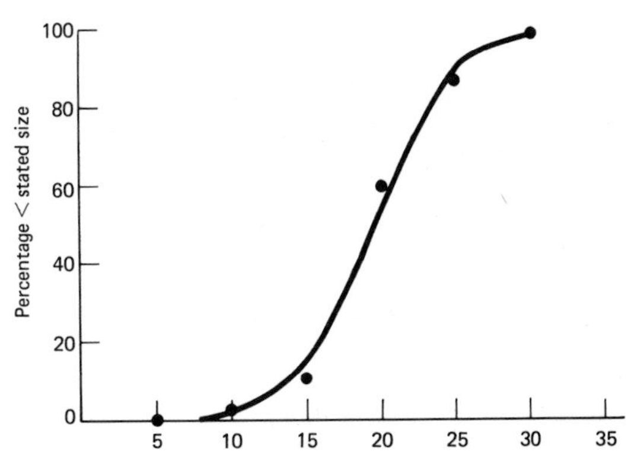

Figure 11.3 Cumulative percentage mass–frequency plot using linear scales.

contained within 5 μm size fractions from 0 to 40 μm. The main disadvantage is that it requires considerable experience to recognize what could be important differences between samples. Such differences are much more readily apparent if the results are plotted graphically. One method is to plot the quantity obtained, be it mass, volume, surface area or number of particles in each size fraction against size, both on a linear scale. This is called a relative frequency plot and Table 11.1 has been transferred in this way to Figure 11.2.

Students with a little understanding of statistics will be tempted to compare this with a normal or Gaussian distribution (also shown). In practice, Gaussian distributions are not very common with powder samples but this simple example is useful to illustrate a principle.

11.6.1 Gaussian or normal distributions

The equation for a Gaussian distribution curve is

$$y=\frac{1}{\sigma\sqrt{2\pi}}\exp-\left[\frac{(x-\bar{x})^2}{2\sigma^2}\right]$$

where $\int y\,dx$, the area under the curve, represents the total quantity of sample (again number, mass, volume, etc.) and is made equal to 1. The symbol $\bar{x}$ represents the arithmetic mean of the distribution and σ the standard deviation of the distribution is a measure of the spread. These two parameters uniquely define a Gaussian distribution. It can be shown that 68.26 per cent of the total area under the curve is contained between the boundaries $x=\bar{x}\pm\sigma$. In this case we have plotted the values of $y\,\delta x$ for equal 5 μm increments. We could just as easily have drawn a histogram. At this point it should be stated that if any one of the distributions should turn out to be 'normal' or Gaussian, then none of the other plots, i.e. number, volume, surface area distributions, will be Gaussian.

An advantage of the above presentation is that small

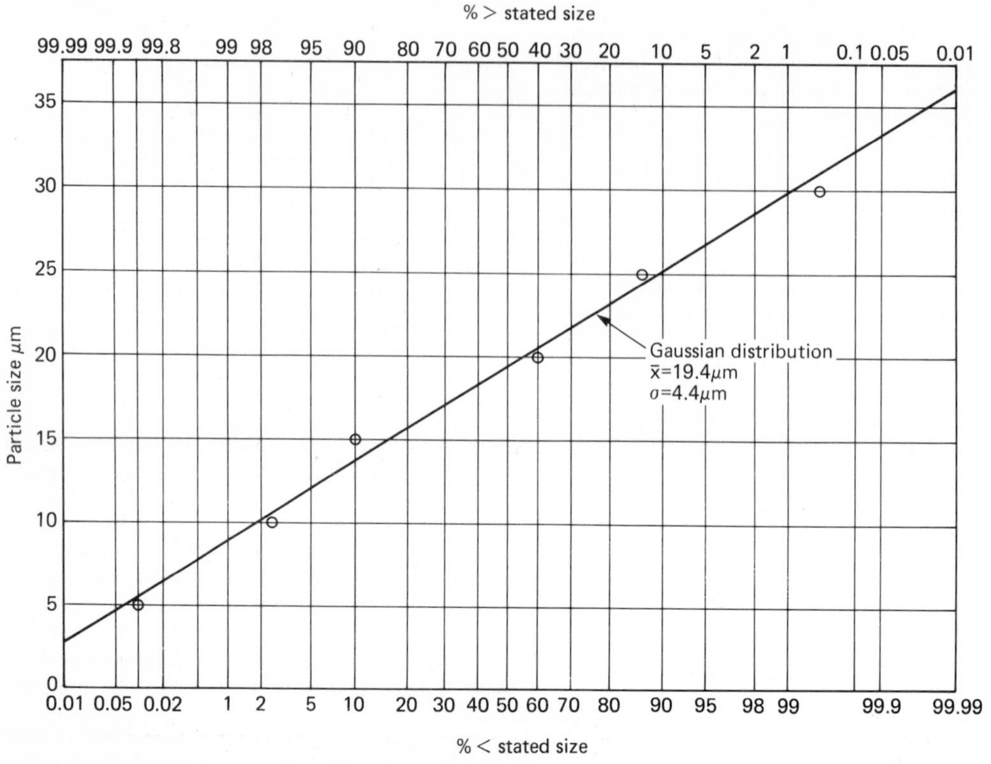

Figure 11.4 Cumulative percentage mass-frequency plot using linear × percentage scales.

differences between samples would be readily apparent. However, it would be useful to be able to measure easily the values of x and σ and this is not the case with the above. Two alternatives are possible. One is to plot a cumulative percentage frequency diagram, again on linear axes, as in Figure 11.3. In this case one plots the percentage less (or greater) than given sizes. Alternatively, one can plot the same information on linear-probability paper where one axis, the percentage frequency axis, is designed so that a Gaussian distribution will give a straight line, as in Figure 11.4. In a non-exact science such as size analysis, the latter has distinct advantages, but in either case the arithmetic mean $\bar{x}$ is the value of x at the 50 per cent point and the value of σ can be deduced as follows. Since 68.26 per cent of a normal distribution is contained between the values $x=\bar{x}+\sigma$ and $x=\bar{x}-\sigma$, it follows that

$$\sigma = x_{84\%} - \bar{x} = \bar{x} - x_{16\%}$$
$$= \tfrac{1}{2}(x_{84\%} - x_{16\%})$$

because $x_{84\%} - x_{16\%}$ covers the range of 68 per cent of the total quantity.

The closeness of fit to a Gaussian distribution is much more obvious in Figure 11.4 than in Figures 11.2 and 11.3. With probability paper, small differences or errors at either extreme produce an exaggerated effect on the shape of the line. This paper can still be used when the distribution is not 'normal' but in this case, the line will not be straight and standard deviation is no longer meaningful. If the distribution is not 'normal' the 50 per cent size is not the arithmetic mean but is termed the median size. The arithmetic mean needs to be calculated from

$$\bar{x} = \sum (\text{percentage in size fraction} \times \text{mean of size fraction})/100$$

and the basis on which it is calculated (mass, surface area, volume or particle number) has to be stated. Each will give a different mean and median value.

11.6.2 Log-normal distributions

It is unusual for powders to occur as Gaussian distributions. A plot as in Figure 11.2 would typically be skewed towards the smaller particle sizes. Experience has shown, however, that powder distributions often tend to be log-normal. Thus a percentage frequency plot with a logarithmic axis for the particle size reproduces a close approximation to a symmetrical curve and a cumulative percentage plot on log-probability paper often approximates to a straight line, Figure 11.5.

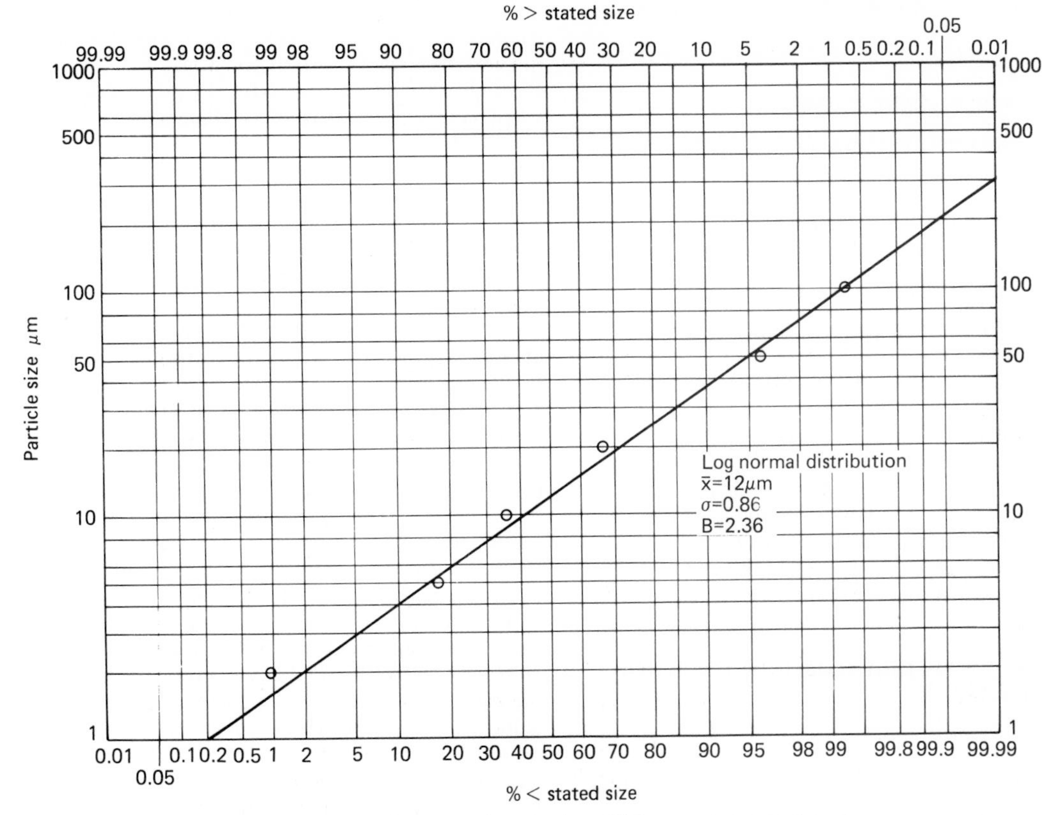

Figure 11.5 Cumulative percentage mass–frequency plot using base-10 log × percentage scales.

In a true log-normal distribution, the equation becomes

$$y=\frac{1}{\sigma\sqrt{2\pi}}\exp\left[-\frac{(\ln x-\overline{\ln x})^2}{2\sigma^2}\right]$$

where now it is $\int y\mathrm{d}(\ln x)$, the area under the curve using a log axis which represents the total quantity, and σ now refers to the log distribution and is not the same as before. The expression $\overline{\ln x}$ is the arithmetic mean of the logarithms of the size so that $\bar{x}$ is now the geometric mean of the distribution. On a cumulative percentage diagram, $\bar{x}$, the geometric mean particle size is the 50 per cent size and σ is found from

$$\sigma=\ln x_{84}-\ln\bar{x}=\ln\bar{x}-\ln x_{16}$$

$$=\ln\frac{x_{84}}{\bar{x}} \qquad =\ln\frac{\bar{x}}{x_{16}}$$

$$=\tfrac{1}{2}\ln\frac{x_{84}}{x_{16}}$$

If x is plotted on base-10 logarithm × probability paper,

$$\sigma=\tfrac{1}{2}\ln 10\log_{10}\frac{x_{84}}{x_{16}}$$

$$=1.15\log_{10}\frac{x_{84}}{x_{16}}$$

Again $\bar{x}$ and σ define the distribution.

Sometimes σ is replaced by $\ln B$ to show that it is the standard deviation of a log-normal distribution

$$B=\sqrt{(x_{84}/x_{16})}$$

Again, if the cumulative percentage plot is not truly linear the derivation of the standard deviation is not truly meaningful and the 50 per cent size is then the median size. However, in practice such curves are commonly used for comparing size analyses and it is sometimes useful for mathematical treatment to draw an approximate straight line.

A feature of a log normal distribution is that if one method of treatment, for example a mass/particle size analysis, demonstrates log-normal properties, then all the other methods will also be log-normal. Clearly the values of $\bar{x}$ will be different. Log-probability diagrams are particularly useful when the range of particle sizes is large.

11.6.3 Rosin–Rammler distributions

Some distributions are extremely skewed, for example, ground coal. Rosin and Rammler have developed a further method for obtaining a straight-line cumulative percentage frequency graph. If the percentage over size x is R, it has been found that

$$\log \log (100/R) = K + n \log x$$

where K is a constant and n a characteristic for the material.

The Rosin–Rammler distribution is included for completeness but its use is not generally recommended.

Sometimes when a distribution covers a wide range of sizes, more than one analysis method has to be used. It is not unusual for a discontinuity to occur in the graphs at the change-over point and this can be due to shape or density effects (see shape factor, Section 11.5).

11.7 Analysis methods that measure size directly

11.7.1 Sieving

Sieving is the cheapest, most popular and probably the most easily understood method of size analysis. It also covers a very wide range of sizes, it being possible to buy sieves (screens) ranging in mesh size from 5 μm up to several centimetres. However, sieving of fine materials requires special techniques and the British Standard 410:(1962) indicates a lower limit of 45 μm. Sieves are made in a variety of materials from non-metallic (e.g. polyester) to stainless steel. The common method of construction is woven wire or fabric but the smallest mesh sizes are electroformed holes in plates. The British Standard gives minimum tolerances on mesh size and wire spacing, etc. American, German and I.S.O. standards are also applicable with very similar criteria. The British Standard nomenclature is based on the number of wires in the mesh per inch. Thus B.S. sieve number 200 has 200 wires per inch and with a specified nominal wire diameter of 52 μm has a nominal aperture size of 75 μm square. In principle all particles less than 75 μm diameter in a sample of spherical particles will pass through a B.S. number 200 sieve. The sample is placed in the uppermost of a stack of sieves covering the range of diameters of interest arranged in ascending order of size from the bottom. The powder is totally enclosed by means of a sealed base and lid. The stack is agitated until the particles have found their appropriate level and the mass in each sieve noted. The tolerance on mesh size introduces a measure of uncertainty on the band widths, and clearly irregularly shaped particles with one or more dimensions larger than the nominal size could still pass through. It is customary therefore to quote particle size when sieving in terms of 'sieve' diameters.

Sieving is by no means as straightforward as it may first appear. For example it is relatively easy for large particles to block the apertures to the passage of small particles (blinding) and there is a statistical uncertainty whether a small particle will find its way to a vacant hole. Both of these are very dependent on the quantity of material placed on the sieve and as a general rule this quantity should be kept small. It is not possible to give an arbitrary figure for the quantity since it will depend on the material and its size distribution, particle shape and surface structure, its adhesive qualities and to some extent the sieve itself. The same comments apply to sieving time. Optimum times and quantities can only be found by experiment, assessing the variation in size grading produced by both factors. Generally a reduction in the quantity is more advantageous than an increase in sieving time and it is normally possible to obtain repeatable results with less than about 10 minutes sieving. The analyst is cautioned that some friable materials break up under the action of sieving.

A number of manufacturers produce sieves and sieving systems using various methods of mechanical agitation, some of which include a rotary action. The objective, apart from reducing the tedium, is to increase the probability of particles finding vacant holes by causing them to jump off the mesh and to return in a different position. Figure 11.6 is an example of one that uses vibration. The vibration can be adjusted in amplitude, and it can be pulsed.

Figure 11.6 Fritsch Analysette sieve shaker.

A feature of any vibrating mechanism is that parts of it can resonate and this is particularly relevant to sieving where it is possible for the sieve surface to contain systems of nodes and anti-nodes so that parts of the surface are virtually stationary. This can be controlled to some extent by adjustment of the amplitude, but although the top sieve surface may be visible, through a transparent lid, the lower surfaces are not and they will have different nodal patterns. One solution to this dilemma is to introduce into each sieve a small number (5 to 10) of 10 mm diameter agate spheres. These are light enough not to damage the sieves or, except in very friable materials, the particles, but they break up the nodal patterns and therefore increase the effective area of the sieve.

A useful feature of dry sieving is that it can be used to obtain closely sized samples for experimental purposes in reasonable quantities.

Although most sieving is performed in the dry state, some difficult materials and certainly much finer sieves can be used in conjunction with a liquid, usually water, in which the particles are not soluble. The lid and base of the sieve stack are replaced by fitments adapted for the introduction and drainage of the liquid with a pump if necessary.

Sieving systems are now commercially available which introduce either air or liquid movement alternately up and down through the sieves to prevent blinding and to assist the particles through the sieves.

Results are usually quoted in terms of percentage of total mass in each size range, the material being carefully removed from the sieve with the aid of a fine soft brush. In wet sieving, the material is washed out, filtered, dried at 105 °C and weighed. Many powders are hygroscopic so that the precaution of drying and keeping in a dessicator until cool and therefore ready for weighing is a good general principle. Convection currents from a hot sample will cause significant errors.

11.7.2 Microscope counting

11.7.2.1 Basic methods

With modern microscopes, the analyst can enjoy the benefits of a wide range of magnifications, a large optical field, stereoscopic vision and zoom facilities, together with back and top illumination. These and calibrated field stop graticules have considerably eased the strain of microscope counting as a method of size analysis but it is still one of the most tedious. It has the advantage, however, that, as well as being able to size particles, the microscope offers the possibility of minute examination of their shape, surface structure, colour, etc. It is often possible to identify probable sources of particles.

The optical microscope can be used to examine particles down to sizes approaching the wavelength of light. At these very small sizes however, interference and diffraction effects cause significant errors, and below the wavelength of light the particles are not resolvable. Microscope counting is covered by British Standard 3046.

Smaller particles, down to 0.001 μm diameter can be examined using the electron microscope.

The two major disadvantages of microscopy are: the restricted depth of focus which means that examination of a sample with a wide size range involves continual re-focusing and the real possibility of missing 'out-of-focus' particles during a scan; it depends more than most other methods on good representativeness.

Several techniques are available for the preparation of slides, the all important factor being that the sample is fully representative. The particles also need to be well separated from each other. A common method is to place a small fraction of the sample onto the slide with one drop of an organic fluid such as methanol or propanol which disperses the particles. Subsequent evaporation leaves the particles suitably positioned. The fluid obviously must not react with the particles, but it must have the ability to 'wet' them. Agitation with a soft brush can help. If the particles have a sticky coating on them, it may be necessary to remove this first by washing. One technique is to agitate, perhaps in water, to allow ample time for all the particles to settle and then to pour off the fluid carefully, repeating as necessary. Obviously the particles must not be soluble in the fluid. Sometimes the material is first agitated in a fluid and then one drop of the particle-laden fluid transferred to the slide. Representativeness can only be tested by the repeatability of results from a number of

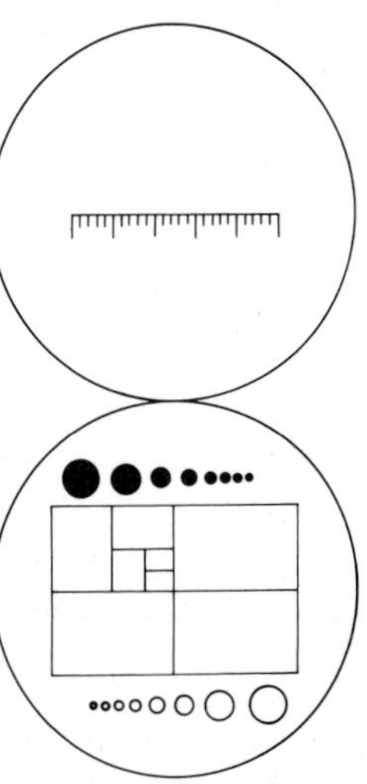

Figure 11.7 Examples of eyepiece graticules.

samples. Techniques have been devised for transferring samples from suspension onto films within the suspension. It is sometimes possible to collect samples directly onto sticky slides coated with grease, gelatine or even rubber solution.

Earlier methods of microscope counting involved the use of an optical micrometer by which a cross-hair could be aligned with each side of each particle in turn and the difference measured. As can be imagined this was slow and tedious and now the most commonly used methods involve calibrated field graticules. The graticules are engraved with a scale, Figure 11.7, nominally divided for example into 20 μm, 100 μm and 1 mm steps. Calibration is dependent on the magnification and this is usually finely adjustable by moving the objective relative to the eyepiece slightly, or by adjusting the zoom if available. Calibration is effected by comparing the field graticule with a stage graticule, similarly and accurately engraved. When set, the stage graticule is replaced by the sample slide.

The slide is scanned in lateral strips, each strip an order or so wider than the largest particles, the objective being to cover the whole of the slide area containing particles. Typically one edge of a chosen reference particle will be aligned with a major graticule line using the longitudinal stage adjustment. The slide will then be traversed laterally along that line and all particles to the right of that line will be counted, and measured using the eyepiece scale. The slide will then be traversed longitudinally to the right until the original particle is in the same relative position but for example five major graticule lines further over and the counting process is repeated for particles within the strip formed by the two lines. The process involves selecting new reference particles as necessary. To avoid duplication, if a particle lies on one of the strip edge-lines, it is counted as if it were in the strip to the right. Particles are allocated to size bands suitably chosen to give say 10 points on the distribution curve. The tedium is relieved if operators work in pairs, one observing, one recording, alternately.

Some graticules have been designed containing systems of opaque and open circles, the sizes arranged in various orders of progression. This can assist the classification of particles by comparison into size bands, each bounded by one of the circles.

When sizing irregularly shaped particles, microscope counting introduces a bias because the particles tend to lie in their most stable orientation. By making measurement of a distribution of randomly orientated particles on a slide along a fixed direction, one obtains a two-dimensional statistical mean diameter.

The method outlined above using a line graticule measures the mean two-dimensional Ferêt diameter, the direction being fixed parallel with the long edge of the slide. It is equally possible to measure the mean two-dimensional Martin's diameter, projected area or image shear diameter.

To obtain three-dimensional mean diameters, it is necessary to take special steps to collect and fix the particles on the slide in a truly random fashion.

11.7.2.2 Semi-automatic microscope size analysers

Semi-automatic methods are those where the actual counting is still done by the analyst but the task, especially the recording, is simplified or speeded up.

The Watson image-shearing eyepiece is a device that replaces the normal eyepiece of a microscope and produces a double image, the separation of which can be adjusted using a calibrated knob along a fixed direction, which again can be preset. The image spacing can be calibrated using a stage graticule. In the Watson eyepiece the images are coloured red and green to distinguish them. The technique in this case is to divide the slide into a number of equal areas, to set the shear spacing at one of a range of values and to count the number of particles in each area with image-shear diameters less than or equal to each of the range.

Some methods have been developed for use with photomicrographs, particularly with the electron microscope. Usually an enlargement of the print, or a projection of it onto a screen, is analysed using comparison aids. The Zeiss–Endter analyser uses a calibrated iris to produce a variable-diameter light spot which can be adjusted to suit each particle. The adjustment is coupled electrically via a multiple switch to eight counters so that pressing a foot switch automatically allocates the particle to one of eight preset ranges of size. A hole is punched in the area of each particle counted to avoid duplication.

11.7.2.3 Automatic microscope size analysers

Several systems have been developed for the automatic scanning of either the microscope field or of photomicrographs. In one type, the system is similar to a television scanning system and indeed the field appears on a television screen. Changes in intensity during the scan can be converted to particle size and the information analysed in a computer to yield details of size in terms of a number of the statistical diameters. It can also calculate shape factors. One system, the Quantimet, now uses digital techniques, dividing the field into 650 000 units.

11.7.3 Direct optical methods

Malvern Instruments Ltd. use a laser and forward-scattering to analyse particles in suspension. The parallel light from the laser passes through a lens, producing an intense spot at the focus. Light falling on any particle is diffracted and is brought to a focus in a system of Fraunhofer diffraction rings centred on the axis and in the focal plane of the lens. The diameters correspond to the preferred scattering angles which are a function of the diameters of the particles. The intensity of each ring is proportional to the total cross-sectional area of the particles of that size. The variation of intensity therefore reflects the dize distribution. Irregularly shaped particles produce blurred rings. A multi-ringed sensor located in the focal plane of the lens passes information to a computer which calculates the volume distribution. It will also assess the type of distribution, whether normal, log-normal or Rosin–Rammler.

The position of the particles relative to the axis of the lens does not affect the diffraction pattern so that movement at any velocity is of no consequence. The method therefore works 'on-line' and has been used to analyse oil fuel from a spray nozzle. The claimed range is from 1 to more than 500 μm.

There are distinct advantages in conducting a size analysis 'on-line'. Apart from obtaining the results generally more quickly, particles as they occur in a process are often agglomerated, i.e. mechanically bound together to form much larger groups which exhibit markedly different behavioural patterns. This is important for example in pollution studies. Most laboratory techniques have to disperse agglomerates produced in sampling and storage. This can be avoided with an on-line process.

11.8 Analysis methods that measure terminal velocity

As already discussed, the terminal velocity of a particle is related to its size and represents a useful method of analysis particularly if the area of interest is aerodynamic. Methods can be characterized broadly into: sedimentation, elutriation and impaction.

11.8.1 Sedimentation

A group of particles, settling for example under the influence of gravity, segregates according to the terminal velocities of the particles. This phenomenon can be used in three ways to grade the particles.

(a) The particles and the settling medium are first thoroughly mixed and changes in characteristics of the settling medium with time and depth are then measured.
(b) The particles and settling medium are mixed as in (a) and measurements are then made on the sediment collecting at the base of the fluid column.
(c) The particles are introduced at the top of the fluid column and their arrival at the base of the column is monitored.

Group (a) is sometimes termed incremental, i.e. increments of the sedimenting fluid are analysed.

Group (b) is sometimes termed cumulative referring to the cumulative effect on the bottom of the column.

Group (c) is also cumulative, but it is sometimes distinguished by the term 'two-layer', i.e. at the initiation of the experiment there are two separate fluids, the upper one thin compared with the lower and containing all the particles, the lower one clear.

11.8.1.1 Incremental methods

Consider at time $t=0$ a homogeneous distribution of particles containing some special ones with terminal velocity V. Ignoring the minute acceleration period, after a time t_1 all the special particles will have fallen a distance $h=Vt_1$. The concentration of those special ones below the depth h will have remained unchanged except on the bottom. Above the depth h, however, all the special particles will have gone. The same argument applies to any sized particle except that the values of h and V are obviously different.

It follows that a measurement of the concentration of all the particles at depth h and time t is a measurement of the concentration of those particles with a terminal velocity less than V, and we have therefore a method of measuring the cumulative distribution.

The following methods use this general principle.

Andreasen's pipette This consists of a relatively large (~550 ml) glass container with a pipette fused into its ground-glass stopper. A 1 per cent concentration of the sample, suitably dispersed in a chosen liquid, is poured into the container to a set level exactly 200 mm above the lower tip of the pipette. Means are provided to facilitate the withdrawal of precise 10 ml aliquots from the container via the pipette.

After repeated inversions of the container to give thorough mixing, the particles are allowed to sediment. At preselected times after this, e.g. 1 minute, 2 minutes, 4 minutes, etc., 10 ml samples are withdrawn and their solids content weighed. Corrections are applied for the change in depth as samples are removed. Samples are removed slowly over a 20-second period centred around the selected times to minimize errors caused by the disturbance at the pipette tip. The results yield a cumulative mass/terminal velocity distribution which can be converted to mass/size etc., as already discussed. With suitable choice of liquid, the method can be used for particles ranging in size from about 1–100 μm. The conditions should be controlled to be Stokesian, i.e. laminar flow, and of course the terminal velocity is appropriate to the fluid conditions, i.e. it depends on the liquid density and viscosity which are also dependent on temperature.

Density-measuring methods Several techniques involve the measurement of the density of the fluid/particle mixture at different times or at different depths at the same time. Initially, after mixing, the density is uniform and depends on the fluid, the particle densities and the mass concentration of particles. After a period of sedimentation, the density varies with depth.

One method of measuring the density uses a hydrometer. This is complicated by allowance having to be made for the change in the overall height of the fluid caused by the immersion of the hydrometer tube. Also, any intruding object causes a discontinuity in the settling medium, some particles settling on the upper surface of the hydrometer bulb, none settling into the volume immediately below the bulb. Motion around the bulb is not vertical. These problems tend to outweigh the basic simplicity of the method.

A neat method of hydrometry which overcomes the overall height problem uses a number of individual hydrometers, commonly called divers. Each consists of a small body which is totally immersed in the fluid, but with its density individually adjusted so that after the preselected time, the divers will be distributed vertically within the sedimenting column, each at the depth appropriate to its density. Accurate measurement of the positions yields the required information. The main problem in this case is being able to see the divers.

A specific-gravity balance can be used. The change with time in the buoyancy of a ball suspended from one arm of a balance at a fixed depth again gives the information required.

Photosedimentation In a photosedimentometer, the sedimentation is observed by a lamp and photocell system (see Section 11.3). The observation distance is small and for particles greater in size than about 15 μm, the value of K, the scattering coefficient, progressively reduces from 2 to 1. We know that

$$\text{optical density } D=0.4343Ka/A$$

where a/A is the area concentration. With no particles present in the liquid, let the values of D and K be D_0 and K_0. With all particles present, thoroughly mixed, let the corresponding values be D_1 and K_1. At time t and depth h, $h=Vt$, where V is the upper limit of the terminal velocity of the particles present. If the corresponding values of D and K are D_V and K_V, the fractional surface area of particles with terminal velocity less than V is given by

$$\left(\frac{D_V}{K_V}-\frac{D_0}{K_0}\right)\bigg/\left(\frac{D_1}{K_1}-\frac{D_0}{K_0}\right)$$

We thus have a method of measuring cumulative surface area terminal velocity distribution.

Proprietary sedimentometers are available which measure D at a fixed height, or scan the whole settlement zone. It is usual to assume $K_V=K_1=K_0$ and to compensate the result appropriately from supplied tables or graphs. Most photosedimentometers use narrow-beam optics in an attempt to restrict the light to maintain the value of K as 2. The WASP (wide-angle scanning photosedimentometer) has the photocell close to the fluid so that most of the diffracted light is also received and the value of K is nearer 1. The 200 mm settling column is scanned automatically at a fixed rate and the optical density continuously recorded giving a graph which can then be evaluated as a cumulative mass size or cumulative surface area size distribution.

X-ray sedimentation is similar to photosedimentation except that X-rays replace light and the intensity of transmission is dependent on the mass of the particles rather than the surface area. Again

$$I_T=I_0\exp(-Kc)$$

where c is the mass concentration of the particles and K is a constant. The x-ray density is

$$D=\log_{10}\frac{I_0}{I_T}$$

11.8.1.2 Cumulative methods

Sedimentation balance Consider at time $t=0$ a homogeneous suspension of particles contained in a column which includes in its base a balance pan.

Let W_1 be the mass of particles with terminal velocity greater than V_1. If h is the height of the column, at time $t_1=h/V_1$ all those particles will have arrived on the balance pan. However the mass M_1 on the pan will also include a fraction of smaller particles that started part-way down. It can be shown that

$$M_1=W_1+t\frac{dM}{dt}$$

and measurements of M and t can be used to evaluate W. British Standard 3402 part 2 suggests that values of M should be observed at times t following a geometrical progression, for example 1, 2, 4, 8, etc. seconds. Then t/dt is constant, in this case 2. It follows that comparing the nth and the $(n-1)$th terms in the time progression,

$$W_n=M_n-2(M_n-M_{n-1})$$

The final value of M is assumed to be equal to the initial mass introduced.

An alternative method, useful if M is continuously recorded, is to construct tangents as in Figure 11.8. Then W is the intercept on the M axis. Unfortunately, because of the inaccuracy of drawing tangents, the method is not very precise, especially if the overall time is protracted, with a wide size distribution. The

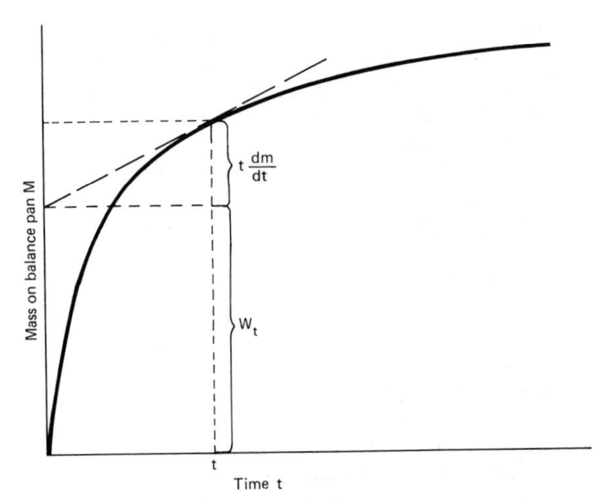

Figure 11.8 Sedimentation balance—plot of mass against time.

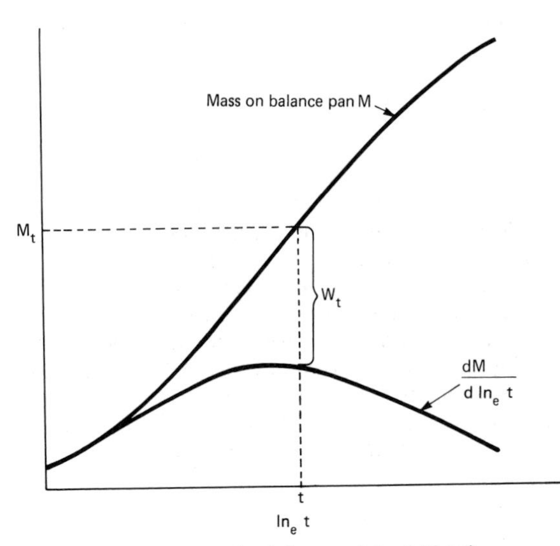

Figure 11.9 Sedimentation balance—plots of M and $dM/d \ln t$ against $\ln t$.

method can be improved by replotting M against $\ln t$ instead of t.

Since

$$\frac{dM}{dt}=\frac{1}{t}\frac{dM}{d(\ln t)}$$

the above expression can be rewritten

$$M=W+\frac{dM}{d(\ln t)}$$

A plot of M against t on logarithmic paper, Figure 11.9, enables tangents to be drawn with greater precision making it possible to compute $dM/d(\ln t)$, the gradient at time t. From a further plot of $dM/d(\ln t)$ against $\ln t$ on the same graph, W can be derived by difference. The method relies on none of the initial material being lost to the sides of the column or round the edges of the pan and that the initial quantity beneath the pan is insignificant. These factors do lead to errors.

Several commercial liquid sedimentation balances are available, notably Sartorious, Shimadzu and Bostock. They have means for introducing the homogeneous suspension into the column above the balance pan. In some, the fluid beneath the pan initially contains no dust. The pan is counterbalanced incrementally by small amounts to minimize pan movement although some is bound to occur and this causes pumping, i.e. some of the finer particles transfer from above to below the pan. All the columns are contained in thermostatic jackets, constancy of temperature being important to the constancy of fluid viscosity and density.

Sedimentation columns A sedimentation column works on the same principle as a sedimentation balance but instead of weighing the sediment continuously the sediment is removed at preset times and weighed externally enabling a higher quality balance to be used.

The ICI sedimentation column, Figure 11.10, tapers at the bottom to a narrow tube a few centimetres long. It is fitted with taps top and bottom. A side branch in the narrow section connects to a clear fluid reservoir.

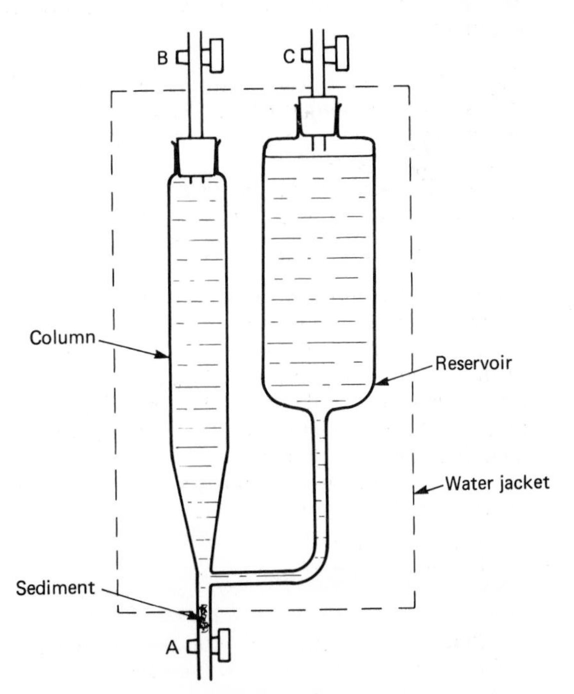

Figure 11.10 ICI sedimentation column.

The dust sample is introduced into the main column and mixed using a rising current of compressed air through tap A, with tap B also open and tap C closed. At time $t=0$, taps A and B are closed and C is opened. Particles sediment into the narrow tube below the side branch. At preset times, tap A is opened allowing clear fluid to wash the sediment into a centrifuge tube or beaker. Negligible sedimenting fluid is lost. The sediment is filtered, dried and weighed.

The BCURA sedimentation column also uses an air supply for mixing, Figure 11.11. In this case, however, the lower tap and narrow tube are replaced by a length of 1 mm capillary tubing. With the top tap closed, surface tension in the capillary supports the column of fluid. At the prescribed times, a container of clear fluid is brought up around the open capillary, breaking the surface tension, and the sediment passes out into the container. The container is then removed. In principle, no sedimenting fluid is lost, but usually a small initial loss occurs until a partial vacuum forms at the top of the column.

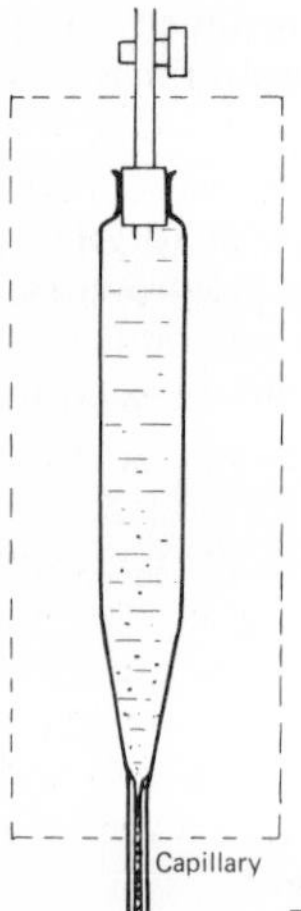

Figure 11.11 BCURA sedimentation column.

The above systems have the advantage of cheapness, but they are subject to errors because the tapered walls affect sedimentation and particles adhere to the tapered walls.

Manometric methods have been used to assess the sedimentation. A manometer fused into the side of the column near the base and filled with the clear fluid will register the change in mean pressure of the column with time and this of course depends on the mass of material still in suspension. Pressure differences are very small.

Beta particle back-scattering has been used to measure the mass of material at the base of a column. The intensity is proportional to the atomic number and the thickness, i.e. the weight of sediment, provided the thickness does not build up to saturation level.

Decanting If a homogeneous fluid/sample mixture is allowed to settle for time t_1 seconds and the fluid down to a depth h is then removed using a pipette, particles removed would all have a terminal velocity less than h/t_1. In the decanting method, this process is repeated several times, replacing the removed fluid with clear fluid and re-mixing until the supernatant fluid is clear. The process is then repeated but with a shorter time, t_2. The removed fluids are analysed for dust content, each containing the fraction of the total mass of material of terminal velocity between h/t_n and h/t_{n-1}. The accuracy depends on the precision of h, t, the rate of removal of fluid, and the number of repeated decantations at each value of t; so it is not high.

Two-layer methods If the upper layer is significantly thinner than the lower layer at time $t=0$, then after a time $t=t_1$, the only material to have reached the base of the column will be those particles with terminal velocity greater than h/t_1, where h is the height of the column, and a measurement of the weight of those particles gives the cumulative distribution directly. Liquid two-layer methods are not common because of the difficulties of arranging the starting condition. The Granulometer uses a shutter system to maintain separation until $t=0$ and a manometer to measure the pressure change as particles sediment.

The Sharples Micromerograph uses an air column approximately 2 m tall. The sample is injected using a puff of compressed nitrogen between two concentric cones to disperse the particles and break up the agglomerates. An electronic balance coupled to a pen recorder monitors the arrival of particles at the base of the column. The column is jacketed to maintain thermal stability. Errors are experienced due to the loss of some fine material to the walls of the column. These can be reduced to some extent by anti-static treatment. The time scale of the recorder is adjustable, fast for the initial phase, slow for the later phase of the sedimentation. With friable particles care has to be exercised at the injection point.

Centrifugal methods For small particles, gravitational systems are very slow-acting. There is also a lower limit to the size of particle that can be measured because of the effects of Brownian motion and convection. While it is possible to use gravitational systems for particles as small as 1 μm in water and about 0.5 μm in air, in practice the lower limit is usually taken to be about 5 μm. These problems can be reduced by the use of centrifugal enhancement of the settling velocity.

The theory for centrifugal settling from a homogeneous fluid mixture is complicated in particular because the terminal velocity varies with distance from the centre of rotation. Approximations have to be made which limit the usefulness of the techniques.

The theory for two-layer systems is exact and therefore these are more attractive. Unfortunately, a phenomenon known as 'streaming' can occur, in which particles tend to agglomerate and accelerate in a bunch instead of individually, behaving as a large particle; this renders the results useless. Streaming has been prevented by using extremely low concentrations of particles in the starting layer. A technique using a third, intermediate layer of immiscible fluid has also been used successfully.

Theories always depend on the applicability of Stokes's law to the particle motion and this imposes a restriction on the maximum particle size, depending on the speed of rotation. Further problems exist for larger particles with respect to the acceleration and decleration of the centrifuge.

In spite of the many problems, the techniques have advantages for very small particles, as small as 0.01 μm and systems are available paralleling many of the gravitational techniques. The most promising appear to be the three-layer methods and the use of optical detection devices.

11.8.2 Elutriation

A group of particles suspended in a fluid which is moving upwards at a velocity V will undergo separation, those particles with a terminal velocity less than V travelling upwards, the others settling downwards. This process is called elutriation. The fluid is usually water or air depending on the particle sizes. Strictly, an elutriator is a classifier rather than a particle sizer. It divides the group of particles into those above and those below a given cut size. In the perfect system, the fluid would clarify except for the few particles with terminal velocity exactly V, and the settled particles could be removed and would contain no undersized particles. The system, however, is not perfect. Proper Stokesian conditions do not exist because practical considerations make the tubes too short compared with their diameters. Also, the velocity at the cylinder walls is considerably less than at the centre, causing a circulation of some particles up the centre and down the walls. The cut point therefore is not sharp. A multiple elutriator consists of a number of elutriators connected in series but with increasing diameters. Each section therefore collects progressively smaller particles.

Both water and air elutriators are commercially available. In use, the sample is introduced into the smallest section and the fluid velocity set to a preset value. When the fluid has cleared in all the sections, the system is switched off and the sediment in each weighed. The last section is usually terminated by a filter. In some designs, the separating section is short and followed by a conical reducing zone to hasten removal of the undersize particles to the next section.

The elutriators described so far are counter-flow elutriators. Acceleration (i.e. gravity) and drag are in opposite directions. Elutriators have been designed for transverse flow. If the sample of particles is introduced slowly into the upper level of a horizontal laminar stream of fluid, two-layer sedimentation takes place but the sediment is separated horizontally, different-sized particles following different trajectories. The particles are collected on judiciously placed pre-weighed sticky plates.

11.8.2.1 Centrifugal elutriation

Elutriation is also used in the centrifugal field, usually with air as the fluid. In principle, air with entrained particles travels inwards against the centrifugal force. Particles with terminal velocities sufficiently low also pass inwards; the rest pass outwards.

The natural flow of air in a spinning system is radially outwards. In order therefore to obtain a counterflow, the air must be driven. In some systems a separate pump is used. In others, the air is introduced at the centre, passes radially outwards under centrifugal force, turns 180° to travel radially inwards for a short distance, of the order of half a radius, and finally through another 180° to pass to the circumference. Elutriation takes place in the inwards-flowing section. In this case, no pump is necessary because the net airflow is outwards.

Adjustment of either rotation speed or air velocity will affect the cut size. Air velocity is usually set by a throttling mechanism.

A variety of centrifuge systems is available, their design and size making them particularly suitable for different size ranges. Some for example are very sensitive in the range 2–12 μm, while others are better at larger sizes. Some are capable of a continuous and large throughput which makes them especially suitable for producing quantities of closely-sized particles. The devices are then being used for their original purpose which is classification rather than size grading.

A cyclone is a centrifugal device normally used for extracting dust from carrier gases. It consists of a conically shaped vessel. The dusty gas is drawn tangentially into the base of the cone, takes a helical route towards the apex where the gas turns sharply back along the axis and is withdrawn axially through the base. The device is a classifier in which only dust with terminal velocity less than a given value can pass through the vortex formed and out with the gas. The particle cut-off diameter is calculable for given conditions. Systems have been designed using a set of cyclones in series with increasing gas velocities for size analysis.

The Cyclosizer Analyser uses liquid instead of gas and has five equal-sized cyclones with different inlet and outlet diameters to obtain the velocity variation. The cyclones are arranged, apex uppermost. Thus the coarse particles retained in a given section fall back many times for reclassification, thereby obtaining good separation. In this case the range is 8–50 μm.

11.8.3 Impaction

When a fluid containing a suspension of particles is made to turn a corner, particles with terminal velocity in excess of a value determined by the fluid velocity and the geometry of the bend are deposited or impacted. A cascade impactor consists of a series of orifices each accurately positioned above a collector plate. The orifices can be round holes or slots. The holes in successive stages are reduced in size to increase the impaction velocity. The particles pass through the holes and are either deposited on the adjacent plate or pass on to the next stage. There are typically between six and ten stages covering an aerodynamic size range from about 0.4 μm to 15 μm.

The Andersen cascade impactor is designed to work 'on-line' incorporating a nozzle for isokinetic sampling from a gas stream. A precyclone removes particles $>15\,\mu$m and a filter catches those $<0.4\,\mu$m. The Sierra, designed for room or atmospheric air measurement, covers a range 0.05 μm to 10 μm. The collected particles are removed and weighed. California Measurements Inc. markets an instrument with piezoelectric crystal mass monitors at each of ten stages giving immediate automatic readout.

Impaction surfaces frequently require the aid of an adhesive to prevent re-entrainment from one stage to the next.

11.9 Analysis methods that infer size from some other property

The methods discussed so far either measure size directly or measure a fluid-dynamic effect dependent on the particle terminal velocity which, although dependent on size, is also affected by density, shape and surface structure. The following methods do not measure size directly nor are they dependent on terminal velocity.

11.9.1 Coulter counter

The Coulter counter uses the principle that the electrical resistance of a conducting liquid is increased by the addition of an insulating material. Particles are assessed individually. To obtain adequate sensitivity the volume of liquid measured must be similar to the volume of the particle.

These criteria are achieved by containing the electrolyte in two chambers separated by a narrow channel containing an orifice, the dimensions of which are accurately known. An electric current from a constant-current source passes through the orifice from one chamber to the other. The voltage across the orifice is therefore directly proportional to the resistance of the orifice.

The sample, suitably dispersed, is placed in one of the chambers. An accurately controlled volume of the well-agitated electrolyte is then passed through the orifice. The concentration of the sample (of the order of 0.1 per cent) is such that particles pass through individually. Each particle causes a voltage pulse and a pulse-height analyser increments one of a set of counters, each representing a size maximum.

The theory of the Coulter counter is complicated, particularly for randomly shaped particles but it has been shown that, to a first approximation, the pulse height is directly proportional to particle volume, errors being less than 6 per cent when the particle size is less than 40 per cent of the orifice diameter. This size limitation also represents a reasonable practical limitation to avoid blockage of the orifice. Although the resistivity of the particles should affect the result, in practice, surface-film effects make this insignificant. The method also works with conducting particles.

The lower limit on particle size is set by the electronic noise in the circuit and in practical terms is usually taken to be about 4 per cent of the orifice diameter. Orifices are available ranging in size from 10 μm up to 1 mm giving a particle-size range (using different orifices) from 0.4 μm to 400 μm. Samples containing a wide range of sizes need to be wet-sieved to remove those larger than 40 per cent orifice size. With small sizes, as always, care has to be exercised to avoid contamination. Bubbles can cause false signals. Aqueous or organic electrolytes can be used. It is usual to calibrate the instrument using a standard sample of latex polymer particles. The technique permits several runs on each sample/electrolyte mix and it is easy to test the effect of changes of concentration, which should be negligible if dilution is adequate.

Models are available with 16-channel resolution and the output can be in tabular form giving particle frequency volume or particle cumulative volume or can be in the form of an automatic plot.

11.9.2 Hiac automatic particle sizer

The Hiac analyser can be considered to be the optical equivalent of the Coulter. In this, the cylindrical orifice is replaced by a two-dimensional funnel-shaped orifice which guides the particle stream through a very narrow light beam located at its throat. A sensor measures the obscuration caused by each particle as it passes through. The responses are proportional to the particle cross-sectional areas and are sorted by a pulse-height analyser. A range of orifices is available to suit particle sizes from 2 μm up to 9 mm, each covering a size range in the ratio 30:1. Although the measurement on a given particle is along one axis, an irregularly shaped particle will not tend to be orientated in any particular way so that statistically the area measured will be a mean cross-sectional area. The optical method has an advantage over the conductivity method in that it can operate in any liquid or gas provided it is translucent over the very short optical path length (typically 2–3 mm of fluid). Scattering-coefficient problems are reduced by calibration using standard samples. The instrument has been used 'on-line' to measure the contamination of hydraulic fluid. The number of particles in a fixed volume is found by counting while timing at a constant flow rate.

11.9.3 Climet

The Climet method involves measuring the light scattered from individual particles which are directed accurately through one focus of an elliptical mirror. Light is focused onto the particles and it is claimed that about 90 per cent of the scattered light is detected by a photomultiplier at the other focus of the ellipse. Direct light is masked. The response is pulse-height analysed.

11.9.4 Adsorption methods

In some processes, a knowledge of the surface area of particles is more important than the actual size. Optical techniques may not be appropriate since these tend to give the 'smoothed' surface area rather than the true surface area—including roughness and pores. Some gases adsorb onto the surface of substances, i.e. they form a layer which may be only one molecule thick on the surface. This is not to be confused with absorption in which the substance is porous and the gases penetrate the substance. The subject is too large for a complete treatment here. The principle is that the particles are first 'cleaned' of all previous adsorbates and then treated with a specific adsorbate, e.g. nitrogen, which is then measured by difference from the adsorbate source. If the layer is monomolecular, the surface area is readily calculated; corrections have to be applied because this is generally not the case. Results are given in terms of surface area/volume or surface area/mass.

11.10 References

For a more comprehensive treatment of this whole complex subject, *Particle Size Measurement* by T. Allen, and *Particle Size Analysis in Industrial Hygiene* by L. Silverman, C. E. Billings and M. W. First are recommended.

Index